Yale Studies in the History of Science and

The Emergence of Agricultural Science

Justus Liebig and the Americans, 1840–1880

Margaret W. Rossiter

New Haven and London   Yale University Press

1975

Copyright © 1975 by Yale University.
All rights reserved. This book may not be
reproduced, in whole or in part, in any form
(except by reviewers for the public press),
without written permission from the publishers.
Library of Congress catalog card number: 74-29737
International standard book number: 0-300-01721-9

Designed by John O. C. McCrillis
and set in Baskerville type.
Printed in the United States of America by
The Murray Printing Co., Forge Village, Mass.

Published in Great Britain, Europe, and Africa by
Yale University Press, Ltd., London.
Distributed in Latin America by Kaiman & Polon,
Inc., New York City;
in India by UBS Publishers' Distributors Pvt.,
Ltd., Delhi; in Japan by John Weatherhill, Inc., Tokyo.

For My Parents
and
Twin Brother Charles

Contents

Illustrations

Acknowledgments

Of all the many people who have helped me in the course of writing this book, I owe the most gratitude to Frederic L. Holmes and A. Hunter Dupree, who have given generously of their time and advice. They are also the nicest and kindest of men, and I have always profited greatly from talking with them. George Pierson, G. Evelyn Hutchinson, and Martin Klein offered encouragement at key points. Charles Rosenberg, John Greene, Roger Hahn, Joseph Fruton, Derek J. de Solla Price, Samuel Haber, Hubert Vickery, and Nathan Reingold also read all or part of the manuscript and had perceptive criticisms. I also owe much to Michele Aldrich, who has shared her wide and critical knowledge of related topics. Many other friends have also helped along the way. I was able to complete my study thanks to a traineeship grant from the United States Public Health Service, a postdoctoral fellowship from the National Science Foundation, and a research grant from the Penrose Fund of the American Philosophical Society. It is a pleasure to acknowledge their support.

The Yale University libraries have been the source of most of my material; and the staff of the Yale University Archives, especially Herman Kahn, Judith Schiff, and Lawrence Dawler, was especially helpful. Elsewhere I was very lucky to have the aid of Barbara Takacs at the Connecticut Agricultural Experiment Station; Samuel Rezneck and K. J. Bauer at Rensselaer Polytechnic Institute; Andrew Fiske of Shelter Island, Long Island; John Clayton, Jr., at the University of Delaware; John W. Spaeth, Jr., at Wesleyan University; and several other archivists in both the United States and Germany who very kindly answered my inquiries. Finally, I wish to thank Christine M. Tattersall and Charles S. Fineman for their superb typing of the manuscript, Judy Yogman for an excellent job of copyediting, and Janice Palumbo for vigilant proofreading.

Berkeley, California　　　　　　　　　　　　　　　　　M. W. R.
August 1974

Introduction

Research laboratories and agricultural experiment stations play such an important role in twentieth-century America that it is hard to imagine modern life without them. Yet institutions such as these have not always existed in the United States. They had to be envisioned, created, imported, and sustained, often in spite of a hostile or apathetic audience or environment. An examination of the early years of these institutions reveals much about the precarious place of science, research, and the higher learning in mid-nineteenth-century America.

Alexis de Tocqueville raised the issue of the relative places of pure and applied science in America in his famous chapter, "Why the Americans are more addicted to Practical than to Theoretical Science" (*Democracy in America*, 1835). Since then several scholars have followed his lead and belabored the Americans' apparent indifference to basic science before 1880. A curious secondary literature has resulted, emphasizing what may not have been present in this period rather than examining what was. It has created stereotypes about the period that persist despite evidence of the widespread popularity of anthropology, botany, astronomy, and chemistry in antebellum America. Nor has this "indifference literature" spawned the interest in the history of applied science that one might have expected. This neglect is unfortunate, since, as we shall see, the study of applied science reveals far more of a society's attitude toward science than does the study of the more abstracted pure science.

Agricultural chemistry is a particularly interesting science to examine, since it has both pure and applied aspects and since it aroused such a variety of strong and conflicting emotions between 1840 and 1880. Spokesmen for the field could respond to the changing moods and demands of society and of its own practitioners by shrewdly stressing its practical applications at one moment and then its contributions to pure science at the next. For example, the role and source of nitrogen in plants was a very important theoretical problem in the 1840s and 1850s, but it also underlay the practical problem of the use and manufacture of chemical fertilizers. Such spokesmen had to be careful, also, of what tone they used with various audiences, since the public's reaction to agricultural chemistry was ambivalent and changeable. The scientists found themselves popular enough to be imitated by quacks and to have their books pirated by unlicensed publishers, but they were not popular enough to raise money for their causes or to get bills passed by legislatures. Their work excited the farmers, who needed them, admired them, and listened to them, but also distrusted them and ridiculed their failures. The picture that emerges shows science's role in American life in the mid-nineteenth century to be far more pervasive and dynamic, but also more complex and ambivalent, than has usually been thought.

Yet even if the public was far from indifferent toward agricultural chemistry, the institutionalization of the science did suffer from the "withering influence," as Richard Shryock has called it, of American social attitudes and economic conditions. Research work that was expected and subsidized in Germany was unusual and costly in America, where industrial opportunities and financial rewards lured the ambitious out of the laboratory and into business. Despite the best efforts of several American scientists who were determined to overcome such conditions, they and their institutions too fell victim to the demands for practical results; and in 1880 research was still costlier and its rewards less tangible in the United States than in Germany.

The focus here is on three related events in the history of science in America—the reception during the 1840s of the works on agricultural chemistry by the eminent German scientist Justus Liebig, the sudden craze over soil analysis and subsequent reaction against it, and the importation of the first chemical research laboratories and agricultural research stations from Germany into the United States. The story necessarily involves aspects of social history, agricultural history, and the history of education as well as the history of science, which together give a broad picture of the greatly expanding role of science in America in the formative period 1840–80.

The story takes place against the backdrop of the overall decline of agriculture in the eastern United States after 1830. Poor soil and western competition meant that decline and adjustment were continuing problems for Eastern farmers in this period, despite their efforts to change and improve. If they were to compete for markets at all, they would have to specialize in certain crops and adopt new techniques, such as the use of chemical fertilizers. Although farmers as a group may have been generally reluctant to change, competitive pressures in the 1830s and after made many of them increasingly receptive to new ideas.

Agricultural chemistry also underwent its own internal development between 1840 and 1880. Problems that at first glance seemed simple and, as Justus Liebig said, capable of "easy solution by well-known facts," were indeed highly complex and certainly beyond the limits of agricultural science in the nineteenth century. Thus our story has the added twist that the scientists, who are normally seen as forces of progress and who usually criticized the farmer for failing to adopt the latest ideas rapidly enough, suffered the embarrassment of finding themselves in error after all and of having to reverse their earlier buoyant optimism. After reassessing the state of agricultural chemistry in 1853–55, they began to stress the need for long-term experimentation into agricultural problems as the only hope for improvement. Trying to reconcile the complexities of agricultural science with the public demand for practical benefits became a continuing problem for agricultural scientists. These dual pressures were institutionalized into the experiment stations in the 1870s and 1880s, and after a period of great frustration and tension, the stations eventually lived up to the early hopes of the scientists and became a source of fruitful agricultural innovation as well. It was in this area of institution-building, with the importation of methods and ideas from Germany, that agricultural chemistry showed its most important and long-lasting influence in this period.

Most of the vast secondary literature on the German influence on the American university is quite general and fails to consider the important financial side of the growth of laboratories and universities in the nineteenth century. It also leaves the impression, in regard to science, that most Americans who studied at German universities sought Ph.D. degrees and pursued "pure science." But the earliest group of American chemists in Germany cared little for degrees and clearly sought to study applied science, which they were eager to use on the practical problems facing the farmers of New York and New England in the 1840s.

Agricultural chemistry between 1840 and 1880 also had some of the flavor of the reform movements of the time. Like other reformers, agricultural scientists faced problems of overcoming apathy and creating concern for their objective. Their movement, which hoped to save the farmers from themselves, aroused the same sort of righteous humanitarian emotions and attracted much the same sort of driving, selfless crusaders as did the temperance and abolitionist movements.

Finally, although agricultural chemistry attracted wide popular interest in mid-nineteenth-century America it was the professional specialty of a very small group of men. In fact, we can survey the American side of the subject with justice from the vantage point of three men active in the movement, Eben Norton Horsford, John Pitkin Norton, and Samuel W. Johnson. They had different backgrounds, motivations, attitudes, and experiences; but they were responding to similar forces and facing similar problems. From a study of their different experiences but common goals, one can learn something of the difficulties that faced men trying to import foreign ideas and institutions like research laboratories and experiment stations into the United States between 1840 and 1880.

PART I

Agriculture and Science

1

"Worn-Out Soil"

Twentieth-century Americans take it for granted that their agri-culture is the most efficient and productive in the world. Yet Ameri-can farming has not always been so successful, and before 1860 it was by all accounts quite backward and inefficient. Visiting Euro-peans, used to more intensive and careful farming methods abroad, often made negative comments about the Americans' seemingly wasteful practices. Professor James F. W. Johnston, a noted Scottish agricultural chemist, described American agriculture in 1851 as "in a very primitive condition" and pointed to soil exhaustion as a serious problem.[1] But, ironically, by the time of Johnston's visit in 1850, American agriculture was already in a state of recovery, and his very invitation to come to the United States to lecture on agri-cultural topics was just one more sign of it. By 1850 farmers were already well aware of the problem of "worn-out soil," and many were taking steps to correct it.

Worn-out soil throughout the East and South by 1830 was largely the result of earlier farm exploitation. Frontier economies are usually enormously destructive of the soil, since with land abundant and labor scarce, farmers find it most advantageous to skim the land for quick profits. Then, when the soil's fertility has declined from such treatment, they leave the worn-out soil for cheap virgin land else-where. This cycle of events—of settlement, exploitation, and "ruin" —was already well under way in those parts of the United States settled before 1830.[2]

The phenomenon was most destructive in the South, where little urbanism and economic differentiation took place in the antebellum period. In the North, however, its effects were less pronounced, since the soil had been less fertile to start with,* and the Indian

*William Bradford's story of how the friendly Indian Squanto showed the Pilgrims how

3

threat had long limited the new lands available. Besides, once westward expansion began in the North around 1790, the problem of
worn-out soil became just one part of the larger process of regional
differentiation. This process, which would cause some areas to
prosper and others that failed to adjust to decline, would intensify in
succeeding decades as railroads and canals replaced river transportation and as eastern cities could stretch their supply routes
farther and farther into the West.[3]

The New England colonists had quickly spread out from the
original coastal settlements in search of good agricultural land
along the rivers. But since the Indians presented a threat in northern
and western New York until the 1790s, even poor and rocky land
inside the Indian line had been cleared for cultivation. Many stone
walls, built then with backbreaking toil, still remain throughout
New England, marking hilly, rocky fields that were exceedingly
unsuitable for farming. As the Indians receded, new agricultural
lands in the Mohawk Valley became available. The resulting surge
of migration from New England, especially from Vermont, into
eastern New York rapidly populated the area, overwhelming the
old Dutch outpost at Albany and creating whole new cities such as
Troy, Hudson, and Catskill between 1790 and 1810.[4]

It was one of nature's tricks, however, that the soil of central
and western New York was, for reasons to be explained by geology
and the modern soil science, pedology, much more fertile than that
of New England (see fig. 1). In Paleozoic times a sea had extended
over most of western New York. When this sea receded, it left behind
vast limestone deposits, which would later make soils in the area
particularly fertile. New England, however, lacked this sea and
came to be covered with coniferous forests, which flourished in its
cool, humid climate. Over the succeeding ages, according to modern
soil science, the moisture of this climate and the vegetable acids from
the trees leached the carbonates from the soil and left it acidic and
clayey. Over geologic time, therefore, New England soils became so
acidic and poor in lime that they were suitable for cultivation only
when heavily fertilized. But in central and western New York the
underlying bed of limestone replenished the supply of carbonates,

---

to plant maize by burying a dead fish in the soil with the corn demonstrates that some
New England soils were so poor as to require fertilizers even before 1620. William Bradford, *History of Plymouth Plantation, 1620–1647*, 1:215.

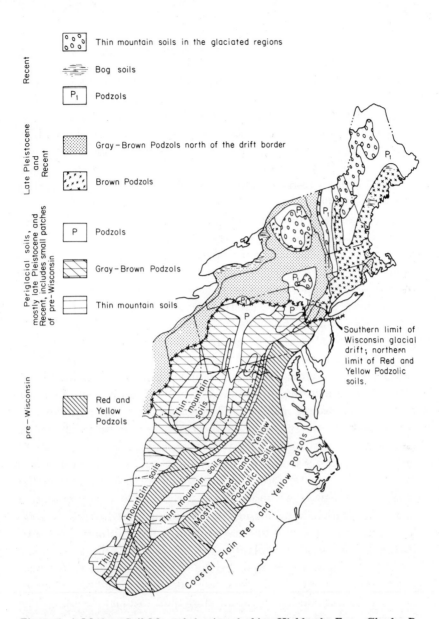

Figure 1. A Modern Soil Map of the Appalachian Highlands. From Charles B. Hunt, *Physiography of the United States* (San Francisco: W. H. Freeman and Company, copyright © 1967), p. 193; reproduced by permission. *Definitions*: (1) podzols = light-colored leached soils of cool, humid forested regions; (2) brown podzols = brown leached soils of cool-temperate, humid forested regions; (3) gray-brown podzols = grayish-brown leached soils of temperate, humid forested regions; (4) red and yellow podzols = red or yellow leached soils of warm-temperate, humid forested regions. In (1), (2), and (3) more aluminum and iron than silica are leached from the soil; in (4) the reverse is true.

and these soils long remained fertile without the use of lime or other fertilizers.[5]

The settlers on this virgin and limestone soil were much more successful in growing wheat than were their relatives who had remained in New England. The resulting competition spelled the doom of the New England wheat culture around 1800–10.[6] New England farmers responded to this economic dislocation in a variety of ways. The most popular solutions seem to have been: (1) moving to Boston, Albany, or other cities and taking up a trade; (2) migrating westward themselves; (3) turning to sheep raising; (4) taking up dairying and truck farming if near the city; or (5) sending children to work in factories. For the most part, after 1800 New England offered greater opportunities off the soil than on it.

But the supremacy of western New York and its limestone soils was also short-lived, for with the completion of the Erie Canal in 1825 the pace of westward expansion began to quicken, and soon even the famed Genesee Valley south of Rochester began to feel competitive pressures. Although a major purpose in building the canal had been to make the new agricultural lands along its route accessible to eastern markets, the effects of the canal went beyond that original aim; and, in fact, the canal helped bring about the decline of the very agriculture it was meant to help. The canal not only made it easier to move food products east as planned, but also made it much easier for emigrants to move west. Studies of the traffic on the Erie Canal show that as early as 1825 load after load of emigrants and their belongings were moving west from New England and New York into the new Ohio country. Within a few years, in the 1830s, these transplanted easterners were able to compete with the Genesee Valley and, by the 1840s, to surpass it in wheat production. Western New York was, like New England before it, forced to change to sheep raising and then to dairy farming. The pattern would continue westward, as Ohio soon yielded to Wisconsin and later to Kansas and the Dakotas.[7]

The New York economy was thus in a state of transition in the 1830s and 1840s, and its farmers were beginning to mutter about their worn-out soil. Under these conditions some of the more prosperous farmers and professional men, also concerned about the declining crop yields and western competition, were stirred to become quite innovative.[8] They popularized ideas of crop rotation, deep plowing, and fertilizing which they had drawn from traditional lore, their own experience, or, occasionally, from recent science. Once a number of farmers had accepted the idea of "book-farming" or scientific agriculture, the innovators began new farm journals in order to press for such other institutions as state agricultural surveys, schools and colleges, societies, and boards to disseminate still further the doctrines of scientific agriculture.[9] The cycle of recovery was by then well under way.

But the process of agricultural improvement in nineteenth-century America was much more complicated and emotional than the gradual diffusion of worthy innovations would imply, for the farmers comprised a very complex group. At the one extreme there were farmers who sought panaceas for their ailing farms and were anxious to try every new fad that came along, such as silkworms in the 1830s and electroculture in the 1840s. It is impossible to determine the size of this group accurately, for, although often denounced, it was probably quite small. At the opposite extreme to the faddists were the large number of farmers who had a strong prejudice against book-farming or improvement of any sort. Their fathers had shown them how to farm, and they clung to these old ways, despite the changing economic conditions and the warnings of reformers. The innovators found the fierce resistance of these farmers exceedingly difficult to overcome and repeatedly underestimated their tenacity. Despite all the reformers' efforts starting in the 1830s, such resistance to agricultural improvement was still a strong force forty years later.

The coexistence of these two almost contradictory attitudes toward agricultural improvement, faddish enthusiasm and outright rejection, in upstate New York in the 1830s and 1840s should not be surprising, for this area was the famed "Burned-over District" known for its extremes of religious enthusiasm and violent prejudices.[10] In comparison with the area's prejudices about religion (anti-Mormon, anti-Catholic), nationality (anti-Irish), and politics (anti-Masonic), its anti-intellectualism seems a mild trait indeed. Although emotion ran high on the subject of scientific agriculture, the resistant farmers were content with ridicule and verbal rejection and did not resort to the riots and lynchings that marked their other prejudices. At least there are no recorded lynchings of professors of scientific agriculture in New York at this time.

Although the farmers were certainly justified in being somewhat wary of agricultural "improvements," since, as this book will show, not every innovation was immediately practicable or beneficial, other innovations, especially in the area of animal breeding, were sources of great advancement in American agriculture between 1820 and 1880. Nevertheless, the agricultural editors and reformers who selected worthwhile innovations and recommended them to this emotional audience knew they were in a very delicate position. They had, on the one hand, to encourage the farmers to adopt new ideas and practices, but, on the other, to prevent them from expecting too much, since overzealousness could, in the case of disappointment or failure, lead to such bitterness and resentment as to set the whole movement back considerably. The agricultural editors tried to guide their readers aright, but occasionally even they were wrong, for the true action of soils, crops, and manures eluded even the most knowledgeable of men in the nineteenth century.

Between 1820 and 1860 Albany, with Troy and Schenectady, constituted a cultural center of growing importance. It was the state capital, with headquarters of the state agricultural society, the state geological survey, and the state library; and an educational center, with institutions like the Albany Academy, the Albany Institute, the Albany Female Academy, Rensselaer Polytechnic Institute, Union College, and the Albany Medical and Law colleges. In the 1840s, Albany was a city that foreign scientists such as Louis Agassiz and Charles Lyell hastened to visit. By the 1850s it was hosting national meetings of the American Association for the Advancement of Science and projecting a national university and the Dudley Observatory.[11]

The major forces behind Albany's cultural development were the continued patronage of the old Dutch patroons (especially Stephen Van Rensselaer) and the interest of the "new men" in business, industry, and the professions. Edward C. Delavan in wine and real estate, Erastus Corning in ironware and railroads, and Charles Dudley in law were intermarrying with the Schuylers, Bleeckers, and other old Dutch families and turning to philanthropy. These "gentlemen farmers" could afford to experiment with scientific agriculture on their private estates outside the city. Together with publicists like Jesse Buel and Luther Tucker, they hoped to direct New York's response to worn-out soil.

Jesse Buel, an Albany newspaper editor and Whig politician, who experimented on his farm outside the city, was in 1832 one of the founders of the New York State Agricultural Society, which would play an important part in the careers of Eben Horsford, John Pitkin Norton, and Samuel W. Johnson. In 1834 Buel started the *Cultivator,* one of the most important agricultural journals in the nation, as the society's mouthpiece. When Buel died in 1839, Luther Tucker, the editor of the *Genesee Farmer* in Rochester, moved to Albany and took over the *Cultivator.* Both men were vigorous leaders who used their dual position in the society and on the journal to endorse the state geological and agricultural surveys and to push for a state agricultural college. They were also advocates of the new agriculture, discussing manures, draining, and crop rotation. They frequently drew their material from British agricultural journals, for Britain was, after the work of Arthur Young in the 1790s, the world center of improved farming.[12] But of all the new ideas and techniques that Buel and Tucker popularized in the 1830s, they especially favored things "scientific." The *Cultivator,* whose motto was "To improve the soil and the mind," considered studying science an excellent way to do both. It urged young men to study science, anything from astronomy to veterinary science, but its favorite was agricultural chemistry. It has special columns directed to such youth, explaining elementary science, and made a regular practice, from its start in 1834, of publishing excerpts, sometimes whole chapters, from the latest works on agricultural chemistry. Most of the books and journals were British or French, with J. A. Chaptal being serialized all through 1837. Buel was quite well informed, writing an article in the *American Journal of Science* in 1835 on a current plant doctrine and urging in 1838 the translation of works by Albrecht von Thaer and Karl Sprengel, two of the leading German agricultural chemists.[13] Since the circulation of the *Cultivator* was about 23,000 in 1838, a large group of Americans were coming into contact with fairly sophisticated agricultural chemistry even before Justus Liebig's book appeared in 1840.[14] The agricultural editors were expecting chemistry to solve the problem of worn-out soil and wanted to prepare their readers for it. Whether or not the subscribers understood the chemistry, some of their sons surely did, for several of them made up the group that would go to Europe to study with Liebig.

2

The Science of Agricultural Chemistry

To Americans concerned about their agricultural problems and believing strongly in science and its applications, Justus Liebig appeared as a savior in 1840. His book, *Organic Chemistry in Its Applications to Agriculture and Physiology,* published in London and Germany that year, was so popular in America that Professor John W. Webster of Harvard College promptly issued two American editions (see appendix 1). Scientists and farmers alike received the book with tremendous enthusiasm and hope. The first American review appeared in the *American Journal of Science* for October-December 1840, where the ebullient Benjamin Silliman, Jr., threw all caution to the winds. He thought that Liebig's book would constitute "an era of great importance in the history of agricultural science. Its acceptance as a standard is unavoidable, for following closely in the straight path of inductive philosophy, the conclusions which are drawn from its data are incontrovertible." Silliman summarized the basic arguments of the book; admitted himself thoroughly impressed by Liebig's "profound knowledge, extensive reading, and practical research"; and hailed the book's "invincible power" and the "importance of its reasonings and conclusions."[1] Likewise, the *North American Review* recognized the book's appearance and devoted over twenty pages to a review which acclaimed it as "a contribution . . . of extraordinary value" and predicted it would have a great effect on American agriculture.[2]

The *Cultivator* devoted its front two pages in May 1841 to a more balanced review of Liebig's work. It congratulated him for a stimulating book but noted that it contained a few errors:

> Prof. Liebig has given to the public a work to be read and studied; one that commands assent to the positions assumed by the clearness and force of the arguments; and which, if not correct in every particular deduction, will, we are confident,

notwithstanding the novelty of some of the positions assumed by
him, be found to be sustained in the main by facts and experience. . . . It is to be presumed that some of the positions taken
by Prof. Liebig may require some modification; and on some
points he may prove not perfectly correct, but for the manner
in which he has taught us how the principal operations of vegetation are performed—and the understanding this constitutes
the whole philosophy of agriculture—the farming public are
very greatly indebted, and we cannot question its influence will
be widely felt.[3]

Though Americans, like their counterparts in Europe, criticized
parts of Liebig's theories, they generally received his ideas on agriculture enthusiastically. This attitude was in distinct contrast to the
American reception of Liebig's ideas on physiology expressed in his
Animal Chemistry in 1842. At that time Charles Caldwell, a Louisville
physician of "vitalistic" leanings, vehemently denied that chemistry
could say anything at all useful about physiology.[4] Although vitalistic
elements persisted in agriculture into the 1840s (especially in the
realm of organic manures), few doubted in the 1830s and 1840s that
chemistry could solve the problems of agriculture.

Precisely why Americans should have responded so strongly to
Liebig's agricultural chemistry is at first hard to determine. Liebig
had a worldwide reputation as an eminent chemist, but he was little
known outside professional circles. His book, written in a clear style,
though using chemical terminology, was not readily understandable
without additional notes. Most scholars would have one believe that
Liebig's book was the first appearance of agricultural chemistry in
the United States,[5] but this is incorrect, since, as we have seen, the
farm journals of the 1830s contained, and even stressed, agricultural
chemistry. Besides, Humphry Davy's *Elements of Agricultural Chemistry*
was one of the few chemistry books in the nineteenth century that
outsold Liebig in America.[6] Liebig's great appeal, therefore, was
certainly not in the novelty of applying chemistry to agriculture.

It seems more likely that Americans reacted so strongly to Liebig
primarily because they *did* know so much about agricultural chemistry[7] and therefore recognized and appreciated the advance he had
made. To the farmer or layman the book seemed to explain for the
first time the scientific basis of certain empirical farming practices.

But, besides appearing to solve pressing agricultural problems, the book also suggested answers to some long-standing scientific questions. In order to understand Liebig's impact, therefore, it is necessary to look at the state of knowledge about agricultural chemistry in the 1830s.

Agricultural journals of the 1830s were urging farmers to adopt new practices like draining, new crops like turnips, and new manures like gypsum. Articles or letters from farmers described methods that they had found effective but were unable to explain. The farmers knew, for instance, that gypsum worked better in some areas than others and on certain crops, but they could not explain these differences. The explanations they did offer were usually vague and more confusing than convincing. Most authors gave up the attempt and admitted that understanding was lagging behind empirical practices. One such article, "On the Use of Gypsum," in the *Cultivator* in April 1838, was typical:

> There is no longer any doubt, in our mind, of the advantage of applying gypsum to all our meadow lands, in the spring, which are beyond the influence of marine atmospheres, and which are habitually dry. There are instances recorded, to be sure, of its not producing perceptible benefits the first year, and some instances where it did not seem to operate even the second year, and yet it ultimately developed its fertilising properties.
>
> We do not design now to discuss the question *how* gypsum does operate—but to inquire and state from the facts within our reach, to what crops its application is particularly beneficial—on what soils its effects appear to be greatest—how much should be applied to the acre, and at what season it is best applied. We are satisfied, that if the value of gypsum was better known, it would be much more extensively used than it is; and that the more it is used, the greater will be our agricultural surplus.[8]

Despite the ignorance of why gypsum and other mineral manures worked, there was in the 1830s a standard, though increasingly inadequate, corpus of knowledge on agricultural chemistry. This traditional understanding grew out of Davy's *Agricultural Chemistry* of 1813 and subsequent editions. This work was a compendium of views and experiments by Theodore de Saussure, Albrecht von

Thaer, J. L. Gay-Lussac, Louis Thenard, and others. It was popular in the United States and England but not in Germany, where different ideas were prevalent.[9]

For our purposes the essential elements of this traditional British view of plant-soil relationships were Humphry Davy's ideas on two important and related but relatively new topics—the role of the soil and its constituents in plant growth, and the action of humus and manures, especially the new mineral manures. Davy's views on these key issues were, however, unclear and inconsistent, for they skirted around unresolved questions of the time: (1) Were organic processes such as plant growth completely chemical, or were certain non-chemical vital processes also involved? and (2) How did one account for the presence of inorganic minerals, such as silica, in living organisms such as plants? Davy's uncertainty reflected the uncertain knowledge of the time. Due to the work of Priestley, Ingenhousz, Saussure, and Senebier on photosynthesis and gas chemistry, more was known in 1813 about the water, oxygen, light, and carbon dioxide relations of the plant than about its soil or mineral relations. In particular, Davy was trying to reconcile Saussure's recent data, which showed that minerals played a role in plant life, with the older vitalistic theories, which stressed the uniqueness of living processes and the role of the humus.

One result was Davy's ambivalence as to the role of the soil and its constituents in plant life. On the one hand, he was quite sure that the soil had only a minor passive, almost mechanical, role in plant growth—that of simply supporting the plant so that the roots could absorb their true food, dissolved organic matter.[10] But on the other hand, Davy admitted elsewhere that the soil must also have a "chemical" role, since the plant stem was known to contain silica, which it could obtain only from the soil. Although such minerals served to strengthen the plant stem (pp. 154–55), Davy was uncertain how they were assimilated and put into action: "The conversion of matter that has belonged to living structures into organised forms, is a process that can be easily understood; but it is more difficult to follow those operations by which earthy and saline matters are consolidated in the fibre of plants, and by which they are made subservient to their functions" (p. 270). But, Davy felt, whatever problems they raised, minerals in plants were of such minute quantity, of such different kinds, and of such unknown functions that their role could be rejected as trivial: "The earths afforded by plants, are applied to no uses of common life; and there are few cases in which the knowledge of their nature can be of importance, or afford interest to the farmer" (p. 100).[11]

These "earths" or minerals were not so easily dismissed, however, when Davy began to take a closer look at their probable role within the soil. Sensing that the minerals were somehow related to fertility but reluctant to allow them direct access to the plant, Davy presumed that they worked through water and humus, traditionally the "proper" foods of the plant (pp. 11, 134). In particular, he thought them quite helpful in attracting the right amounts of water and humus to the plant, in regulating the rate of decomposition of the humus, and in helping it enter solution (p. 161). Yet this theory neither explained the presence of minerals in the plant nor elucidated the earths' mode of action. To solve this latter problem, Davy hypothesized that the earth particles attracted the water particles to the humus through their power of "cohesion" (p. 159). But why the humus should need such help was unclear, since Davy went on to say that the animal and vegetable matter in the soil was even more effective in attracting water particles than the earths were (p. 159). Here Davy was stumbling upon one of the major problems of the old humus theory. The humus was presumed to be insoluble (by definition it was the insoluble portion of the vegetable matter of the plant), and yet it was also considered essential to plant nutrition.[12] How could anything known to be insoluble enter the plant? In 1813 ideas of solubility, cohesion, attraction, and the functions of particles were not very well defined, and such contradictions not readily apparent. But by 1840 they would be sufficiently clarified for Liebig to demolish the old humus theory by ridiculing the inconsistencies of the soluble insoluble humus. Unfortunately Liebig would go too far, for neither he nor Humphry Davy could have suspected the modern view, worked out by soil microbiologists in the twentieth century—that the humus is not just dead organic matter but is rather the home of many microorganisms which in turn play an important role in ammoniafication and nitrification and, further, that the humus itself is both formed and decomposed by the complex microbial processes outlined in figure 2.

Undeterred by these difficulties with the action of the soil, minerals, and humus, Davy went on to explain the action of organic

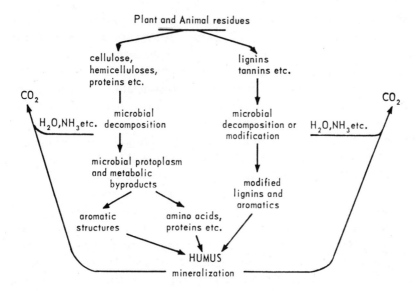

Plant and Animal residues

cellulose,
hemicelluloses,
proteins etc.

lignins
tannins etc.

CO_2

H_2O, NH_3 etc.

microbial decomposition

CO_2

H_2O, NH_3 etc.

microbial decomposition or modification

microbial protoplasm and metabolic byproducts

modified lignins and aromatics

aromatic structures

amino acids, proteins etc.

HUMUS

mineralization

Figure 2. Current View of Humus Formation. From Firman E. Bear, *Chemistry of the Soil*, 2nd ed., p. 258. © 1964 by Litton Educational Publishing, Inc. Reprinted by permission of Van Nostrand Reinhold Company.

manures, and here he made an improvement over traditional theories. Although the effectiveness of animal and vegetable manures had been known since antiquity, chemists in Davy's time were only beginning to understand the complex reactions involved. As with the humus, such reactions were usually explained loosely in terms of "solubility," but Davy reframed the problem in terms of "fermentations and putrefactions," a set of diverse and complex biochemical reactions likewise little understood at the time. Here Davy quickly dropped the difficult problems presented by the nonnitrogenous vegetable matter and talked mostly of the reaction involved in the decomposition of nitrogenous animal substances, which were known from long experience to putrefy rapidly on exposure to air. Davy related this easy putrefaction of animal substances to their chemical composition, especially to their relatively high percentages of carbon, nitrogen, hydrogen, and oxygen, as shown in analyses of gelatin, fibrin, and urea by Gay-Lussac and Thenard and Fourcroy and Vauquelin (pp. 238–41). As they putrefied, these compounds gave off ammonia, carbon dioxide, and water—products that were essential for an effective manure, as in the guano described by

Alexander von Humboldt on the Peruvian islands (pp. 258–59) and various other ammoniacal salts, which were known to be powerful manures. On the basis of these few but suggestive facts, Davy concluded his chapter on organic manures by sketching hastily a simplisitc chemical theory of their action. Just as animal matter putrefied and emitted noxious ammoniacal gases when exposed to air above the ground, so too by a similar series of "fermentations" and "putrefactions" animal matter would decompose, emit ammonia, and become an effective manure beneath the soil (p. 269). By modern standards Davy's description of the process was exceedingly vague, but it constituted an adequate explanation for the time and was widely accepted. Practical men had long known and used the related process of alcoholic fermentation, as in brewing and wine making, but the exact cause of this whole cluster of reactions had eluded Lavoisier and would elude Saussure, Liebig, and other chemists until Louis Pasteur demonstrated the dependence of these reactions on yeast and other microorganisms in the 1850s and 1860s, and Eduard Buchner related them to enzymes in the 1890s.[13] Nevertheless, the hypothesis proved to be a fruitful one and may well have been what attracted Liebig to the study of agricultural chemistry.

But such "fermentations and putrefactions" would not explain the action of the new "mineral" or inorganic manures (lime and gypsum) that were coming into use after 1800.* This new class of manures represented the real challenge for the agricultural chemistry of Davy's time, since being inorganic they would have no "humus," vital principle, or putrefying substances that could enter the plant. Inorganic substances did not enter the plant, or did they?

Saussure had shown in 1804 that plants contained minerals which seemed to come from the soil, and not, as many chemists of the time thought, from a transformation of air particles within the plant. Davy accepted this view (p. 273) and derived from it two possible explanations for the effects of mineral manures: "They must produce their effect, either by becoming a constituent part of the plant, or by acting upon its more essential food, so as to render it more fitted for

---

*"Mineral" manures should not be confused with "artificial" manures that manufacturers started to develop in the late 1830s. Most of the latter were inorganic or mineral, as superphosphates, but a few others like poudrettes and urates were organic.

the purposes of vegetable life" (p. 274). Not surprisingly, since he had used it before with the minerals in the soil, Davy preferred the second alternative of the mineral manures' "acting upon" the other "more essential" organic food of the plant. Luckily, lime, one of the most popular mineral manures, seemed to follow this pattern. Its hitherto puzzling action could now be explained.

Lime occurred in three different states: quicklime, slaked lime, and limestone or marl. In all three states it was usually mixed with organic manures before being applied to the soil. Its use had, however, led to certain problems. The three forms had been observed to have different effects on the soil. Quicklime was much too strong and killed all vegetation with which it came into contact (not a good trait for a fertilizer!). Slaked lime (hydrate of lime) gave up its excess water and absorbed carbon dioxide from the other manures, thus making them more soluble. The limestone or marl did not affect solubility but slowed the rate of the manure's decomposition by "preventing the too rapid decomposition of substances already dissolved" (p. 278) and thus ensured a constant supply of soluble matter to the plant. Lime did not, therefore, add anything to the plant. It merely "acted upon" the organic manures with which it was mixed (pp. 278, 160). Davy's explanation of the action of lime had the added advantage that it could also account for the phenomenon of worn-out soil. Too much lime could, he thought, exhaust the soil by using up all its organic matter. The vitalist explanation of the action of lime was that it acted as a "stimulant" to the other manures. The modern view is that the lime neutralizes the excessive acidity of the soil, which was essentially the American Edmund Ruffin's explanation in the 1820s, based on his interpretation of Davy.[14]

Though Davy could explain the effects of lime, he realized gypsum was a different matter. It attracted water from the atmosphere but retained it too tightly to be useful as a source of moisture. Furthermore, as Davy learned from a few experiments, gypsum did not hasten the putrefaction of organic manures as lime did. It obviously did not work through organic matter and therefore presented a serious problem for Davy's system. He did not solve the problem satisfactorily, and one of the immediate advantages of Liebig's book was that it seemed to explain the action of gypsum.

Davy was therefore forced to broach the idea that the plant

might absorb the gypsum directly as a kind of food (p. 16). It seemed plausible since gypsum was most effective on clover, rye, and sainfoin, all of which showed large quantities of calcium in their plant ashes (p. 289). Davy suggested that they probably absorbed the gypsum as part of their wood fiber, much as they did a fraction of the earths in the soil. Davy even ventured to add that gypsum might one day make a better fertilizer than hitherto thought (pp. 290–91). In reviewing the effects of other known mineral manures, Davy also added the observation that phosphate of lime was "probably necessary to corn crops and other white crops" (p. 293), but he left these ideas undeveloped.

For future reference, we should note in passing that Davy was aware that nitrogen played a role in plants, but he could only speculate on its source (free nitrogen in the atmosphere) and suggest further experiments (pp. 186, 203). He himself made some field experiments with ammoniacal salts as fertilizers and was quite struck with the effects of ammonium carbonate (pp. 296–98). He seemed, however, unable to connect the nitrogen in the plants with the ammonia in the fertilizer. The former probably came from the atmosphere, and the latter presumably remained in the soil. They remained in two different corners of his mind, quite separate from each other and the known effects of guano. He neither formulated nor explored the nitrogen problem.

But this is to stress the inadequacies and weaknesses in Davy's system rather than its widespread acceptance and influence. The problems of soils and manures were only beginning to receive attention, and the contradictions between old assertions and new facts were not yet noticed. The interactions of water, oxygen, and carbon dioxide, in plants had yielded important results to the new gas chemistry between 1790 and 1810. Most research interest was focused on those studies, and the problems of the role of nitrogen and minerals in plants were allowed to remain on the sidelines until additional and more persistent evidence forced the whole matter of their significance to be reconsidered.

This basic view of agricultural chemistry remained practically unchanged in the next twenty-seven years, although there were great advances in analytical chemistry.[15] Most agricultural chemists devoted themselves to the detection of the organic acids in the humus, and a typical achievement was Berzelius's isolation of the "crenic" and "apocrenic" acids in the humus in 1833. Only Karl Sprengel was interested in the minerals in the soil and did extensive studies of them, but he too was a German vitalist who believed that organic substances and the humus were the most important foods of the plant. Equally important, however, were Thomas Graham's work on the phosphates, Dumas's new combustion method for the determination of nitrogen, and Liebig's own new methods for organic analyses. Heinrich Rose also invented and perfected many tests for inorganic elements and codified them in an important textbook. Speedy and systematic procedures were becoming available for analyzing organic and inorganic substances.

American farmers, for their part, read Davy and some did their own field experiments. Almost every issue of agricultural journals in the 1830s printed a letter from at least one such farmer. The usual outcome of such experiments was that the farmer had somehow failed to obtain the expected results. These experiments frequently had too many variables, such as climate and rainfall as well as soils, and usually lacked controls; but however faulty they were, the feeling was growing up in American farm circles in the 1830s that the traditional explanation of the action of soils and manures was unable to cope with observed phenomena. Popularizer Henry Madden, for instance, tried in vain in 1839 to describe how manures work:

> Those substances which either alter the texture of the soil, or more especially such as supply saline matter to the plants themselves, may be said to be directly beneficial; whereas those which merely act as chemical agents in hastening the decomposition of the organic matter existing in the soil, can be said to be benefitting the plant in an *indirect* manner only. . . . Moreover, the whole subject is as yet involved in so much doubt, that we should well deserve the imputation of rashness, were we to attempt any classification of these substances founded upon mode of action.[16]

Then Liebig's book appeared in 1840. Amid all the confusion of the 1830s on the role of soils and manures in plant nutrition, Liebig was able to pick out the principal issues and come immediately to the heart of the problem. He was concerned with what elements a plant needed, where it got them, and which farm practices helped most. He organized his book as an argument focused on three essential points: (1) the destruction of the humus theory, (2) the elaboration of a nitrogen cycle, and (3) the explanation of the role of minerals. His book was more of a critique of the present state of the field, as Lyon Playfair pointed out in his preface to the second edition, than a systematic treatise on agricultural chemistry. This was an arrangement at which the argumentative Liebig excelled. Out of his critique emerged a wholly new picture of plant-soil relationships.

Liebig's attack on the humus theory was in several ways typical of his style of argument and showed both the strengths and weaknesses of his personality and scientific approach. First, he incisively critic-ized attempts to define and isolate the "humus." It was called by different names by different investigators whose analyses had shown it to contain 58–72 percent carbon. Such variation might have been tolerated earlier, but organic analysts by the 1840s were arguing over differences of 1–5 percent (as in the Liebig-Mulder controversy over proteins). Liebig pointed to the discrepancy but, unfortunately, insulted other investigators in the process.

He then calculated how much carbon a given area of land pro-duces, whether for forest, hay, or straw. After a lot of fast work with numbers (for which he gave no source), he concluded that the "incontestable facts" had shown that all fields of "average fertility," whether of meadowland or forest, put out equal quantities of carbon. Thus type of soil seemed to make little difference in the amount of carbon in the plants grown on it.[17]

He then asked a surprisingly simple and direct question: If "hu-mus" is decayed plant matter, and if all plants need it, where did the first plants get their humus? This would seem to have been a basic flaw in all vitalistic arguments, where all life was said to come from preexisting life, and Liebig used it to good effect.

He next put plant respiration within a larger context. If men breathe in oxygen and emit carbon dioxide, how does the percent-age of each in the atmosphere ever remain constant? The answer must be that the plants complete a cycle, taking in carbon dioxide and emitting oxygen, as, he noted, Priestley, Ingenhousz, and Senebier have already told us (p. 19).

Having "rediscovered" Saussure, Liebig then unfortunately entered a long tirade against botanists and physiologists who had scorned chemistry and experimentation on plants because of their vitalistic ideas. His attack was part of the general reaction against earlier German vitalistic and antichemical attitudes, but it was probably quite difficult for an organic chemist in 1840 to realize how primitive and limited his beloved chemical analysis had been in 1804 and to understand that plant anatomy and morphology had probably presented more promising avenues for research at that time. In any case, the unnecessary polemic enraged his fellow scientists. It was Liebig at his worst.[18]

Having shown that the carbon dioxide in the atmosphere, rather than the carbon in the humus, contributed to the carbon in plants, Liebig then discussed humus in a more sympathetic light. Before plants grow the leaves with which they can absorb the carbon dioxide of the air, they are dependent upon the carbon dioxide in the humus. He did not seem to notice that his third argument above could also be used against this explanation: Where did the first plant get its humus? His final conception of the role of the humus was somewhat subdued: "Humus does not nourish plants, by being taken up and assimilated in its unaltered state, but by presenting a slow and lasting source of carbonic acid which is absorbed by the roots, and is the principal nourishment of young plants at a time when, being destitute of leaves, they are unable to extract food from the atmosphere" (pp. 59–60). It seems, in retrospect, rather a minor accomplishment to have distinguished between the carbon and the carbon dioxide in the humus, and perhaps the outrage in Liebig's arguments was not really justified. But to have subjected a rather vague concept like the humus theory to chemical scrutiny was a lasting achievement and one that cleared the way for a more detailed analysis of plant nutrition.

After dealing with humus, Liebig discussed the role of nitrogen in plants. This argument, which was really the first formulation of the problem of nitrogen in plants, showed brilliant insight, was based on numerous analyses and farm practices, involved elaborate calculations, and yet was wrong. But by being wrong, or by being several steps beyond the reliable evidence of the time, it stimulated others like Boussingault and Ville in France and Lawes and Gilbert in England to work out the actual details in fifteen years of tedious experiments. With these subsequent events in mind, it is interesting to watch the great mind in action.

Liebig started out by stating that "we know that nitrogen exists in every part of the vegetable structure" (p. 69). This generalization derived from a great many analyses of plant substances undertaken by Liebig and several French chemists and pharmacists during the 1830s. Dumas had devised a new method for determination of nitrogen which made much of it possible. Workers in animal nutrition were also suggesting that nitrogen was an important and little understood constituent of many organic substances, and the source of this nitrogen was of considerable interest to them.

Yet here both Liebig's evidence and his logic were faulty. He pointed to Edward Lukas's experiments in which a plant reportedly grew successfully in charcoal and rainwater (p. 70). How could this happen if the plant, as evidence showed, needed nitrogen? The nitrogen, he reasoned, must be dissolved in the rainwater, either as uncombined nitrogen or as ammonia, the only two forms known to be soluble in water. In his haste to simplify the problem, Liebig apparently overlooked the nitrates which are also soluble in water. Here Liebig made a serious error which was only corrected years later by J. B. Boussingault (see chapter 8). Liebig found little evidence for the free nitrogen but much for the ammonia. Ammonia was known to be very reactive; bodies containing nitrogen putrefied easily and emitted much ammonia. There must therefore be a significant amount of this stray ammonia in the atmosphere. But there was a problem, since, as Liebig noted, "All the analyses of atmospheric air, hitherto made, have failed to demonstrate the presence of ammonia, although according to our view it can never be absent. Is it possible that it could have escaped our most delicate and most exact apparatus?" (p. 74). There was, however, room to hope that the theory might be preserved in spite of this awkward fact, because the experiments of Gustav Schübler and others made in Liebig's own laboratory expressly for this purpose revealed that ten cubic inches of rainwater contained 0.000000048 of a grain of ammonia. This was one grain in 20,800 cubic feet of air. However, a quick juggling of figures would reveal this to be enough to supply the average field the nitrogen necessary for its plants.[19] Thus Liebig skillfully avoided a serious obstacle. The discovery of ammonia in rainwater impressed practically all of Liebig's reviewers, and many investigators proceeded immediately to find it themselves.

But Liebig immediately encountered another even greater obstacle. Was ammonia the real source of the plant's nitrogen? Liebig was confident that, despite the lack of experiments on this point, "this question is susceptible of easy solution by well-known facts" (p. 78). "The most convincing proof" came from the use of ammoniacal manures by farmers. Studies had shown that the amount of gluten (one of the few proteins known at the time) in a plant was variable, and that it was greatest when ammoniacal manures had been used. In wheat the percentage of gluten varied greatly—from 3.3. to 26.7 percent. Guano, urine, and excrements were all excellent manures because of their high nitrogen content. Wild plants, like forests, it was true, survived quite well without any of these ammoniacal manures, but the quantities they obtained from the rainfall were "not sufficient for the purposes of agriculture" (p. 85). Since Liebig later changed his views on the value of nitrogen as a fertilizer (see chapter 3), it is important to note what a crucial position nitrogen manures had in his first formulation of his theory that ammonia entered the roots directly. It was practically the only evidence Liebig offered. Ironically, however, those who challenged and eventually disproved his ammonia theory of plant nitrogen, Jean-Baptiste Boussingault and Georges Ville, upheld and strongly supported the need for nitrogen fertilizers.

On the basis of his theory, Liebig was ready to explain the hitherto baffling problem of gypsum. He asserted that its effect on grasses "depends only upon its fixing in the soil the ammonia of the atmosphere, which would otherwise be volatilised, with the water which evaporates" (p. 86). But then the question arose, If the ammonia in the atmosphere was all that mattered, why should gypsum be effective only on clover and rye? This was a problem that the farm journals would bring up again and again, for Liebig's answer was inadequate. He considered only atmospheric and not soil factors as important and attributed gypsum's frequent ineffectiveness to a dry atmosphere (p. 88). But Liebig was not enough of a farmer to know about these underlying problems and, therefore, in his typically exaggerated way, reiterated his simple theory: "No conclusion can then have a better foundation than this, that it is the ammonia of the atmosphere which furnishes nitrogen to plants" (p. 91).

If Liebig's first two strokes were to deflate the humus and to elevate nitrogen, the third was to explain the role of minerals in plants. This was a problem that was only dimly perceived before him. It was his lasting achievement not only to formulate it as a problem but also to explain it and offer practical suggestions on how to solve it. Though he, as usual, overstated his case, his work on minerals was valid long after his nitrogen theory had been overthrown (see chapter 8). The analyses of Saussure and Davy's time were not precise enough or numerous enough to pinpoint which minerals appeared in which parts of which plants. Some were known to be present sometimes, but no one knew why or how they got there. Succeeding decades had seen many newer analyses which Liebig began to pull together. His review of this work led him to a radically new interpretation of Saussure's experiments: Minerals, despite their small quantity, were not trivial; they were essential. There were certain variations and substitutions, but in general potash, soda, lime, and magnesia were present in all parts of all plants (p. 98) and were not "accidental" as others had thought. Two alternative explanations of the variations between plants were then possible. Either the plants were somehow selective and absorbed only the proper minerals, he reasoned, or else they absorbed minerals indiscriminately, as Saussure had shown, and excreted the nonessential. Liebig adopted the second view and used the questionable Candolle/Macaire-Princep theory of plant exudations to support it. He found more evidence that certain minerals were essential to plants in phenomena observed around the farm. When alkalies were absent from the soil, the growth of plants was frequently stunted in some way. When alkalies were added to crops, as in the potash of ashes, the crops thrived. Potash had been observed to be even more effective than gypsum (p. 106). The potash was acting as a replacement for a deficiency in the soil. With this explanation one could now make sense out of other phenomena—such as the depleted state of the tobacco lands of Virginia, which had formerly been so productive. This was due to no vague loss of humus, but to a simple exhaustion of the alkalies in the soil. This "deficiency" concept could also explain why some rotations of crops worked better than others. The trick was to arrange them so that what was excreted from the first plant as a "poison" (such as phosphate of magnesia) would be a necessary food to the next crop in the rotation (pp. 168–72).

Not only were such bases of the inorganic salts as potash, magnesia, and soda necessary; acids were also required (p. 154). Silicic and especially phosphoric acids were both essential. This discovery (and its consequences for phosphatic fertilizers) was a clear example of how improved analysis helped Liebig. Saussure had shown that phosphates were important, but he had had great difficulty in isolating them and kept getting double salts.[20] Davy had barely mentioned them, but they had received much attention in the 1830s. Phosphates, Liebig thought, were especially helpful to wheat crops. Developing better tests for the phosphates, which were frequently taken for alumina, was a continuing problem for agricultural chemists.

Assuming minerals to be essential to plants, the action of manures could now be explained in a new way. They supplied the inorganic elements that were lacking in the soil, as animal dung provided silicates of potash as well as small amounts of nitrogen, ashes provided potash, and bone dust provided phosphates. Perhaps someday, Liebig suggested, these elements could be produced artificially, just as calico manufacturers were using artificial phosphate of soda instead of cow dung to brighten and make fast their dyes.

Liebig, however, did not close his first edition in this optimisic vein. Instead, he stressed once again that supplying crops with nitrogen was "the most important object of agriculture" (p. 188). Much nitrogen was being wasted in animal and human urine. But now that gypsum had been shown to fix ammonia, stables could be strewn with it to collect the urine. Since for each pound of urine lost, Liebig calculated sixty pounds of wheat were lost, this was no joking matter. Thus both nitrogen and alkalies were necessary, but in 1840 nitrogen seemed the most pressing, since there was not enough available in the form of ammonia in the atmosphere.

Liebig thus managed in less than two hundred pages to put together a wholly new synthesis of agricultural chemistry.[21] It was probably one of the most important scientific books ever published and marks the beginning of a "scientific revolution." The book had great impact because it came suddenly from an unexpected, though greatly respected, quarter and seemed to solve long-standing and gnawing problems. It created order out of the previous thirty years of agricultural chemistry and outlined a program for the next thirty years. By being sketchy and outlining problems rather than by doing experiments himself, for which Berzelius criticized him,[22] Liebig directed a whole generation of workers, who solved more problems than he, if he had had the patience, could have solved in a lifetime.

But the results of this important book were not limited to scientists.

Liebig had made his solution seem so simple, had taken so many of his arguments from known farm practices, and had written at a time when such problems were becoming so urgent, that the popular reaction was immense and led to long-term consequences. "Liebig" and "agricultural chemistry" became, for better or for worse, synonyms and entered the popular mind as symbols of the progress and usefulness of science.

Who, then, was this German professor Justus Liebig on whom popular attention was so suddenly focused in 1840? Liebig was, at the age of thirty-seven, at the height of his powers and already one of the leading organic chemists of Europe. His work on agriculture and physiology in the 1840s would extend this professional reputation even further and make him one of the most widely known and influential chemists of all time. He discovered and analyzed numerous organic compounds, but his best-known work was his joint discovery with Friedrich Wöhler of the benzoyl radical in 1832. It led to knowledge of a whole series of compounds, on which theories of organic structure could be based, and during the 1830s Liebig battled with Dumas of Paris and Berzelius of Stockholm over their meaning and theoretical explanation. Throughout his career Liebig showed a knack for isolating the key problem, solving it and thereby opening up a new area, and then moving on to another problem. His quick impulsive, energetic temperament was more suited to this style of research than to patient, systematic studies of one set of compounds, which another chemist, such as Gerhardt Mulder of Utrecht, was doing on proteins.

Liebig had studied with the French chemist Gay-Lussac in Paris and, through the patronage of Alexander von Humboldt, had been able to obtain a professorship at an early age in the tiny town of Giessen in his native Hesse-Darmstadt. He had struggled to build up a small laboratory there and under rather difficult conditions had managed to do his path-breaking research. Liebig's laboratory, one of the few in Europe open to students in the 1830s and 1840s, before such institutions became popular, was very helpful to a professor of his temperament. The fame of his researches in the 1830s and the needs of pharmacists seeking training had brought large number of students, even foreign ones, to his laboratory, years before his popular work on agriculture appeared. He could direct these students, who were doing original research but who needed some direction, to topics that interested him. As editor (with his friend Wöhler) of one of the major chemical journals of the day, the *Annalen der Chemie und Pharmacie*, Liebig was exceptionally well informed of the newest areas of investigation and the latest interpretations. In the course of his career he went through distinct phases of interest in organic, agricultural, and physiological chemistry.[23]

It is not clear from the published sources how Liebig became interested in agricultural chemistry, but several conjectures are possible. The opportunity to write the book arose when the British Association for the Advancement of Science, which Liebig was visiting in 1837, asked him to write a review of the state of organic chemistry. The subject had gone through a tremendous period of growth in the 1830s, and the BAAS had a tradition of requesting such topical progress reports. Liebig was about to write a textbook on organic chemistry anyhow and accepted the assignment. The book he presented to the association three years later was really the introduction to his three-volume textbook, *Traité de chimie organique*, which appeared only in French.[24] But no one suspected that he would choose to discuss agricultural chemistry exclusively. The BAAS certainly did not direct him to the topic.

Yet the 1837 visit to England may have given Liebig some ideas about agricultural chemistry, for there was in Britain at the time a group of men very actively interested in scientific agriculture. Perhaps Liebig saw or heard something from them that started him on the topic. His visit with Thomas Graham the chemist is known to have turned his interest toward the phosphates. This hypothesis of British influence is especially inviting since one of the papers delivered that year at the BAAS meeting had some of Liebig's essential ideas in it. Yet appealing as this theory is, Liebig wrote home that day that he was having such a hard time understanding the English spoken at the meeting that he had spent the day at the beach.[25]

A different source of Liebig's interest in agriculture in 1840 may have been the economic situation in Giessen at the time. Giessen in the 1830s and 1840s was at the very heart of an extremely poor agricultural area of Germany. The Giessen Emigration Society was one of the most active groups in Germany in helping improverished families flee to America.[26] Perhaps they interested Liebig in the humanitarian goal of improving agriculture.

But Liebig's own previous publications show only moderate interest in agricultural chemistry. An analysis of the articles in his *Annalen* in the years before 1840 shows that he published one by Macaire-Princep on the rotation of crops in 1833, one by Sprengel on constituents of wood ashes in 1835, and one by Boussingault on nitrogen in cattle feeds in 1837.[27] In a sense, therefore, Liebig had been interested in agricultural chemistry all along, but none of these papers would furnish a clue to his intensive interest in it by 1840.

One last suggestion is possible. Liebig wrote the book in 1839 just after Saussure had published a paper on fermentation which discussed the humus. Liebig immediately noticed it and used it to bolster his own arguments for an oxidative-catalytic theory of fermentation, which was also his major concern in the second part of his book. Perhaps Saussure led him to the humus, and he then taught himself rapidly all he could about agricultural chemistry. This explanation seems fairly likely, since it would explain Liebig's great interest in the humus in 1840 and his feeling of rediscovering Saussure's earlier work. Fermentation may well have been the topic that brought Liebig and Saussure together.[28]

In any case, it seems that after his visit to England and while working on his textbook, Liebig came upon agricultural chemistry unexpectedly. He surveyed the literature, did a few quick experiments, wrote his ideas up quickly, and took everyone completely by surprise. Most—like the Americans Samuel L. Dana and Charles T. Jackson, who had been interested in agricultural chemistry as part of their work on various state agricultural surveys—could at first only sputter about the humus and the apocrenic acids. The larger influences of Liebig and his laboratory were yet to come.

3

From Ammonia to Phosphates

In the early 1840s Liebig's ideas spread rapidly in America as they were published in numerous inexpensive editions, popularizations, and agricultural journals. The original English edition sold for $3.50, but one pirated American edition sold for as little as 25 ¢ a year later.[1] The *Cultivator* of Albany, New York, was probably the first American journal to incorporate Liebig's views into its articles and editorials, since it started immediately upon receiving and reviewing his book. Liebig's influence in America dates, therefore, from May 1841. The *Cultivator* was particularly prompt in taking up Liebig's ideas, since one of its editors, Willis Gaylord, had a special interest in manures and scientific agriculture. He vigorously praised new developments, and since he always spelled out his reasons, his comments provide a useful barometer of Liebig's fluctuating reputation in America. Unfortunately, he died in March 1844 at a key point in the excitement over Liebig scientific agriculture in the United States.[2]

Although the chemistry of soils is in one sense a fairly "applied" science, there were varying degrees of usefulness, and Liebig's book was not practical enough to direct a farmer, who needed to know how much of a substance to use and how and when to use it. The agricultural journals tried to fill this gap between the scientist and the farmer in the 1840s. The editors not only popularized new theories but also, by encouraging experiments, reporting successes and failures, and determining what methods seemed to work best, acted as clearinghouses for those trying to implement the new theories.

Liebig's book presented special problems, since it was written more for other chemists than for farmers. As he discussed the humus, nitrogen, and minerals, Liebig reviewed a great many farm practice, such as the rotation of crops, fallowing, and the use of manures of all sorts. He asserted so much that it was hard to derive a clear-cut program for improved farming from it all. Even worse, it was not very clear from the text whether he preferred ammonia or minerals. He seemed to stress both equally, but at the end he urged most emphatically that plants be provided with additional sources of ammonia. It was the central role of ammonia that struck his contemporaries most forcibly. Liebig specifically recommended gypsum or powdered charcoal for attracting ammonia from its two most abundant sources, urine and the atmosphere.[3]

Before following the fate of these two suggestions in the farm journals of 1841–45, we should pause to consider an important difficulty underlying the verification of any agricultural theory at that time. The problems were far more complex than anyone in the 1840s could have realized. Neither farmers nor scientists would have a working knowledge of statistical verification and proper controls until the early twentieth century. Furthermore, these farmers were trying both to implement and to verify Liebig's theories at the same time. Just what, then, did a given "success" or "failure" prove? For example, if a farmer's experimental crop failed, was it because (1) he had used too little (or too much) gypsum or his technique was otherwise faulty; (2) other factors like rainfall, field drainage, or type of soil had entered in; or (3) Liebig's explanation was wrong or inadequate? All too often they blamed apparent failures on Liebig's theory rather than on their own experimentation. If, on the other hand, the farmer had a successful crop (larger than usual), which of the many factors involved was the true reason—this year's charcoal or the lime he had been using all along? Since most experiments were rather muddled and imperfectly reported, it was usually hard to tell what they meant, and one could interpret them however he chose. Nevertheless, the farmers did their "experiments," reported their results, and then came "scientifically" to their conclusions.

Editors and readers alike were constantly calling for more and more experiments on the various innovations of the period. Their quest for rational proof seems to have been only rarely fulfilled, however. More often experimental results were used to buttress whatever one already wanted to believe. Besides, farmers were generally reluctant to report failures, since they feared ridicule.[4] This self-censorship made it harder for editors to find negative evidence and increased their bias in favor of crazes and innovations. But despite these difficulties, the editors' faith that amateur home experimenters would be able to choose the correct over the incorrect method remained strong throughout the 1840s. Later, agricultural reformers were able to use this faith and these frustrated hopes as important arguments for the establishment of state agricultural experiment stations.

Liebig's ideas on gypsum were the first part of his book to attract the farmers' scrutiny, since by 1841 Americans, especially those in upstate New York, had already had a great deal of experience with this fertilizer. As already mentioned, almost all reviewers acclaimed Liebig's solution of the long-standing gypsum problem. His explanation that gypsum attracted the ammonia from the atmosphere and from the manures and fixed it in the soil as ammonium sulphate was a more satisfactory theory than Davy's had been. Yet it, too, had difficulties, for gypsum was not universally successful—its effects wore off, it did not affect some soils at all, yet it affected others for years. Liebig could, in short, explain the "successes" satisfactorily but could not predict the "failures." In spite of this problem Liebig's theory was the best available in 1841 and was readily accepted, though, as the *Cultivator* put it, with "some modification."[5]

But in the spring of 1842 Samuel L. Dana of Lowell, Massachusetts, presented an alternative theory in his *Muck Manual for Farmers*. It was essentially a vitalistic theory based on Berzelius's and Mulder's ideas of the organic acids in the humus (or "geine," as Dana preferred to call it, from the Greek earth goddess Ge). Dana had used the humus concept while working with Edward Hitchcock on the Massachusetts geological survey in the 1830s. The survey's final report was just going to press in 1841 when Liebig's book appeared. Dana inserted a special "postscript" prominently near the front of the volume to summarize his and Liebig's differences.[6] But he did not develop his theory fully until faced with the necessity of delivering a series of public lectures. With his invaluable experience of making soil analyses for the state survey, Dana should have been the American most able to appreciate Liebig's theory. Such strong opposition by the nation's leading agricultural chemist is therefore quite significant.

In 1840 Dana was already an accomplished physician, geologist, and agricultural chemist; but he was, and still is, best known for his work in industrial chemistry. A graduate of Harvard Medical School in 1818, he published a geology of greater Boston with his brother James Freeman Dana* that same year. He then settled down to a medical practice in Waltham, Massachusetts. Becoming more interested in chemistry than in medicine, he started a sulphuric acid plant in nearby Newton in 1826 to supply the textile mills in Waltham. In 1833 he was hired away by the Merrimac Print Works of Lowell, where he remained until his death in 1868. Textile industrialists were at this time quite interested in chemistry, since they faced important problems in the bleaching and dyeing of calicos. Dana went abroad to look into French solutions to the problem and started reading a French translation of Berzelius's textbook, which contained a lengthy section on dyes. Dana struck upon the idea of substituting sodium phosphate for the cow dung used by American firms in the dyeing process, an early and important step in the replacing of organic dyes and mordants with artificial substitutes.[7]

The source of such phosphates now became an important problem for the company and one which led Dana from industrial into agricultural chemistry. He had been involved with the first Massachusetts state geological survey in 1830–33, but was even more active on the second survey of 1837–40, which stressed practical geology such as analyses of soils. When, on the survey, he discovered that Davy's method of soil analysis gave an excess of alumina, he developed a new one. He also grappled with the elusive concept of geine, which was currently under attack by Charles T. Jackson of Boston. In his survey of Rhode Island, Jackson had said not only that geine did not exist, but also that it was a nitrogenous combination of the crenic and apocrenic acids. Dana insisted it was non-nitrogenous.[8] A controversy with Jackson was thus flaring in 1841, but this was minor compared to Liebig's attack on the humus theory.

Although Dana completely condemned Liebig's theory at first, within a year he adopted the idea of ammonia.[9] In a letter written to Hitchcock in June 1841, just a few hours after Dana had seen Liebig's book, he bristled with rage. John W. Webster obligingly published this and some other items representing Dana's and Jackson's views in the appendixes to his first and second American editions of Liebig's books and also added their criticisms of Liebig's ideas to the notes in

*Not to be confused with James Dwight Dana (1813–95) of Yale.

the text. In these notes, Dana, who advocated replacing cow dung with artificial phosphates in the factory, remained too much of a vitalist to accept Liebig's dismissal of the humus for plant growth. His statements do not seem to have met very many of Liebig's arguments—he just reiterated the Berzelian doctrine. Even Berzelius himself had been more open-minded.

It would be easy, therefore, to dismiss Dana as an uncomprehending "old fogy," but the episode is not so simple. Later in 1841 the local lyceum in Lowell asked Dana to lecture on the suddenly popular subject of agricultural chemistry. Dana did so and published his lectures in 1842 as the *Muck Manual for Farmers*. It is a most peculiar book, outdated and modern at the same time. Dana took some of Liebig's ideas, such as the ammonia theory, and cast much of his argument in a form reminiscent of Liebig—emphasizing probable sources and quantities of each necessary element. He also skillfully used Liebig's own earlier statements to discredit him, as in citing a textbook Liebig helped edit in the late 1830s for an analysis of humus.[10] In other places he went beyond Liebig and included climatic, geological, and physical aspects of soil chemistry, far in advance of his time.

Dana's argument is quite difficult to follow. Mainly he attributed the growth of plants to the interaction of the geine with salts. He warned, though, that plant growth could not be investigated too far, since the mysterious vital principle would elude all men. The geine was by definition insoluble, but the salts made it soluble and so able to enter the plant. His theory was somewhat reminiscent of Davy's, but went beyond it. Sulfates (like gypsum) and carbonates (like marl) made effective manures, since when they broke down the silicates, which make up a large part of the soil, they freed a base to combine with the geine. Here then was an alternative theory for the action of mineral manures. In the case of gypsum, the sulfate attacked the inert silicates, thus freeing both its own lime (Ca^{++}, in modern terminology) and the silicic acid (SiO_3^{--}) of the soil. The lime then formed a soluble salt with the geine, while the extra silicic acid remained free in the soil:

$$CaSO_4 + \underset{\text{(insoluble)}}{geine} + \underset{\substack{\text{silicate} \\ K_2SiO_3}}{alkaline} \rightarrow Ca^{++}\text{-geine} + \underset{\text{(soluble salt)}}{K_2SO_4} + SiO_3^{--}.$$

If some of the soil contained lime silicates, $CaSiO_3$, then a chain reaction would be set up, and the prolonged effects of gypsum, sometimes over several years, would be explained:

$$CaSO_4 + geine + CaSiO_3 \rightarrow Ca^{++}\text{-}geine + CaSO_4 + SiO_3^{--}.$$

Liebig had not included any such soil factors in his explanation and certainly not any geine, but if the geine were allowed to contain ammonia (as Charles Jackson was beginning to think), then both Liebig's and Dana's explanations would come down to the same reaction:

$$CaSO_4 + (NH_4)_2CO_3 \rightarrow (NH_4)_2SO_4 + CaCO_3.$$

The sources of their ammonia would, however, be very different, being the atmosphere for Liebig and the geine for Jackson and Dana. But Dana had expressly defined geine as nonnitrogenous, although he described it as emitting ammonia! Dana's theory might have had the advantage over Liebig's, since it depended on the nature of the soil, which contained a great many sulphates, carbonates, and silicates, as well as geine. But Dana minimized these mineral differences in soils and considered the organic geine of greater importance than the salts.[11]

Dana's theory was therefore riddled with internal inconsistencies, but it allowed for variable results; while Liebig's theory was chemically more consistent but unable to account for the variety of phenomena. Both were in the light of modern knowledge, partially correct, each tackling and oversimplifying a different aspect of a very complex problem.[12] In the long run Dana's view would find support; but in the short run, the next eight to ten years, Liebig held sway.

The reception accorded the two theories by the farmers and the scientists offers an interesting view of the two different communities. Both, as we have seen, accepted Liebig—the scientists (with the exception of Dana) enthusiastically, the farmers with qualifications. With Dana's *Muck Manual* the reactions was the reverse. This time the scientists were over the years much less enthusiastic than the farmers. Benjamin Silliman, in a lengthy review in the *American Journal of Science,* predicted that although he had "never met with so luminous and satisfactory a view of the mutual and complicated action of silicates, salts, and geine," the book was so aphoristic as to overlook important exceptions and to cause minunderstandings. He was correct, for the book made little impact on the agricultural chemists of the time, who made only one reference to it in the next thirty years, and that was unfavorable. The book, as far as scientists were concerned, seems to have dropped out of sight shortly after publication in 1842. The farmers, however, hailed the book and bought so many copies of it through the 1860s that it went through four editions. In American farming circles Dana's *Muck Manual* was an all-time best seller.[13]

One can only speculate as to reasons for this tremendous difference. The problems being considered were much too complicated for the techniques and concepts of the 1840s. Dana's views were comprehensive, but since they centered on the humus, whose action was far too complex for the chemistry of the time (see fig. 1), they were so muddled and vague that they could provide no clear starting point for further work. The proper study of the humus awaited the development of new microbiological, biochemical, and pedological techniques and concepts in the 1880s and after. Liebig's theory, by contrast, drastically but skillfully oversimplified the problems involved and pointed directly to nitrogen and minerals—two subjects that could be studied by techniques available in the 1840s. The advantages of Liebig's theory over Dana's were obvious to scientists. Unfortunately, in failing to pursue Dana's theory, the scientists missed entirely his valid views on the importance of reactions within the soil. But in the 1850s and 1860s enough dissatisfaction with Liebig's theory would build up for soil factors to seem important. Only then would scientists begin to study the ideas Dana had put forth in 1842. Agricultural science, like agricultural innovation, appears in general to progress now in one direction and then in another, as successive improvements in ideas and techniques at first excite and then disappoint their practitioners and finally make way for another that appears even more fruitful.

The farmers' reaction to the two books was very different. They saw no contradiction in approving Dana on gypsum and Liebig on humus, even though such a stand involved a double inconsistency, for accepting Dana's view of gypsum required an important role for the humus, which Liebig denounced.[14] The farmers were much more eclectic than the scientists and were willing to invoke the one or the other as the case required. Consistency was not important to them;

they were willing to accept whatever theory seemed to make the best sense out of a given phenomenon and were content to follow several at once if it meant better crops. This attitude led to what has been called a certain "anti-intellectualism" among farmers, as, for example, when Gaylord talked of the two conflicting theories of the action of manure: "So far as the farmer is concerned, it matters but little which of these two theories is the correct one, or whether (as we are inclined to believe) they are both partly true, since the value and the necessity of the application of manures remains the same."[15] Yet impatient as farmers were with the details of scientific controversies, their eclecticism was really an open-mindedness when compared to the attitude of the scientists, who had to focus on a few of the simpler aspects of a complex problem, pursue them as far as possible, and then try another approach. The farmers, however, had to face the problem in its bewildering totality and do what seemed safe at the time. The two communities could hardly have differed more in their approach to agricultural problems.

It was typical of the eclectic farmers that their skepticism toward one of Liebig's ideas did not prevent them from trying out his second suggestion for attracting ammonia, the use of powdered charcoal. The episode was quite unlike the gypsum case, since the Americans had no previous experience with charcoal and had to be persuaded to try it. Instead of an encounter of theory with practice, therefore, the charcoal episode illustrates the promotional campaigns undertaken by the farm journals of the period to spread a new technique.

The first phase was active publicizing of the advantages of powdered charcoal. Before results of the earnestly sought experiments were forthcoming, instances of "successes," recollected from as far back as twenty years, were sprinkled in the journals as wonder stories to keep the interest alive.[16] But, of course, the greatest publicist for charcoal's benefits was Liebig himself. He had been quite optimistic about it in the first edition of his book, asserting, "Plants thrive in powdered charcoal, and may be brought to blossom and bear fruit if exposed to the influence of rain and the atomsphere." The evidence for this was not that any farmers had been successful with it, but that charcoal "surpasses all other substances in the power which it possesses of condensing ammonia within its pores, particularly when it has been previously heated to redness. Charcoal absorbs 90 times its volume of ammoniacal gas, which may be again separated by simply moistening it with water."[17] The *Cultivator* cited this chemical fact again and again in the early 1840s as evidence that the use of charcoal promised bigger crops to farmers.[18]

Liebig based this strong recommendation of powdered charcoal on certain experiments by Edward Lukas in Munich in 1837, which were Liebig's sole experimental evidence for the central role of ammonia in plants. Lukas claimed that about fifty varieties of his plants had flourished in a soil of charcoal watered with rainwater. Willis Gaylord reprinted in the *Cultivator* the appendix to Liebig's book that described Lukas's experiments, along with comments encouraging farmers to try it and see for themselves.[19]

Meanwhile, John W. Webster, in the preface to his first American edition of Liebig's book, had also encouraged readers to try their own experiments in the coming summer season. Already several indoor experiments had been undertaken in the Boston area. For instance, James E. Teschemacher, a Boston businessman and horti-culturalist later interested in guano, had used charcoal and ammonia to good effect on geraniums at the Boston Conservatory. Webster himself had applied charcoal, rainwater, and extra ammonia to a large pine kept indoors in a tub. It had grown six inches in thirteen weeks, significantly more than the four to five inches it usually grew in six months. Wealthy John Lowell had allowed experiments to be made at his greenhouse in Roxbury, but there had been "no very obvious results" among fruit trees or vines, though among vegetables there had been some effect with beans. Webster attributed the several failures to "an oversight of the gardener" who had not understood the directions properly, but attributed the "success" with the beans to the charcoal. Webster hoped to include the results of more experiments in later editions but never did.[20] The use of powdered charcoal thus led to mixed results with domestic plants, but the promoters' optimism for it remained strong.

Over the next few years several farmers experimented with charcoal on their farms and reported their results to the *Cultivator*. One farmer in Alabama reported a complete failure, but Gaylord insisted that he must not have pulverized the charcoal finely enough. Another, Robert Pell of Ulster County, New York, reported phenomenal success with charcoal on his wheat—seventy-eight bushels per acre (for less than half an acre). He accordingly believed charcoal "to be the most valuable substance now known as manure, being pure, incorruptible and lasting." A description of Pell's farm that appeared a few months later, however, reported that he generally used lime extensively on his farm, up to thirty bushels per acre.[21]

Then, suddenly, in May 1844 an alert reader pointed out that Liebig himself no longer favored charcoal. After this, the Americans' first inkling that Liebig had changed his views on ammonia, articles on charcoal became more skeptical. A. J. Prime of Newburgh, New York, considered the current "mania" for charcoal quite unfounded, lacking adequate proof of its effectiveness, and called for more precise experiments, but none were forthcoming. Now even a past "success" was reported unfavorably. In January 1843 Zachary Drummond of Virginia had written to the *Cultivator* for advice on some charcoal experiments, but he had not reported his results. A Michigan farmer inquired in December 1844 what had happened. Drummond responded that he had had a 15 to 20 percent increase on both wheat and corn, which earlier would have been hailed as successful. But Drummond was not enthusiastic about charcoal. He attributed about half the increase to his plot's hillside location and did not consider the remainder worth the added cost of the charcoal. He thought ashes would be just as effective and much cheaper.[22] Thus the American farmer pointed out the important matter of prices, which Liebig the scientist had not considered in his recommendations.

Even worse, Liebig's facts were shown to be wrong. In 1851 John Pitkin Norton reported that Thomas Anderson of Edinburgh had shown that charcoal did not absorb ammonia after all (less than 1 percent after several days). Charcoal absorbed the gaseous ammonia, and so its smell, but nothing more. It would therefore make an effective deodorizer of manure heaps or city sewerage, but it could not be a fertilizer.[23]

In practice, then, Liebig's recommendation for the use of charcoal did not lead to the great new manure that both he and the editors of the *Cultivator* had predicted in 1841. Like other crazes of the period, the charcoal fad went first through a period of optimism, fed by the editor's encouragement, wonder stories from past recollections, and a few seemingly successful experiments; and secondly through a period of skepticism, led by a few alert and discriminating readers, who subjected the muddled nature of the "successes" to closer examination. In this case the additional factor of Liebig's change of heart brought the fad to an early end. Neither of Liebig's first two suggestions for improved farming, therefore, wrought noticeable changes on American farms. His theory on gypsum was inadequate, and his facts on charcoal were wrong. Agricultural panaceas were not as easy to find as Liebig had thought.

In the realm of fertilizer theory, however, Liebig was much more successful. As one farmer put it, "Liebig's theory appears to me the only one as yet promulgated, on which a farmer could apply plaster understandingly."[24] Although Liebig's ammonia theory had taken everyone by surprise in 1841, almost all had rapidly embraced it, for it provided a very adequate explanation of known fertilizer phenomena. Proven manures, like human and animal urine and excrements, contained a significant percentage of ammonia compounds, or at least they smelled as if they did. The action of other manures, like gypsum, could be explained in terms of fixing the ammonia. Furthermore, two new fertilizers of the period seemed, at first, to support this view.

Sir Humphry Davy was probably the first person to introduce guano to Americans when he discussed its effects in his *Agricultural Chemistry,* but its use was never as popular in the United States as it was in Britain. It was not commercially available in America until 1844, and then its supply was irregular and its price high until about 1848–50. It reached its height of popularity in the 1850s, chiefly in the South on depleted tobacco lands. Although it was not widely used in the United States in the period 1841–44, it attracted wide interest in scientific as well as agricultural circles, since it was so phenomenally effective.[25]

At first glance guano's high nitrogen content, which had been known since Louis Vauquelin and Martin Klaproth analyzed it for Alexander von Humboldt, explained its powerful effects; and Liebig used it, as we have seen, as strong evidence for an ammonia theory. But a spate of new improved analyses in this period, by Karl Völckel in Wöhler's laboratory at Göttingen and by James E. Teschemacher of Boston, showed that guano also contained a high percentage of phosphates. On close inspection, therefore, guano could provide evidence for either an ammonia or a mineral theory of fertilizers.[26]

Bone dust or pulverized bones had been recognized as an effective fertilizer during the 1830s. As with other fertilizers, the reason for its effectiveness remained a much-discussed problem, and two schools of thought about it had developed by 1841. The more widespread one held that bone dust was effective because of the nitrogenous gelatin or animal matter that it contained, though after 1840 the gelatin idea was usually dropped in favor of ammonia. The opposing viewpoint attributed the effectiveness of bone dust to its phosphate content—55 percent according to Berzelius. Liebig was ambivalent about bones in 1840, stressing at one point their phosphate content and at another their animal matter and ammonia. There seemed to be no conclusive evidence either way.[27]

An ammonia theory thus provided an acceptable explanation for known fertilizer phenomena in the early 1840s. Most evidence strongly favored ammonia, and the rest was at least neutral. The chief problem of the time was whether all the nitrogen was really in the form of ammonia. Nitrates might be equally important, as the French agricultural chemist Boussingault was to suggest.[28] But for Liebig to develop a mineral theory that stressed phosphates and deemphasized nitrogen would run counter to current thinking and would require potent new evidence. The path Liebig took is therefore of some interest.

Liebig's first step away from ammonia and toward minerals was rather a hesitant one. He published a second edition of his epoch-making book early in 1842 which was largely unchanged but had "very numerous additions." By far the most important addition was the forty-six–page "supplementary chapter" on soils and soil analysis. Though he remained an adherent of his ammonia theory in the main text, the new chapter was strongly in favor of minerals. Alkalies, earths, and phosphates he now considered "perfectly indispensable" (p. 199). Different plants need different acids, as only grapes need considerable quantities of tartaric acid. The various salts, which are necessary to the formation of certain acids, do not, therefore, appear in all plants. Knowing which salts a plant needs will help a farmer determine which fertilizer to apply to it. To show the usefulness of this approach, Liebig appended sample analyses of forty-seven soils and added to each brief notes on their performance and suggestions for possible remedies. Most of the samples were taken from Karl Sprengel's *Die Bodenkunde* (*The Science of Soils*) of 1837; but a few were culled from Davy and Berzelius, and two were unidentified analyses from Ohio. These examples were not very persuasive, since the amount of phosphate of lime in one soil ranked "fertile" might be less than that in the next one marked "barren."[29] A skeptic might wish to consider many other factors before concluding with Liebig that the quantity of salts was the crucial one. Few conclusions were drawn, however, and the samples were left to speak for themselves.

Unlike his predecessor Humphry Davy, Liebig did not encourage farmers to run out and give their own soils a quick calcium carbonate test. Accurate analysis was far too complex for that now, for as Liebig noted, "It is unnecessary to describe the *modus operandi* used in the analyses of these soils, for this kind of research will never be made by farmers, who must apply to the professional chemist, if they wish for information regarding the composition of their soils" (p. 208). Only a few Americans seem to have picked up this hidden hint of where Liebig's ideas would eventually lead.

This second edition of Liebig's book appeared in America in four printings—two edited by John W. Webster of Cambridge and two in Philadelphia. Since these editions were less expensive than the first had been, they may have reached an even wider American audience than the first had. Yet no separate reviews of this edition appeared in the journals. Everyone, it seemed, thought both editions of Liebig were the same.

Appearing almost simultaneously with the second edition was another book by Justus Liebig, the *Animal Chemistry* of 1842. It represents the second step Liebig took toward a mineral theory of fertilizers, though at first it seems somewhat irrelevant, for plant and animal chemistry had traditionally been rather separate studies. It was Liebig's genius to show them to be intimately related. One of the main themes of the *Animal Chemistry* was that the plant food eaten by an animal already contained the proteins that later appeared in the blood and muscles. Analyses of the blood (and of other proteins, though he usually talked of the blood) revealed the presence of phosphorus and sulphur as well as nitrogen.[30] Liebig's acute mind immediately focused on the probable source of these elements. Where did the plant get them? Since they were not present in the air, they must come from the soil, probably in the form of phosphates and sulphates.

Liebig now (1842–August 1843) undertook the third and final step toward his "mineral theory," a complete revision of the text, stressing all indications that minerals were important and deemphasizing all evidence that nitrogen alone was adequate. The final effect was ambivalent—the necessity of both, but the greater necessity of minerals. Whenever Liebig mentioned in the third edition that the addition of nitrogen and ammonia was important, he always added immediately that mineral fertilizers were even *more* necessary: The plant could survive, if not thrive, on the nitrogen in the atmosphere, but it had no atmospheric source of minerals. The change in emphasis is neatly summarized in this comparison of two similar passages in 1842 and 1843:

1842 (2nd ed., p. 84)	*1843 (3rd ed., p. 54)*
Cultivated plants receive the same quantity of nitrogen from the atmosphere as trees, shrubs, and other wild plants; and this is not sufficient for the purposes of agriculture. Agriculture differs essentially from the cultivation of forests, inasmuch as its principal object consists in the production of nitrogen under any form capable of assimilation; whilst the object of forest culture is confined principally to the production of carbon.	Cultivated plants receive the same quantity of nitrogen from the atmosphere as trees, shrubs, and other wild plants; and this is quite sufficient for the purposes of agriculture. Agriculture differs essentially from the cultivation of forests, inasmuch as its principal object consists in the production of the CONSTITUENTS OF THE BLOOD: whilst the object of forest culture is confined principally to the production of carbon. But the presence of ammonia does not suffice for the production of the nitrogenous ingredients. Other conditions likewise are essential.

Liebig chose his evidence very carefully and defended his new mineral theory in his usual highly polemical style. He now cited Saussure's work on plant minerals more than ever and mentioned numerous times the recently published prize paper by Wiegmann and Polstorff, "On the Inorganic Constituents of Plants," putting much of its supportive data in his appendix. Liebig also minimized and distorted the interpretation of certain field observations on the effects of nitrogen manures in order to support his own view and, apparently without reason, increased 100-fold his figure on the amount of ammonia in the atmosphere (from .000000048 to .00000-48). Either there had been a mathematical error before, or else Liebig, in his eagerness to maximize the ammonia in the air, was not above shading his figures a bit. He also dropped more than five pages of his previous discussion of the effects of guano, which he had attributed to its ammoniacal salts. Most unfair of all was his deliberate attempt to disprove and ridicule recent experiments by his nemesis Boussingault, which pointed more toward nitrates than toward minerals as the essential food of plants.[31]

Liebig's usual tactic in recasting his argument was the skillful addition and deletion of paragraphs, sentences, and even whole chapters in order to leave a distinctly opposite impression on the reader. A few examples may suffice. Whereas in the earlier edition he stressed that the nitrogen in urine must be the effective ingredient (he never seemed to think several might be essential) because the salts were only 1 percent of the total volume, he now dropped these figures and said that the salts are present in the urine in the same percentage that they are in plants (tiny in both). He applied the same argument to his greatly shortened discussion of guano, so that now instead of considering the salts trivial, he left the reader to conclude that the similarity of their percentages could hardly be coincidental.[32]

In another place, where he had formerly said that the nitrogen harvested in a crop and sent to a city was lost to the farmer forever, he now chose to minimize the problem by dropping this whole idea, valid though it was, and considering only the related but minor problem of the loss of nitrogen in deceased animals and people. He could then reassure the reader that such loss was only apparent because the dead bodies would decompose and return their share of the nitrogen to the soil. He thus subtly minimized the magnitude of the danger of nitrogen depletion which had appeared so imminent in his first edition.[33]

But not all of his changes were merely ingenious argumentation. In his completely revised chapter "On the Rotation of Crops" he came up with an entirely new explanation of this phenomena. He dropped the dubious Macaire-Princep theory of poisonous plant excretions, which Berzelius had criticized earlier, in favor of his own new one of deficiencies. Later called the "law of the minimum," it attributed the decreasing yields of much-used fields to a depletion of one or more of the essential minerals, rather than to any emission of poisons by previous crops. This idea was one of his great achievements, for when extended to nitrogen and other minerals it made possible the advance from empirical fertilizing of the 1830s and 1840s to the more scientific fertilizing of later periods.[34]

That scientific fertilizing was not as easy as it seemed in the 1840s is clear from Liebig's own adventure with it in England. In 1845 he and a student, James Muspratt of Liverpool whose father owned a large industrial works there, took out a patent for a mineral manure (#10616, October 15, 1845). Liebig developed six kinds of fertilizer suitable for different crops: (1) wheat, rye, barley, and oats; (2) potatoes and turnips; (3) grass; (4) clover, peas, and beans; (5) tobacco; and (6) flax. They were sold for the growing seasons of 1846 and 1847, but very little reached the United States. After great hopes had been aroused for this new and cheaper alternative to guano, the fertilizer turned out to be a fiasco. The theory was not wrong, as far as it went, but in his efforts to keep the minerals from being washed away by the rain, Liebig had made them too insoluble to enter the plants, and a crust (probably like plaster of Paris) developed on the fields. The whole episode caused a great stir in English agricultural circles, whose strong criticisms thoroughly embittered Liebig toward the British, with whom he had previously had fairly close relations. The British reaction caused Liebig to maintain his mineral theory all the more strongly and served to exacerbate the debates with his British critics in the 1850s.[35]

Liebig was aware that his ideas led to a whole new field for the application of chemistry; and at times, in moments of humility, he noted how few analyses of plants, soils, and manures had been done. It was a task to keep many people busy for decades (see chapter 8). But in other moments he seemed to forget the paucity of data and the conflicting evidence and grossly overstated his case. He asserted that fertilizers were useful not according to the amount of ammonia in them, but only according to the amount of minerals in them. He even went beyond all evidence and claimed that their effectiveness was in direct proportion to the quantity of minerals—as if adding twice the minerals would yield twice the crop![36] This was to be emphatically disproven in the 1850s by two Englishmen, one a former student of Liebig and the other John Bennet Lawes, the "superphosphate" king.

The subtle change in Liebig's thinking from ammonia to phosphates had certain important implications, though he did not even hint at them in the third edition. Fertilizers must now be scientifically tested, as must all plants and all soils. Only then might the farmers hope to match their crops and soil with the fertilizer that was right for them out of the many now available. But only trained chemists could perform these analyses. Now higher education for chemists, paid positions for them, and regulation of the fertilizer industry would be necessary. No longer could a farmer expect to increase his crop just by applying gypsum or charcoal or even by applying a test for lime. A whole new day of "rational agriculture," as Liebig put it, was dawning.

This new doctrine with its great implications reached the Americans and was actively taken up, but the pathway of its transmission was by no means as clear as with the first edition. The third edition does not seem to have ever appeared in America (see appendix 1). The *Cultivator* made no reference to it at all, but perhaps this can be attributed to the sudden death of Willis Gaylord in late March 1844. Subsequently readers of the *Cultivator* were depending on other readers for reviews of major books in agricultural chemistry. However, the recently founded *American Agriculturalist* in New York City reprinted a rather mixed review of the third edition from the English *Gardeners' Chronicle* in February 1844.

The transmitter of the new message seems not to have been the third edition itself, but another Liebig book, the *Familiar Letters on Chemistry and Its Relations to Commerce, Physiology, and Agriculture,* which Liebig completed just about the same time as the third edition. One of the most influential scientific books of all time, it was translated into many languages and published in numerous editions, including two in the United States in 1843. It was a collection of newspaper articles Liebig had written on the nature of chemistry and its applications to medicine, industry, and agriculture. As Liebig said in the Preface, the letters "were intended . . . for the especial purpose of exciting the attention of government, and an enlightened public, to the necessity of establishing Schools of Chemistry, and of promoting, by every means, the study of a science." The recent progress in agricultural chemistry was one of Liebig's strongest arguments for governmental support. Six of the sixteen letters in the first edition dealt with scientific agriculture. At the end of one letter on the role of minerals in plant and animal nutrition, Liebig spelled out his hopes for scientific agriculture. All the uncertainties of farming promised to yield to modern science. Once all cultivated plants and their soils have been analyzed, "the farmer will be able to keep an exact record of the produce of his fields in harvest, like the account-book of a manufactory; and then by simple calculation he can de-termine precisely the substances he must supply to each field, and the quantity of these, in order to restore their fertility." The idea was very appealing to those who were facing starvation in Germany or merely "worn-out soil" in New York State.[37]

The first American notice of the *Familiar Letters* in February 1844 detected no major change, but within a few months there was a noticeably abrupt shift in the subjects of articles in the *Cultivator*. Mention of ammonia practically disappeared. Among the last references to it was the item about charcoal in May 1844 by the reader of the *Familiar Letters* who had detected Liebig's new em-phasis on minerals and phosphates. Great interest in soil analysis erupted immediately. In April 1844 the first advertisement for a $2–$5 analysis appeared. In May it was reported that Ebenezer Emmons had performed a soil analysis at a meeting of the New York State Agricultural Society. If farmers wished, Emmons would now accept $10 for the analysis of two or three soils. "A Practical Farmer" added that New York State needed a soil analyst. In June he wrote in again to ask James Hall of the geological survey where there were phosphates in New York, since Liebig said they were important. In July a notice appeared of a new agricultural college, Franklin College in Nashville, Tennessee.[38]

Thus in the spring of 1844 there was a sharp change in the columns of agricultural magazines, as readers picked up copies of the 6.25¢ *Familiar Letters* and began to think about soil analysis. It was no coincidence that at just this time young Eben Horsford of upstate New York decided to go to Giessen to study agricultural chemistry with Justus Liebig.

PART II

Liebig's Laboratory in America

4

Eben Norton Horsford and Giessen

As soon as Liebig's books started appearing in the United States, Americans began wondering why they had no agricultural chemists of their own. They were so dazzled by the recent achievements of European chemists that for a while they overlooked the work of their own Edmund Ruffin, Charles T. Jackson, and Samuel Dana and expressed a feeling of decided inferiority to Europe.

> If we have as yet no such men as Van Thaer, Chaptal, Davy, Liebig, Dombasle, &c., it is because the exigencies of our country have not demanded them. The talent, the zeal, are here; in short, we have the *men* among us, and nothing is wanting but to have these qualities called out, and directed to the pursuits which have given so much usefulness and honor to the individuals we have named.[1]

According to this view, America's economic needs would call forth a sufficient number of agricultural chemists for the nation to overcome its inferiority to Europe in this science. In the long run this rough outline was fairly accurate. It only failed to mention that the mechanism directing this change was to be the agricultural college. By 1841, when this editorial appeared, New York State, and New England before it, had already begun to feel the prescribed "exigencies" in the form of increasing competition from the West and decreasing yields from their own worn-out soil. Awareness of the problem in New York State led to agitation for new agricultural colleges in the period 1841–44. In 1844 Daniel Lee, editor of the *Genesee Farmer* and a statewide lecturer on agricultural problems, brought a bill before the legislature to establish a state agricultural college. It passed the Assembly but failed in the Senate and marked the beginning of a long campaign, which led eventually to the establishment of college of agriculture at Cornell University in the 1860s.[2] The impulse of Liebig's books and the promise of jobs in the new agricultural institutions suddenly made the career of agricultural chemist an attractive possibility for young men interested in science in the early 1840s.

But where were these "American Liebigs" to be trained? Since there were as yet no suitable facilities in the United States, they were forced to study abroad, perhaps in Liebig's own laboratory at Giessen, Germany. Although there had long been a fairly strong American tradition of foreign medical training, especially in Edinburgh, and although several Americans, starting with George Ticknor, Edward Everett, George Bancroft, and Joseph Cogswell, had studied at the German universities, it was still a rare occurrence for an American to study abroad. Only one American, J. Lawrence Smith, had yet been to Liebig's laboratory, and he was more interested in minerals than in agricultural chemistry. Costs were low once one arrived in Germany, but the total for two years of study might amount to $1,500 to $2,000. Germany was still a long voyage away and well-nigh an impossibility for anyone who lacked the money and ability to speak German. Without some assurance of a job on his return, a young man would be foolhardy to risk such a costly venture. But for Eben Horsford a few loans, several Albany connections, and a lot of hard work would eliminate these obstacles, for he had strong personal reasons for wanting to go to Giessen.[3]

The Horsfords were primarily an agricultural family, but with some claim to political prominence in upstate New York. Eben's father Jerediah (1791–1863) and his mother Maria Charity Norton had moved from Vermont to the fertile Genesee Valley (south of Rochester) in 1814–15, when farm prices were low. At first his father, a veteran of the War of 1812, ran a missionary school for the few Seneca Indians left in the area. When the area became a major commercial farming district, Jerediah Horsford became a progressive agriculturalist—purchasing one of the first Hussey reapers (1834), advocating a scientific approach to the potato blight, and developing a successful cattle food when the area turned to livestock raising. He also interested himself in local education, in abolitionism, and in politics. He served in the New York Assembly in the early 1830s and in the United States House of Representatives as a Whig under President Fillmore from 1851 to 1853. His chief interest when in Congress was the Patent Office's annual agricultural report, and in 1852 he spoke in favor of an independent bureau of agriculture. Eben Horsford's father, therefore, was a progressive farmer in a region facing the problems of worn-out soil in the 1830s and after.[4]

Eben Norton Horsford was born in 1818 in Moscow (now Leicester), New York, and spent his youth at local schools in Livingston County, where, as he mentioned later, the teaching was not very inspired. At home he showed a certain inventive or mechanical skill, great ability in sketching, and unbounded interest in collecting specimens from the rich fossil deposits on the family farm. At about age sixteen he took up a series of jobs—teaching school at LeRoy, New York, making a survey of iron in the Adirondacks for a Mr. McIntyre of Albany, and making preliminary surveys for both the New York and Erie Railroad and the Auburn and Rochester Railroad. He might have continued with the railroads if it had not been for the arrival in the area of James Hall of the newly organized New York State Natural History Survey in 1837.[5]

The survey had been started in 1836, but the first geologist for the Genesee Valley area, Timothy A. Conrad, had been reassigned after one year; and Hall, who had been an assistant in another district, replaced him. Since the Genesee Valley provided the key to much of the geology of western New York, and since well-trained assistants were in short supply, Hall was delighted to discover that the son of a local politician knew the area and collected rocks and fossils. Hall, a recent graduate of Amos Eaton's Rensselaer School, was so impressed with the young Horsford that he wrote Eaton to accept him for the next year free of charge. In return, Horsford performed the duties of an assistant professor in civil engineering (linear and perspective drawing) and was a monitor of student discipline. In one year (1838) Horsford earned his Bachelor of Natural Science in Engineering. He then helped Hall both in the field and in his Albany headquarters and may have continued teaching at the Troy school. It was thus Hall and the state geological survey that brought Horsford to Albany and turned him toward a career in science—not yet chemistry, but geology, which at times on the state surveys could be fairly closely related.[6]

From about 1838 until 1844 Horsford's activities centered in Albany. He joined the faculty of the Albany Female Academy in 1840, where for $800 he taught mathematics and natural history.

He seems to have been very popular at the school and to have led a happy life with the other faculty members and the young men who lived at the boarding house. His aspiration at this point was to become the headmaster of the school within a few years.[7]

Horsford also entered quite actively into the scientific life of the capital. The arrival in Albany of the Scottish phrenologist George Combe in January 1840 for a series of lectures at the Female Academy aroused great interest. Another phrenologist of conflicting views, J. Stanley Grimes of Buffalo, had just finished lecturing in Albany; and the two criticized each other sharply in the press. Several leading citizens, including bank president Thomas W. Olcott, formed the Albany Phrenological Society to consider the claims of the two conflicting theories. Twenty-two-year-old Eben Horsford wrote the final report, which weighed the two systems and ended by favoring Grimes's theory. This paper and an 1840 geological report to Hall were Horsford's first scientific publications. The phrenological episode also showed how easily the eager and capable Horsford could pick up a new science and how susceptible he was to scientific crazes.[8]

Horsford, as a protégé of Hall, Eaton, and Ebenezer Emmons (who was also at the Rensselaer School and on the geological survey), was an early member of the new American Association of Geologists and Naturalists that was formed in 1840. The first indication of Horsford's becoming a member was in April 1841 when he attended the Philadelphia meeting. He was also present a year later at the Boston meeting, when Hall, who had grown up in Boston and knew the geologists there, probably introduced him to Charles T. Jackson and George B. Emerson. At this time Horsford may also have met John W. Webster, the Harvard geologist-chemist who prepared several American editions of Liebig's works and who was to play an important part in Horsford's coming to Harvard in 1846–47.[9] Later, when this group had become the American Association for the Advancement of Science, Horsford was acting secretary (substituting for Jeffries Wyman) at the 1849 meeting in Cambridge.

Whether or not Horsford met Webster in April 1842, within a month he recorded in his diary that he had started reading Liebig's *Organic Chemistry*. He must also have read the *Animal Chemistry* as soon as it was available in America, since, according to the *Cultivator,* he attended several meetings of the New York State Agricultural Society and spoke on the value of the geological survey to agriculture in March 1844 and on the fattening of livestock in April. The latter was an application of Liebig's views in the *Animal Chemistry* to farm practice.[10]

Important as these contacts with Liebig's work and with the scientific and agricultural circles were, an even more significant event for Eben Horsford was a romantic interest. It seems that he fell in love with one of his students, Mary L'Hommedieu Gardiner of Shelter Island, Long Island, as early as 1841. Her family on one side descended from a long line of wealthy landowners on eastern Long Island. On the other side, the L'Hommedieux owned large tracts of land around Syracuse, and Mary's grandfather had been an active scientific farmer with the Livingstons and DeWitts around 1800. Mary responded to Horsford's interest, but her father would be much harder to please.[11]

Meanwhile, in August 1843 Horsford heard of an opening for a professor of chemistry and natural history at Newark College in Delaware (now the University of Delaware), where his cousin William A. Norton was already on the faculty. Immediately Horsford mustered all the letters he could to obtain the position. He succeeded and was elected to teach two six-week courses on chemistry each year for $200. Even as the college expanded its faculty, however, it was in a precarious financial state. The same month that Horsford was elected, the president and faculty all took salary cuts of $200. Visiting professors at fractional salaries were one solution, and the chopped-up nature of the curriculum made it easy for them to come and go as their schedules allowed.[12]

Shortly after obtaining the additional job, Horsford wrote to Mary's father about a possible "connection." Samuel Gardiner was enraged that Horsford had been paying attentions to his daughter, prohibited further communication, but must have avoided a definite no because Horsford responded, "I shall look forward to the period when I may be permitted to address you again, with a stronger stimulus to effort, and a brighter view of the future than ever yet has moved me." Mary's father was undoubtedly greatly surprised by Horsford's request, but he was also a widower and not willing to lose his eldest daughter. Besides, the Gardiners were socially a step or two above the Albany schoolteacher. In June 1844 Julia Gardiner, a first cousin of Mary, would marry President John Tyler and become a popular Washington hostess. Samuel Gardiner had not sent his daughter to the Albany Female Academy to fall in love with her instructor.[13]

Horsford, for his part, was crushed. He had tried to make his meager prospects sound appealing, "I have no fortune; and I should assure you that the profession to which I have promised my life offers its measure of happiness in a humbler sphere than wealth sometimes commands," but Mary's father had rejected it. Horsford must now try new ways to win him over. Pleasing Samuel Gardiner and thereby winning Mary's hand became the most important object in Horsford's life. His very ambitious career after November 1843 reflects this driving motivation to please her father. That this was the reason for his excessively hard work at Giessen and his eagerness a few years later for a position at Harvard is clear from a special diary that Horsford kept at Giessen. There he worried constantly about his ability to impress Mr. Gardiner and vowed that no obstacle or sacrifice would be too great for him.[14]

He finished up his duites in Albany and hurried down to Delaware for his first course of lectures. In spite of the friendly atmosphere there with W. A. Norton, his lively wife Lizzy, and Professor John Addison Porter (who would later follow Horsford to Giessen; see chapter 8), Horsford was eager to find a better position. When he heard in February 1844 of an opening at the University of Pennsylvania for a professor of chemistry, he was quick to apply. He roused all his supporters again, but as James Hall noted, his chances were not very good, and he almost wondered what made Horsford think he was qualified. Horsford certainly was not qualified, since he had no previous training in either medicine or chemistry and had not published anything on chemistry; but the thought of Mary was enough to push him into at least applying. He must have realized his chances were poor when Joel Parker of Philadelphia wrote him that anyone from Albany should have a letter from Joseph Henry who, Horsford discovered, was backing another candidate. In spite of Horsford's efforts, the position went to John Frazer of Philadelphia who had both the requisite training and the necessary local connections.[15]

In March 1844, then, Horsford was again defeated and despondent. The chance of his ever obtaining his beloved seemed dim. Efforts to communicate with her were necessarily roundabout and secretive. The most he could find out was that she still cared for him and would wait for him. It was at this time, the spring of 1844, that Horsford decided, undoubtedly with Webster's strong encouragement, to go to Liebig's laboratory in Germany and learn agricultural chemistry. In April he resigned from the Female Academy staff, though he stayed on until graduation in July. In August Webster and his daughter Marianne joined him at Portage, New York, near his family home, to view the spectacular falls and geological sites. Then Horsford was off for five hectic weeks in Delaware giving his semiannual course. He had also been able to get a letter of introduction to Liebig from Joseph Henry at Princeton, who was now very encouraging and assured him that upon his return he would find a better job than the one at the University of Pennsylvania. Before racing back to Albany to take out loans from his distinguished patrons and make final preparations for his departure, Horsford took the chance of writing Mary directly about his plans. He was "to be absent in the pursuit of science at least two years." But she should not get her hopes up, for "though I may be permitted to mingle with men whom the world call great and share the sympathy of the noble and the true of circles in which I may live, in all human probability I shall not be a man of fortune." Specifically, "on my return I expect to hold one of three or four professorships in an Agricultural College, upon a scale commensurate with all the schemes in which New York engages, as a state. Everything connected with the plans I have formed seems to promise this beyond disappointment, and yet it may be that some other sphere is arranged for me."[16]

If these were Horsford's aspirations and expectations on the eve of his departure, what were his abilities? From the recommendations that he had been collecting one can get a certain picture of him. He was very likable, of high moral character, and had a fine intellect. He was known especially as an excellent lecturer who gave clear explanations and could make ready applications of principles to specific cases. Most recently at Newark College he had shown great skill in performing experiments for his chemistry lectures. His outstanding characteristics, which almost every letter about him mentioned, were his great zeal or "enthusiastic devotion to the cause of science" and his tremendous energy and untiring industry. These traits were to be all the more obvious in his stay at Giessen. A more candid appraisal of Horsford in 1844 by John Pitkin Norton, a good judge of character, indicates that what might be called great "versatility of talent" was perhaps a weakness. "Mr. Horsford is evidently a man of much talent but I should think him unstable; he flies from one thing to another & I am afraid will fail in that way. He expects to commence under Liebig in the fall & study agricultural chemistry but I believe not exclusively."[17] A list of the books Horsford left with friends in Albany in 1844 shows a wide variety of interests—moral philosophy, agriculture, and every conceivable science.[18] Horsford was an accomplished geologist, engineer, and surveyor and had studied phrenology and most of the sciences. He lacked, however, systematic training in chemistry and a knowledge of advanced mathematics, German, and French; and sometimes he had difficulties in writing essays. On the whole, his preparation was barely adequate for a German university in the 1840s, but hard work once there might make up for it.

Horsford finally set sail with a cousin, Edmund ("Ned") Sewall of Watertown, New York on October 10, 1844. After rough voyage, during which they were seasick most of the time, they landed in England, on November 8. They spent a few days in London before heading on to Giessen, arriving there on November 23, 1844.

Horsford had idolized Liebig even before he met him and was somewhat disappointed by their first interview. Liebig was distant, preoccupied, and coldly efficient, but Horsford determined to overlook it all. A second interview, after Liebig had read the very warm letter of introduction from Joseph Henry, was much friendlier. Horsford also brought Liebig some seeds of several varieties of American corn, with which Liebig promised to experiment on his new farm outside Giessen.[19] As time went on, Liebig took a distinct interest in his American student and invited him to visit him and his family at home every week. This was a rare privilege extended otherwise to only a few of the English students. Horsford was greatly flattered by the attention, venerated Liebig all the more, and became very uncritical of everything the man said and did. In this he shared a common attitude with the other students at Giessen, for the atmosphere there was full of adulation for Liebig. The students rejoiced in his successes, such as becoming a baronet or "Freiherr", and scorned all his enemies, like Mulder, Boussingault, and recently C. F. Gerhardt. J. P. Norton shrewdly observed, at a farmers' dinner for Liebig in Glasgow the same year, that Liebig would have to be a strong man indeed to withstand all this praise. More likely, he suspected, it would make him more assertive than ever. Some criticism did appear at Giessen, but the students haughtily rejected it. When they encountered criticisms of Liebig outside Giessen, as Horsford later did in Berlin and elsewhere, they reacted strongly, condemning any and all who would dare speak out against the great man.[20]

The years 1844–46 that Horsford spent with Liebig seem to have been a turning point in the German chemist's life. The patent manure was proving to be a failure in Britain, and the criticisms were severe. For a man who prided himself on the applications of his work and who had been expecting to build up a modest fortune, this was a hard blow, though in 1845 he was blaming his British manufacturers and financial agents and did not yet realize that solubility effects were the real problem. Also at this time he was involved in fierce quarrels with several scientists, and the constant round of activities at the laboratory was beginning to weary rather than excite him. When Liebig was in Glasgow in 1844, Norton observed that he "seems quite young. I should judge him about thirty," although he was forty-one. By 1846 Horsford was commenting on how fast Liebig had aged since he had arrived. In his long talks with Horsford and others Liebig occasionally mentioned that he felt "used up"; and now that the grand duke, who had shown such confidence in appointing him in the 1820s, was dead, he no longer felt any compulsion to stay in Giessen.[21] At one point there was a rumor that Liebig might be going to America. In the laboratory, as Horsford noted, he paid very little attention to some of the students, barely passing them by, but concentrated more and more on a few. The longer he stayed in Giessen, the more Horsford, too, became bored with the round of events. The semiannual student dinner for Liebig had at first excited him, but by the time he was leaving he was tired of it and suspected Liebig was too.[22] As early as 1845 Liebig was showing signs of giving up his Giessen laboratory though he did not do it until 1852.

Determined as Horsford was to idolize Liebig, and greatly encouraged for the most part by the brilliancy of his lectures and the generosity and warmth of his family, Horsford found it difficult to admit that Liebig had faults. But it became evident that Liebig, otherwise such a model for youth, did not attend church and drank beer and wine. He even expected Horsford to drink and embarrassed him when he did not. Horsford had been brought up in a religious family, had taken a temperance pledge, and was therefore concerned that Liebig had these faults. He tried to overlook them, but Liebig's moral character was a source of great uneasiness for him. Others in the academic community also shared these practices. At first it seemed enough evidence for Horsford to condemn the whole German people. Later on, however, when he could understand the German sermons better and when he got away from the university town, the realized there was more religion in Germany than he had suspected at first and was greatly relieved. But even then he remained critical of Catholicism, which he considered mere "mummery." Its chief value, he thought, lay in reconciling the poor beggars of the area to their fate and in focusing their minds on the next world.[23]

Horsford also observed the extreme poverty of the area around Giessen, whose problems would make those of upstate New York look trivial indeed. He witnessed the efforts of many people to emigrate. Several, even total strangers, asked him for recommendations to help them get to America; and boats down the Rhine were always crowed with emigrants. At one point he heard that three towns had sold out to a local prince and set sail for America. Another prince had taken a group from Giessen to Braunfels, Texas, a few years before. Horsford observed that the fields near Giessen were tiny and that labor was in oversupply, but other comparisons with American farming were confusing. American plows were vastly superior to German ones, and the lack of threshers in Germany astounded Horsford until he was told that the people were too poor to experiment and their fields too small to make such a machine worthwhile. On the other hand, the Germans seemed to be better farmers than the Americans—they cultivated their land more intensively and used much more manure. They also had educational institutions for farmers that surpassed anything in America.[24]

Horsford thoroughly disapproved of the German students at the university. They seemed to spend their time drinking and dueling, especially over trivial matters that offended their delicate sense of honor. Although the German universities were supposed to be a stage beyond the American college, many of the students there were still adolescents at heart. The scene is somewhat reminiscent of Dink Stover's Yale, where the extracurricular life with one's fellows was much more important than the professors' lectures, no matter how brilliant or world famous they might be. Voluntary class attendance made it even easier to ignore the professors. Of the five hundred students at Giessen University in 1845, about sixty were in chemistry, a sizable but segregated minority. The hours of the laboratory meant that they all ate together later than the other students. Among them discipline was fairly strict, and when Horsford arrived late at the laboratory or missed a lecture Liebig noticed and scolded him. Though the chemists lived somewhat apart from the other students, they could not ignore them completely. When a student rebellion broke out in August 1846, Horsford was afraid to work in the laboratory, even though Liebig advised him to, because he feared it would lead to fights with the German students. Horsford had no problem, but the rebellion did reach the point where the state militia had to be called in to quell it. There was much more going on at the German universities in the 1840s than the quiet disinterested search for truth.[25]

Unlike the Americans who attended the German universities in later decades, Horsford never mentioned the joys of *Lehrfreiheit* or *Lernfreiheit*. These much-proclaimed virtues of the German university were noticeably absent from Giessen in 1844–46. On the contrary, the oppression by the state and the limits on freedom of speech were all too evident for anyone to extol the freedoms of the German university. One outspoken professor had disappeared mysteriously a few years before, and another had last been seen in a nearby prison. Though the grand dukes might have been benevolent in awarding Liebig a job or a baronetcy, they also tended to punish their critics rather mercilessly. Horsford and other Americans in Germany at the time, such as Oliver Wolcott Gibbs at Berlin, greatly criticized this lack of freedom of speech, predicted (quite correctly) revolution, and scorned a people that tolerated such conditions. Political repression, with irreligion and drinking, was one of the first things an American noticed in Germany in the 1840s.[26]

Though Horsford found plenty of reasons to deprecate the German people, especially the students, he had only praise for the professors and his fellow chemistry students. "These never was, and it is altogether probable there never will be again, such a school of chemists as Giesesn has now." According to Horsford, it was the chemistry students who were making the university famous. They were a grand group of fellows who were going to do exciting things. They spent their time studying rather than drinking, though the British chemistry students had some wild drunken brawls of their own. At other moments Horsford was not so sure that all sixty chemistry students were going to be successful, and he frequently bolstered his ego by concluding that he was among the best in the laboratory.[27] Whenever Horsford talked of the greatness of Liebig's laboratory, it was in terms of personalities—Liebig, Heinrich Will, Karl Fresenius, and the students. He hardly mentioned the facilities until the end of his stay, when he went on tour to the other famous laboratories in Germany (Göttingen, Heidelberg, Berlin, Leipzig), and then he merely noted which were based on Liebig's laboratory and which not. From all this it seems that the key ingredients of the greatness of Liebig's laboratory and the aura that came to surround it were the charisma and eminence of the professor and the esprit de corps of the students. The facilities at Giessen were secondary and by the 1840s no longer unique.

The laboratory had been started in 1824 under very difficult circumstances. By dogged persistence (including a threat to quit), Liebig had had it expanded in 1835 and again in 1839. Even before the publication of his *Organic Chemistry* he had space for twenty students in the main laboratory, for forty more in a junior laboratory, and a private laboratory of his own.[28] For a time it was unique.

By the time Horsford got to the laboratory in 1844 it was already world famous. But one should not conclude from this, as others have done, that it was the book that made the laboratory popular. By 1840, when the book appeared, Liebig had been attracting foreign students for over a decade (see appendix 2). In fact, one should not generalize too much from the Americans, for as a group they were quite late in coming, being heavily concentrated in the period 1846–49. Horsford considered Giessen at the height of its fame in 1846 and bragged, "Liebig's school was never in such glory as at this moment. There has rarely been so strong a corps of young chemists at any one time present as that of this winter. The influence of Liebig upon theoretical and technical chemistry was never so extended." But despite these boasts there is evidence that by the time Horsford arrived at the laboratory in late 1844, it was already heading for a decline. Not only was Liebig aging rapidly and beginning to think of a change, but by 1845 there were several other laboratories in Germany where foreign students could seek chemical training—with Rose, Rammelsberg, and Magnus in Berlin; Erdmann in Leipzig; Wöhler in Göttingen; and Gmelin in Heidelberg. In fact, in 1845–46 it seemed to be common talk in Berlin chemical circles that Liebig's golden days were over and his laboratory no longer the greatest in Europe. As soon as the richer and larger universities decided to build laboratories, they might easily outstrip the facilities and number of students at poor little Giessen. Some, like Leipzig, much favored in the late 1840s and especially in the 1850s, were modeled on Giessen. Nevertheless, though the initial attraction of Liebig's laboratory in the 1830s may have been its uniqueness, by the 1840s other places were available to those seeking instruction in chemistry; and many students made it a practice to go to several different laboratories. Wolcott Gibbs, for example, attended Giessen for a few months but did not like Liebig and thought he was learning little when compared with his work with Rose in Berlin. Liebig, in fact, recommended to Horsford that the should spend a semester each in Berlin and Paris.[29] Even the "Master" agreed that there were other places to learn chemistry besides Giessen, however strongly the devoted disciple might disagree.

Horsford spent two full years at Giessen (November 1844 to November 1846), during which the "gigantic world of chemistry" opened to him. In his first year he took a formidable number of lectures in the mornings and spent afternoons in Dr. Will's junior laboratory, learning qualitative and quantitative analysis. In order to use the daylight hours to the utmost, the professors started to lecture at 6:00 A.M., and the laboratory closed at 6:30 P.M. Horsford at one point described his weekly schedule:

Monday	6–8	Dr. Will on Blowpipe Analysis
	8–11	Dr. Will on Quantitative and Qualitative Analysis
	11–12+	Liebig's lecture—Experimental Chemistry
		dine and lounge
	3–6:30	work in laboratory
		walk and lounge
	8–9:30	German lesson
		write and study
	10:30	to bed

Tuesday	7–8	Kopp on Crystallography
		rest as Monday
Wednesday	6–7	Fresenius on Quantitative and Qualitative Analysis
	7–8	Kopp on Crystallography
		rest as Monday
Thursday	6–7	Fresenius on Quantitative and Qualitative Analysis
	7–8	Will on Qualitative Inorganic Analysis
		rest as Monday
Friday	6–7	Fresenius on Economical and Technical Chemistry
	7–8	Kopp on Crystallography
		rest as Monday
Saturday	6–7	Fresenius on Economical and Technical Chemistry
	7–8	Will on Qualitative Analysis
		no laboratory today
	11–12+	Liebig on Experimental Chemistry
		dine
	2–2:30	Kopp—drawing crystals
		balance of day to arrange affairs in town
Sunday	9	church
		rest of day usually on an outing

Needless to say, he was frequently too tired to write much in his journal.[30]

At first he was at a decided disadvantage, being unable to understand much German; but he hired a private tutor, worked hard, and caught on rapidly. His roommate Ned Sewall added a secret postscript to one of Horsford's letters home that was probably an accurate assessment of Horsford's progress, "His course in Chemistry in Giessen, has been one succession of triumphs. The obstacles that met him at the commencement, have given way, and he is pushing on with strides that threaten to overtake many an older Chemist."[31]

During his first year in Professor Will's laboratory, Horsford thought a chlorine process he was working on might be commercially feasible (he was always alert to such things), but Liebig was skeptical and it was dropped. More significant were Horsford's analyses of the ash of red clover, which Liebig published in the *Annalen* and later included in the fourth edition of the *(Organic) Chemistry in Its Applications to Agriculture and Physiology.** Horsford also sent this article home to the *Cultivator,* since it was of great interest to farmers. Clover

*The word *Organic* was dropped from the title of Liebig's book in later editions.

was used in most crop rotations, since it apparently restored nitrogen to the soil. Horsford's analysis also showed a high percentage of minerals, especially sulphates, in the leaves, a finding that seemed to explain why clover responded so well to gypsum. It also suggested that, according to Liebig's mineral theory of manures, these clover leaves would themselves make excellent fertilizers if plowed under the soil.[32]

During the April vacation, Horsford took a long walking tour through the Swiss mountains. Yet, even on vacation he put his opportunity to good use. He picked up a piece of glacier on Mont Blanc, which he melted down in Professor Jean Marignac's laboratory in Geneva. Back in Giessen he analyzed it for ammonia and thereby added support to Liebig's theories on the atmosphere. Liebig, not surprisingly, showed great interest in the analysis and printed up the results in the *Annalen*.[33]

In October 1845 Horsford was at last ready to enter Liebig's laboratory for advanced students. The procedure was for Liebig to suggest a topic from the stock of items of interest to him. For Horsford he chose just the right problem, both in subject matter and in degree of difficulty. He was to analyze the nitrogen content of thirty-one grains in order to determine their nutritive value for the fattening of animals. It was a topic that had recently begun to attract attention back home, and Horsford had delivered a paper to the New York State Agricultural Society in April 1844 on this very subject. Sir Humphry Davy had established food values for different grains, based on the quantity of gluten they contained, but his analyses had been necessarily inadequate and his findings were known by 1839 to disagree with observed farm results. In the early 1840s Boussingault's and Liebig's work on the chemical composition of foods, combined with the American farmers' greatly increased interest in livestock (another response to their worn-out soil), made a detailed study of the comparative nutritive values of different grains a worthwhile project.[34]

Boussingault had recently (1837) determined the quantities of nitrogen in grains using the Dumas method, but Horsford was to use a method that Will and Varentrapp had recently developed at the Giessen laboratory. Horsford probably meant to disprove Boussingault's data if he could, but his conclusions verified them instead (within the degree of experimental error), and he ended up criticizing

Liebig as much as anyone else. Liebig, however, seemed pleased with the paper and published it in the *Annalen*.[35]

The subject Horsford was tackling was a deceptive one. He was thrilled to think that he was establishing for all time the nutritive values of thirty-one grains, but the problem really needed clarification of thought more than any more new analyses. Data collected from animal feeding experiments conflicted with chemical analyses of the foods' content. Horsford's new data, by confirming so closely Boussingault's previous chemical work, led him to criticize the feeding experiments. (He might also have concluded that the theory, which relied only on protein content to determine nutritive value, was in error, but the 1840s were much too early for this.) Once Horsford put his mind to the possible sources of error in farm feeding experiments, he came up with eighteen items ranging from amounts of moisture to the sophisticated problem of animal metabolism. These conclusions, rather than all the data he so laboriously collected, were the paper's chief contribution.[36]

The procedure Horsford used in this paper on grains is also of interest, for it relates to the protein question. As discussed in chapter 3, Liebig knew by 1843 that proteins contained other elements as well as nitrogen or ammonia. Sulphur and phosphorus were essential —essential enough for Liebig to recast his arguments on the value of nitrogen for agricultural chemistry and to greatly expand his earlier views. Yet here in 1845–46 he was letting Horsford use nitrogen alone as an indicator of the protein content (gluten) of grains. Liebig's theorizing about the sulphur and phosphorus in proteins had been based on qualitative data and had run far ahead of precise determinations of their composition and structure. Other students in the laboratory were working on these problems at the very moment Horsford was at work on his grains.

Part of the problem about proteins was one of definition. In a sense they contained sulphur and phosphorus, and in a sense they did not. Gerhard Mulder had thought that "proteine" was a single substance to which he gave the formula $C_{40}H_{62}N_{10}O_{12}$. It contained neither sulphur nor phosphorus, but when added to various combinations of these substances, it yielded the familiar fibrin, albumen, gluten, and casein, as,

$$\text{Casein} = 10 \text{ Proteine} + S$$
$$\text{Gluten} = 10 \text{ Proteine} + 2S$$

Fibrin   = 10 Proteine + SP
Egg albumen = 10 Proteine + SP
Blood albumen = 10 Proteine + S_2P

Thus Mulder could say that "proteine" had no sulphur or phosphorus, and Liebig that fibrin, or the "blood-making substance," did. There the problem stood until 1845 when Liebig had a Russian student in his laboratory, Nicholas Laskowski, redo some of Mulder's "proteine" analyses. There was great glee in Giessen when he showed Mulder to have been in error by finding sulphur in the "proteine." Mulder was incensed and exchanged angry, threatening letters with Liebig. When Liebig would no longer answer him, Mulder wrote a fiery polemic that seemed like the work of a crazed man. Meanwhile, Mulder had asserted that there was another way to prepare "proteine." E. Rüling, also at Giessen, immediately tested this new method. Not only did he discover sulphur in all of Mulder's "proteines," but even more significantly, it appeared in variable amounts. This disproved Mulder's whole hypothesis of a single fixed "proteine" substance and led Liebig to develop his own theories.[37]

Such was the excitement going on around Horsford as he did his two hundred organic combustion analyses. Since he knew from Rüling that gluten had 1.14 percent sulphur, he did not have to analyze the sulphur directly but could calculate how much of it must be present in the protein and attribute the rest to impurities. Since he assumed that all the nitrogen in the grain was in the form of protein and that only one protein (gluten) was present, he could calculate from the amount of nitrogen in a plant its gluten content or nutritive value.

When Horsford finished this piece of solid but painstaking work in February 1846, Liebig suggested he take up another topic related to proteins. Liebig had been following up more of Mulder's work and was now reformulating the concept of protein in his own characteristic way. He conceived of it not, as Mulder had done, as a large fixed substance joined to variable endings, but as a conglomeration of smaller pieces. He suspected one such smaller piece might be "sugar of gelatin" which uric acid yielded when decomposed. This substance had not really been subjected to detailed study. Mulder and Boussingault had tried to obtain formulas for it but had come up with unwieldy giants such as $C_8H_9N_2O_7$ and $C_{12}H_{31}N_6O_{11}$. Horsford redid the analyses and, by using slightly different atomic

weights (the atomic weight of carbon was constantly being recal-
culated), obtained a considerably less complicated formula, C_4H_5
NO_3.* He then combined this substance with a great many acids
and bases and described the series of compounds he made. He
named the substance "glycocoll," but we call it "glycine" today.
It is the simplest amino acid and therefore essential to twentieth-
century studies of protein structure. Liebig's idea of breaking up the
protein and studying its smaller parts was a fruitful one. Berzelius
repeated Horsford's experiments and considered them correct, as he
wrote Mulder, though he disagreed with the atomic weights used.
Horsford's paper was an early venture into biochemistry, but he
never followed it up.[38] This paper and the one on food nitrogen
remained his most solid scientific work. None of his work in America
ever equaled their significance. Instead, in spite of this glorious
start, as Norton had predicted, Horsford flitted from one subject to
another, coming up with interesting connections, useful analyses, and
wild speculations.

Typical of such speculations were his ideas on "waves," to which
he devoted much energy while at Giessen. He was more interested
in them than in the glycocoll analyses, which were dragging on
endlessly at the time. Horsford never wrote up his wave theory,
complaining that he lacked the necessary mathematics, but Heinrich
Buff, professor of physics at Giessen, with whom Horsford had been
working on the paper, published some of the ideas for him. His
theory seems to have been an early precursor of the electrolytic
theory of conductivity. Liebig was very excited by the paper and
thought that publishing it would provide a strong boost to Horsford's
reputation in America, because it was speculative and Americans
would like that.[39] Liebig, it seems, did not share the view that
Americans were simply Baconian fact gatherers.

Aside from these researches, Horsford wrote letters to the *Cultivator* on a variety of topics—daily life, Liebig, Giessen, German
agriculture, chemical analysis, and especially educational institutions. At first his journalistic efforts were not well received, but since
the editor frequently put them on the front page, Horsford ceased
being concerned. He was never as successful as John Pitkin Norton
at agricultural journalism, but his choice of topics was timely. Put-

*This formula is equivalent, on the basis of modern atomic weights and concepts of
molecular structure, to the currently accepted one of $C_2H_5NO_2$.

ting his vacations to good use, he took his father's advice and visited the Agricultural Institute of Wurtemberg at Hohenheim; the forestry program at Giessen; and the manual labor school at Hofwyl, Switzerland, run by Emmanuel Fellenberg, whose doctrines went through a vogue in the United States in the 1830s.[40] Both Horsford and editor Luther Tucker knew that lengthy and critical descriptions of such institutions would fit in well with local efforts to start a state college of agriculture. It is doubtful whether they had any real effect, however.

Since the state legislature had proven unwilling to start such a college in 1845, Daniel Lee, Horsford's friend and chief lobbyist for the new college, decided to start his own agricultural school at Wheatland, New York (near Horsford's home), as an inducement for state support later. In May 1846 he offered the professorship of chemistry to Horsford, who had for years been expecting and planning on such a position. Surprisingly, Horsford declined it. His reasons were indicative of a serious underlying problem. Since the salary was to be dependent on student fees and since he wanted to be free to devote himself to science upon his return, he did not wish to incur the risk of such a precarious financial arrangement. Furthermore, he would need facilities the school could not afford. The problem was one of overeducation or rising expectations. In 1844 he had gone to Giessen expecting to return to a job in a new agricultural college that would be well supported by the state. By 1846 not only had this hope faded, but Horsford's expectations had risen to the point where he now wanted to continue his advanced chemical research on his return to America. But no fledgling agricultural college could offer him the free time for such research or a laboratory like Liebig's. Overeducated though he was, Horsford would probably have taken the Wheatland professorship, if no alternative had been available.

But Horsford was very lucky. His real but unspoken reason for refusing to go to Wheatland, New York, was that by May 1846 he had been negotiating with Harvard University for two months about becoming its new Rumford Professor of the Application of Science to the Useful Arts. Once Horsford scented Harvard, thought of Mary and her status-conscious father, and imagined the chemical facilities Harvard might have, he could not return to New York and a poor agricultural college.

5

Giessen on the Charles

While Horsford was studying at Giessen and dreaming of Mary, the Boston scientific community was in a stir about impending changes at Harvard. The Rumford Professorship had fallen vacant just at the time when President Josiah Quincy was resigning, and those in and out of the university felt that the time had come for some major changes at the nation's oldest college. Although Harvard had been supporting science since its earliest days, it had fallen behind other universities, especially Yale, in the first half of the nineteenth century.

Harvard's strength in 1845 lay in its large number of endowed professorships. The faculty included such important scientists as Benjamin Peirce, John W. Webster, William and George Bond, and Asa Gray. Gray's recent appointment over less-specialized local rivals also indicated that the Harvard Corporation was already alert to the importance of faculty research achievements. In addition, the university had recently started a new astronomical observatory and imported an expensive set of instruments for it. The undergraduate curriculum, moreover, required substantial amounts of science. With all these advantages Harvard seemed to be a major supporter of science with particular strength in mathematics, astronomy, and botany.[1]

Yet Harvard was not all that it seemed, for it also had obstacles to teaching and research. Deadening teaching methods and uneven financial support tended to offset the efforts of even the most devoted and eminent professors. The classes were, for the most part, elementary and taught by daily recitations. Lectures were reserved for the seniors. No one on the faculty in 1845, not even the Rumford Professor, had the charismatic appeal of a Benjamin Silliman or a Louis Agassiz, who would later attract students to the college and make a few eager to linger on and learn more. Such an appeal was necessary for the building up of a center of science in a day when neither the college nor society offered much incentive for advanced work. The only reward for graduate study in 1845 was the master's degree, which could be obtained just as easily without any effort.[2]

Equally detrimental to the pursuit of science at Harvard was the unequal distribution of financial support among the sciences. Despite its new observatory and its impressive stock of demonstration apparatus in physics and astronomy, Harvard devoted little money to building up its natural history collections and equipping its laboratories. Webster complained in 1845 that he had had to fight for every cent for the mineralogy collection and had personally gone $5,000 into debt to furnish his medical school laboratory. Asa Gray also found it nearly impossible to maintain the botanical garden and was able to build up the botanical collections only by making exchanges rather than purchases. Harvard's endowments had over the years favored some sciences at the expense of others.[3]

More serious in 1845 than Harvard's weaknesses in advanced studies and research was its complete lack of training in the applied sciences. The college's total offering in both engineering and chemistry was comprised of the class recitations of John Webster, Erving Professor of Mineralogy and Chemistry, and the lectures of the Rumford Professor of the Application of Science to the Useful Arts. Despite innovations at other institutions in the teaching of engineering and chemistry, Harvard taught all of applied science in a few lectures with demonstrations. Eastern Massachusetts was industrializing rapidly by 1845, and the teaching of applied science was a problem Harvard would have to solve fairly soon.

The opportunity for a change in the traditional thinking about science at Harvard came in 1845–46. Three months after Daniel Treadwell resigned as part-time Rumford professor in May 1845, President Josiah Quincy also resigned in order that Edward Everett, who was returning from his post as the American ambassador to the Court of St. James, might be elected his successor. Since Everett was a rather unusual college president for the time and was, with Professor Benjamin Peirce, the guiding force behind the creation of a "scientific school" at Harvard, his background is of some interest.

At age fifty-one he had already had a brilliant career. Graduating from Harvard in 1811 at the top of his class, he had earned a master's degree and then become minister of the Brattle Street Church in

Cambridge, one of the most influential Unitarian churches in the country. Harvard soon asked him to be its first Eliot Professor of Greek Literature, which he accepted but insisted on preparing himself in Germany first. He became the first American to receive a German Ph.D. He returned to the United States in 1819, taking up in addition to his professorial duties the editorship of the *North American Review,* for which he occasionally wrote articles on the German universities. But Everett was chiefly known for his oratorical powers. Soon friends, especially Daniel Webster, began suggesting political office to him. He became a member of the United States House of Representatives from 1825 to 1835 and governor of Massachusetts from 1836 to 1839, where one of his more important achievements was the organization of the second state geological survey, which employed Edward Hitchcock and Samuel Dana. In 1841 Webster, by now secretary of state under President John Tyler, had Everett appointed to the prestigious post of ambassador to the Court of St. James. In his years in Britain, Everett performed many duties, among them the ceremonial ones of meeting dignitaries and making speeches. He met Justus Liebig when he was visiting England in 1844 and spoke to various agricultural groups on the value of science.[4]

It was from this eminent position that Everett was returning when President Quincy of Harvard resigned. Everyone was eager for Everett to take on the Harvard presidency, but Everett himself was reluctant until his friend Daniel Webster prevailed upon him to accept. Unfortunately, Everett very soon found the position degrading (there were no deans yet, and he had to enforce the discipline personally). Throughout his three years in office he kept threatening to resign. During his brief and unhappy term as president of Harvard, before becoming secretary of state himself, he fostered some of Harvard's first steps toward university status. For Everett the Harvard years were an unpleasant interlude in an otherwise successful career, but for Harvard and American education, Everett's acquaintance with Europeans, German scholarship, and wealthy American businessmen and philanthropists made a rare combination in a college president and enabled him to envision and establish the Lawrence Scientific School.

As soon as he took office in February 1846, Everett started considering a replacement for Treadwell. One of Everett's first steps

must have been to ask the faculty for suggestions for the appointment, for by February 19 John White Webster knew enough to be
able to formulate his own plans. He chose as his candidate Eben
Horsford, who was studying agricultural chemistry at Giessen and
was unaware of any openings at Harvard. Webster's motivation in
choosing Horsford, who did not seem to offer what Harvard wanted,
was not as disinterested as is usually asserted.[5]

The leading candidate for the appointment was Henry Darwin
Rogers, the former state geologist of Pennsylvania, who had been in
Boston for two years lecturing on geology and, it seemed to Webster,
rather obviously hanging around looking for a job. As a geologist
Rogers had had strong interests in Pennsylvania coal and had also
completed a geological survey for the Boston and Providence Railroad Company in 1832. He had recently explored for copper in the
Lake Superior region for some Boston clients. Influential persons in
Boston considered such activities appropriate "applications of science
to the useful arts." Besides, his candidacy was supported by such
eminent scientists as Joseph Henry, C. T. Jackson, G. B. Emerson
(president of the Boston Society of Natural History), and possibly
James Dwight Dana of Yale. Yet Rogers's election was not a certainty. His public adoption of the doctrines of the *Vestiges of Creation*
in 1844 had made him a controversial figure and earned him the
opposition of Asa Gray, Benjamin Peirce, Francis Bowen, and perhaps others. His candidacy threatened to split the faculty into war-
ring factions.[6]

It was not scientific controversy, however, that motivated Rogers's
most formidable enemy, John Webster. Two years before, Rogers
and Emerson had tried to have Webster ousted on charges of in-
competence and Rogers elected in his place. Naturally enough,
Webster had been highly incensed at Rogers and now meant to use
every bit of energy available to prevent his election to the Rumford
chair. The appointment of his young friend Horsford would not only
give Webster a proven ally on the faculty, but it would also relieve
him of instruction in chemistry. He would be left with mineralogy
and geology, an arrangement he greatly preferred. Once Webster
had settled on his course, he worked feverishly for Horsford's cause,
which was a large task, since Horsford was known only to a few
geologists in Boston, and they favored Rogers.[7]

While Webster was advising Horsford in Giessen to pull together all he could in the way of recommendations from his German professors and fellow students, back in Cambridge President Everett was considering Professor Benjamin Peirce's proposals for a major reorganization of the science faculty. This had already been discussed in January 1846 at one of the last meetings of the corporation under President Quincy, but nothing had been decided. Peirce's "Plan for a School of Practical & Theoretical Science" would regroup all the current Harvard science professors plus those in languages, history, and philology under a new faculty to give instruction on advanced and practical subjects. It did not discuss probable sources of income, for no added expenses were anticipated. In fact, if Peirce thought about the finances at all, he probably expected the tuition of the new students to increase the current professors' incomes. He did not plan to hire any new professors or build any laboratories. In this he differed from Edward Everett and Abbott Lawrence.[8]

Thus by the time Everett was inaugurated as president of Harvard n April 1846, some sort of reform and a great deal of intrigue were already under way. There would be a scientific school and a new Rumford Professor, though the exact details of the arrangement and the choice of the professor had yet to be determined. Everett's inaugural address indicated that he looked to the possible creation of a modified German-style university in Cambridge.

> It is a question well worthy to be entertained, whether the time is not yet arrived when considerable expansion may be given to our system, of a twofold character; first by establishing a philosophical faculty, in which the various branches of science and literature should be cultivated, beyond the limits of an academical course, with a view to a complete liberal education, and secondly, by organizing a school of theoretical and practical science, for the purpose especially of teaching its applications to the arts of life, and of furnishing a supply of skillful engineers, and of persons well qualified to explore and bring to light the inexhaustible resources of the country, and to guide its vast industrial energies in their rapid development.[9]

Everett also noted that such an expansion was much more than a reorganization and would require new funds. Although such means were not yet available, he hoped they might soon be.

From the start, both in Peirce's plan in February and in Everett's of April, the practical and the advanced training were united in one school. The conflict between the two would be a source of great frustration to Eben Horsford, but in 1846 no one thought of practical and advanced science as being in conflict. Reaction to Everett's inaugural address was reportedly quite favorable. Now that it was clear that the new president was an expansionist, the whole matter turned on electing the new Rumford Professor.

Despite the various maneuverings of Webster and Horsford throughout 1846, the appointment had reached an impasse as early as April. Webster's campaign had stalled Rogers's chances, but the Corporation could not bring itself to elect a stranger, however highly recommended by German professors. The longer the appointment wore on, the more people became involved in the decision, and the nastier the infighting got. Eventually it seemed every scientist in greater Boston had an opinion.[10]

Horsford in Giessen was meanwhile very anxious and poorly informed of affairs in Cambridge. He had given up his vacation to finish his papers on proteins and waves, but growing impatient, he had left the waves to Professor Buff, borrowed $100 from Liebig and set out on a tour of German laboratories and industrial plants, which Webster had advised would help his chances in Cambridge. Finally, in November 1846, having heard little more, he left Giessen and headed home.[11]

Upon his arrival in New York City in January 1847, he found a despairing letter from Webster saying that his chances had collapsed and all was over, though no election had yet taken place. Horsford, however, decided to go to Cambridge, even if, as he said later, it was just to see what he had missed. His visit seems to have catalyzed the long-delayed decision. After two days with Professors Peirce and Walker, Fellow John A. Lowell, and Treasurer Samuel A. Eliot, his chances revived miraculously; and on January 30 he was elected unanimously by the Corporation. Shortly thereafter his salary was settled at $1,500, and the rules for the new scientific school were fixed. Horsford was ecstatic and could now write Mary's father again. This time he was better received and began to plan rapturously for a summer wedding and a new home in Cambridge. The happiest period of his life was beginning. Both his dreams, of Mary and of Harvard, had come true.[12]

At Harvard, too, the plans of a year before had now been achieved.

Webster had thwarted Henry Rogers, and Peirce and Everett had their scientific school. The new Rumford Professor would teach advanced and practical chemistry rather than engineering in the new school. How to implement the new school was now the problem.

Though previous Rumford Professors had taught technology by lectures and demonstration, Horsford could not teach practical chemistry that way, especially since he had experienced the value of laboratory instruction, first at the Rensselaer School and then at Liebig's laboratory at Giessen. Everett anticipated this problem, for he closed his letter of congratulations to Horsford, "We shall endeavor to give you as much time as possible for the pursuit of your investigations. You shall have a good laboratory, well furnished; and a cordial welcome from all your associates." In promising such a laboratory, Everett was making a rather sharp change in Harvard's financial policy toward chemistry. Harvard at the time did not have the funds for such an outlay. The Rumford fund was producing $1,900 per year, just enough for a full-time professor and his lecture apparatus, but certainly not enough for a laboratory. Webster had been expected to furnish his own laboratory at the medical school, but Horsford, an outsider, could not be expected to undertake such a task. Laboratories were expensive and a "well-furnished" one was beyond the reach of most American universities in the 1840s and 1850s.[13]

Everett was nevertheless confident that there was enough wealth around Boston by now for Harvard to be able to afford one. The fund for the astronomical observatory in 1843 had proven Boston's wealth and willingness to support science by attracting over $30,000. It had set a precedent for large philanthropy in support of science at Harvard.

Harvard's experience with the observatory had provided more than a precedent, for the leader of its fund drive had been Abbott Lawrence, a Boston industrialist and Whig friend of Everett, who was now to endow the scientific school. Lawrence's background is of some interest, since he represents an early example of the self-made man, who in his later years used his wealth to endow institutions he had never attended. Lawrence had been born in 1792 in Groton, Massachusetts, where he had attended a local academy. In 1808 he had joined his brother Amos in his importing firm in Boston and did not attend Harvard or any other college. The importing firm was fairly successful, and the brothers were able to invest in railroads (the Boston and Albany) and in cotton mills at Lawrence, Massachusetts. As their fortune increased, Abbott took a strong interest in Whig politics, serving in the United States House of Representatives in 1835–37 and 1839–40. In Boston Lawrence mingled with Everett and John A Lowell in encouraging the intellectual life of the city. He had been among the sponsors of Benjamin Silliman's first lectures in Boston in 1836 and those of the phrenologist George Combe in 1840. At his new town of Lawrence, he had come to know the value of applied science and the difficulty of hiring good men. Over the years he had hired Dr. Samuel Dana, Charles S. Storrow (a graduate of Harvard and the Ecole des Ponts et Chaussées in Paris and therefore one of the best-trained engineers of the time), and Augustus A. Hayes, a Boston chemist who later became state assayer. In 1846 Lawrence had also tried to hire John Pitkin Norton, but without success. Lawrence's interests in science thus ranged from the sublime to the applied and, when he heard at Everett's inaugural in 1846 that Harvard would be needing funds to create a scientific school for practical and advanced instruction, he was naturally interested.[14]

During April and May 1847, when Horsford was planning his new laboratory with Everett, their conversation turned occasionally to the subject of costs. Horsford and Treasurer Samuel Eliot both thought a suitable amount would be $50,000, by which Horsford meant $30,000 for the laboratory and $20,000 for a maintenance fund. Horsford was joyous at the prospect, but when Lawrence's gift was finally announced with much fanfare, Horsford discovered to his horror that he would receive only half of that amount, or $25,000, because Lawrence wanted to endow a whole school and not just a laboratory. The salaries of a geology professor, an engineering professor, and an engineering building were to come out of the other $25,000. Horsford tried to be appreciative of the "princely" gift in public, but to Mary he admitted that he was concerned. The difference between $25,000 and $50,000 was in the long run crucial.[15]

When Horsford was planning his laboratory, which he told Everett, "You will be enabled to compare with Liebig's," he had no way of estimating the future demand for chemical instruction in America. But buoyed up by Everett's strong interest and assurances of financial support, and believing strongly that America was due for rapid growth in scientific institutions, Horsford planned for one hundred or more students to attend the lectures and for thirty to enroll in the analytical laboratory. This was about how many students Liebig had had at Giessen. This estimate seems also to have been a middle course at the time, since the cautious Reverend James Walker of the Corporation suggested starting with smaller steps and adding later when the demand materialized, and the chemists Samuel Dana and A. A. Hayes advised building an even larger laboratory. Later they would all wish they had paid less attention to Liebig's model and more to American conditions.[16]

Horsford submitted plans in May for a large (80 × 44 foot) building that featured a lecture hall with semicircular seating like Liebig's and a large analytical laboratory with five feet of work space per student. The laboratory also had numerous other rooms for balances, distillation apparatus, storage, a library, a three-room private laboratory for Horsford, and apartments for the janitor and one assistant. A residence for Horsford was also attached, following the Liebig model. The Cambridge laboratory was to be more spacious, better arranged, and better equipped than Liebig's laboratory at Giessen or any other Horsford had visited in Europe.[17]

Among the modern conveniences Horsford meant to provide in the new laboratory were central heating and a system of ventilation. The lack of such facilities at Giessen had made work there uncomfortable and sometimes unpleasant. These problems were beginning to attract attention in the 1840s. The United States Congress had considered a proposal for heating and ventilating the Capitol in 1844, and Horsford had inspected the provisions for ventilating the Houses of Lords and Commons while in England en route home. His predecessor at Harvard, Daniel Treadwell, had in 1837 devised a method for heating the Harvard library, and Dr. Morrell Wyman of Cambridge, the brother of Jeffries Wyman, had just written a treatise on ventilation with Horsford's help. After looking at apparatus at Lowell and elsewhere, Horsford contrived a steam boiler system that would not only heat the laboratory, but also provide it with a supply of distilled water, pump other water throughout the building, and make a steam drying chamber possible. Horsford also devised a ventilating system that would circulate fresh air first through the apartments, then over the sand and water baths, and finally deposit the noxious fumes outdoors. These two ingenious contrivances would make a big improvement over earlier laboratories, but years later the steam boiler would prove to have been a costly mistake.[18]

The episode with the heating was typical of the school's whole formulation. In the first months of planning, when his every wish had been granted, Horsford had not planned the finances very closely. He had been encouraged to plan the best laboratory in the world, which, with his inventive mind and ambitious plans, wide travels, and expectation of $50,000, had been no particular problem. This structure, somewhat toned down, was built in 1847–48. The eventual problem was not in the initial outlay, but in the maintenance costs. Even heating the vast edifice was sometimes more than the school's income could pay for, and fuel bills were an item of constant concern to Horsford. By 1854 he had given up his steam boiler in favor of a gas heater that would only warm part of the building. He had to give up his early grandiose ideas and settle for something more within his means. Likewise, the school as a whole started out with high aspirations that it could not fulfill and had to drop them for others that were more appropriate.[19]

As the building neared completion in the summer of 1848 and Horsford was preparing it for use, the cutbacks began in earnest. Since there was no fund for equipment or maintenance, he was in a difficult position. The conflict between the German ideal and the American reality became acute. He would need large quantities of chemicals for himself and for his students and enough textbooks and journals to equip an adequate library. Though these were inexpensive items in Germany, they were not available in America and had to be imported at considerable cost. Horsford also estimated that he would need one janitor and two assistants, as Liebig had had. But American salaries were much higher than comparable German ones. The discrepancy between Cambridge and Giessen was even greater, since Cambridge had a relatively high cost of living for the United States, and Giessen was considered cheap for Germany. Horsford later figured that the difference was as great as a factor of four: though his salary seemed about four times as large as Liebig's, they were about equal in purchasing power. Treasurer Eliot, who had been much more agreeable in the optimistic days a year earlier, had no precedent for paying such bills and told Horsford to appeal to the Corporation or to Lawrence. Horsford drew up a "Statement on the Condition and Wants of the Laboratory of the Scientific School" which requested $2,000 per year for each of the next two years. Since necessary salaries to the janitor ($400) and assistants ($500 and $400) would amount to $1,300 yearly, perhaps it would be better to rent out the unfinished second floor of the laboratory to students for $1,500 annually and not be at a loss for operating funds. The Corporation referred the request to President Everett, who toned it down and wrote Lawrence that Horsford needed $1,000 to equip the laboratory. Lawrence agreed to pay two-thirds and the Corporation the rest. There was still no maintenance fund, but Horsford was able to open part of the best analytical laboratory in the world in November 1848.[20]

Horsford was trying to build a German laboratory in America, but American costs and wages were so much higher and so many basic items needed to be imported that he had to make major modifications in the German model. Nevertheless, there was still hope in 1849 that once the school got going it might be as successful as planned. To Horsford "success" probably meant, if we can judge by what he said in 1854, a salary of $3,000 and time and quiet for research. Since the professors' salaries depended on student enrollments, Horsford calculated what numbers would be necessary to assure all three of them (Horsford, Agassiz, and now Henry Eustis in engineering) $3,000 salaries. The calculation was difficult since the different departments charged different fees and any new increase in student numbers also meant increases in costs, but Horsford finally concluded that a total of 157 students would be necessary. Considering "the utter hopelessness of such an income and such a number of pupils," he suggested that Lawrence establish a new fund to guarantee them all salaries of $3,000. This Lawrence was not willing to do, though he did rearrange the funds for Eustis and provided for Agassiz for five years out of other money. Lawrence thought that if the students were not prepared to pay the tuition necessary to support the professors, then the school ought to be discontinued. He also thought that professors, like other men, should expect financial insecurity and rather sternly rejected Horsford's arguments that researchers deserved full salaries:

> Nor do I entirely agree with the views pretty distinctly intimated in the communications from the gentlemen of the Scientific

Faculty . . . that it is necessary, or important, or even desirable that the Scientific man should be raised above the necessity of taking care for himself and his household, in order that he may devote his whole soul to scientific investigations. Neither the History of the most important scientific discoveries, nor the facilities for the prosecution of scientific investigations afforded by any institution in the world with which I am acquainted, justifies the belief that such provision is best for the professor or for the science to which he devotes himself. His mind is stimulated to more valuable effort by sharing with the rest of mankind in a degree of uncertainty as to the future.[21]

Unfortunately, the number of students in Horsford's department was never very large. It never reached the forty-six he had figured in 1849 would be necessary to give him a $3,000 salary. Instead, it hovered around twenty, with a low of five students in its first year, 1847–48, and a high of thirty-one in its peak year, 1850–51.[22]

Of those who did come, most sought elementary training in analytical methods which they could then apply in medicine, industry, and elsewhere. Their needs determined the nature of the daily instruction, which consisted of working through Heinrich Will's *Outlines of Qualitative Analysis* (1847) and Karl Fresenius's *Instruction in Quantitative Analysis* (1846) with additional exercises and calculations.[23] The course also featured such practical skills as soil and ash analyses, blowpipe analyses and mineral assays, detection of poisons, pharmaceutical preparations, and medical tests. The work in the laboratory lasted from nine till five and left Horsford exhausted. He later complained that the teaching of the elementary students was the most tiring task of all and appreciated how much Heinrich Will's junior laboratory had freed Liebig for the advanced students. In his eagerness to duplicate Liebig's laboratory in America, Horsford had forgotten the important part Will's laboratory played at Giessen. It had provided a necessary step in his own training, for he had not gone directly from his American training to advanced work with Liebig. Despite his assurances to Everett that he was bringing Liebig's laboratory to America, Horsford found himself duplicating Will's laboratory instead.

A few of Horsford's students, however, went on to do advanced research; and some, like David A. Wells, Joseph LeConte, and

Francis H. Storer, went on to become famous. Few as the advanced students at both Harvard's and Yale's scientific schools were, their papers and those of their professors dominated the chemical sections of the American Association for the Advancement of Science in the late 1840s and early 1850s. Just about the only chemistry being done in the country at the time, aside from isolated mineral analyses, was done in these two laboratories.

By the mid-1850s Horsford's laboratory had taken its place as an intermediate training school for chemists, and several of its graduates went abroad, especially to Wöhler's laboratory at Göttingen, for advanced degrees. Overseer John H. Clifford was not pleased to note in Horsford's 1856 report that in the last two years nine graduates had gone abroad for advanced training. The necessity of foreign training "ought not to exist," but the Overseers, it seemed, were not prepared to do anything about it. Horsford described their ineffectiveness succinctly, "We shall complain of out wants as usual, dine and disperse." Advanced training in chemistry required more extensive support than the Overseers were willing to work for.[24]

The basic problem was that without a very large endowment (and Lawrence's $25,000 laboratory and the $30,000 Rumford fund were not large enough) Liebig's laboratory was not economically feasible in the United States in the 1840s and 1850s. It required too much overhead (expensive fuel bills, chemicals, books) and too much manpower (several professors, privatdocents, and assistants) for the small demand for advanced instruction in chemistry in the United States at the time. Bringing it to America had appealed to Edward Everett's vanity, but sustaining it was beyond the abilities of the Overseers. It was unsuited to American conditions.

More suited to the United States were the smaller private commercial laboratories that existed in a few large cities by the 1840s. C. T. Jackson's in Boston, James Booth's in Philadelphia and Benjamin Silliman, Jr.'s in New Haven combined elementary instruction and modest overhead with comercial analyses of minerals and soils. Even so, they barely broke even. America could support a few of these in the 1840s and 1850s, but only a few, as Charles M. Wetherill learned when he returned from Paris and Giessen in 1849, set up a private laboratory in Philadelphia, but then had to close it down because there was not enough demand in the city for both his laboratory and Booth's.[25]

The only chemical research possible under such circumstances was whatever work these practitioners, or college professors with modest laboratories, could do on the side with equipment already purchased for another purpose. To expect to include research as part of the day's work was neither possible nor considered desirable, as it was in Germany. Even such a relatively enlightened benefactor as Abbott Lawrence did not like the idea. For Horsford to have devoted as much of his time to research as Liebig thought he should, he would have had to hire still another assistant to direct the students. Such an arrangement would cost $400–$500, which Horsford preferred to spend on his family. Yet the addition of another assistant might not have been as impossible as Horsford seemed to think. His salary in 1854 was $2,100–$2,400 ($1,800 from the laboratory and $300–$600 for "occasional analyses"). The assistant's salary would leave him $1,600–$2,000, which was precisely the going salary range at Harvard at the time. It would seem that if he had really wanted to do chemical research, or if his family had been in better health, he might have chosen differently between the time and the extra money.[26]

Horsford's frustration at the Cambridge laboratory arose not, as he wanted to think, from the school's finances but from his own personality and a change in his motivation. A series of events in the years 1852–54, rather than the financial arrangements of the school in 1847–49, changed his earlier drive for eminence in science to an overriding concern for financial security for his family. Hard work at the laboratory and sacrifice at home might lead to a certain amount of scientific, fame and at first this excited him. Later he realized that such a life would never yield the riches he might make much more easily from inventions, and he became eager to change directions. His duties at the laboratory became burdensome, and he wanted to shake them off. His activities in the period 1847 to 1854 and especially his letters to his wife in 1854 reveal this change.

For a few years Horsford struggled hard to live up to Liebig's hopes for him. Horsford had always been a hard worker and, whatever the problems at Cambridge, he had advantages for pursuing advanced chemical studies there that made other chemists envious. Despite his complaints, he had the best laboratory in the country, a relatively high salary, and stimulating collegues (B. A. Gould, Guyot, Gray, Peirce, and Lovering were the most frequently mentioned.) The direction that Horsford's researches at Cambridge took is interesting. He gave up agricultural chemistry entirely, retained some interest in food chemistry, and turned to public health and mineral chemistry, subjects that were of great interest to the other chemists in the area at the time.[27]

In food chemistry one of Horsford's first tasks at Cambridge was to prepare an American edition of two of Liebig's latest publications, the *Researches on the Chemistry of Food* and *The Motion of the Juices in the Animal Body,* which presented Liebig's latest views on Mulder's work on proteins; analyses of kreatine and other compounds found in muscles; theories on the role of phosphates in the blood; ideas on the chemistry of cooked foods, especially soups and broths; experiments on endosmosis and osmosis; and an appendix on the potato disease. It was an undigested miscellany whose importance was nowhere near as great as that of his earlier works, though Liebig wrote Horsford that "I consider this investigation the most important I have ever made." Horsford killed 140 pigeons to isolate the kreatine from their muscles, but he did not follow it up with any more organic work. His only other venture into the area of food chemistry before 1854 was to direct a student, John Dean, in analyses of cornstarch, arrowroot, macaroni, and other nitrogenous foods in a paper that is very reminiscent of his own 1846 paper on food values.[28]

The major problem that Horsford attacked in 1848, even before the laboratory was finished, was the pressing one of the safety of lead pipes for the conveyance of Boston's drinking water. The city would soon be completing its new aqueduct from Lake Cochituate into town and needed to know what type of pipes to use. Lead pipes were cheap and flexible and had been used since Pompeiian times without difficulty for the most part, though cases of lead poisoning were too numerous to be ignored. Several physicians and chemists, including Dr. Samuel Dana, Professors John W. Webster, Benjamin Silliman, Jr., O. P. Hubbard, and Mr. A. A. Hayes, were already trying to solve the question. At the city's request Horsford undertook an exhaustive series of tests which enabled him to account for the conflicting evidence and settle the issue. Upon entering a lead pipe for the first time, water dissolved enough lead particles to cause lead poisoning, but after a few days an oxidized coating formed that would prevent further dissolution, and the pipe became safe for drinking water. Such a practical problem was a very suitable one for the new Rumford Professor, and the city presented him with a silver tea set in gratitude.[29]

Another set of researches undertaken by Horsford in Cambridge related both to Liebig's work and to urban problems. He tested various samples of air taken from the city of Boston for ammonia and possible traces of cholera. He collected air on the wharves and in the city's worst slums, where he needed two policemen to protect him. His results, however, differed greatly from those of Fresenius at Giessen. Horsford admitted in 1856 that his 1850 findings had been "radically erroneous," because the asbestos he had used had been exposed to the air and reused, but he was pleased to report that his latest results of 6.5 grams per million cubic centimeters of air were close to those of a recent European investigation. But by 1856 Lawes and Boussingault had done such detailed studies of the sources of nitrogen in plant nutrition that Horsford's evidence was largely irrelevant.[30]

Horsford also managed in his first years in Cambridge to contribute to another theoretical question that was attracting much interest at the time. Between 1850 and 1869, when Dmitri Mendeleev presented his periodic table, chemists were trying to determine possible connections between the atomic weights and the physical and chemical properties of the elements. Horsford pointed out in 1850 that the atomic weights of magnesium, calcium, strontium, and barium formed a series that corresponded to the intensity of their physical and chemical properties. A similar conclusion, of which Horsford was unaware, had been reached by Johann Döbereiner in 1817 and again simultaneously with Horsford by Max Pettenkofer, a student of Liebig's, in Munich. Josiah P. Cooke, Horsford's colleague at Harvard after 1851 (when he succeeded John W. Webster as Erving Professor), also contributed substantially to this question in 1854; but he had been attracted to the problem more by a year with Dumas in Paris than by Horsford's paper.[31] Horsford, as earlier with the "waves" at Giessen, touched on an important problem, contributed something to it, but then never followed it up.

In addition to these and other researches, Horsford had several professional duties besides the laboratory in the period 1847–50. Shortly after his arrival in Boston, John A. Lowell, trustee of the Lowell Institute, invited him to give a series of lectures of chemistry for $1,200. He was not as successful as Silliman had been in 1841–43, being "too scientific and not popular enough," but the lectures in November and December 1847 served as an introduction to Boston and a welcome addition to his salary. Then in early 1848 he was appointed an Examiner of the Mint in Philadelphia. This task was more exciting than had been expected, since he uncovered some embezzling among the officers. In 1849 Horsford had to replace Jeffries Wyman, who left suddenly for Labrador, as secretary of the American Association for the Advancement of Science, which was meeting in Cambridge that summer. The meetings were a chance to show off the new laboratory in which the chemical sessions were held, but the editing of the *Proceedings* was a time-consuming task. He had barely finished them by November when his friend John White Webster was arrested for the murder of a fellow Harvard professor, Dr. George Parkman of the Medical School. The trial, which attracted widespread popular attention and became one of the most colorful in Boston's history, lasted through April 1850 and occupied much of Horsford's time. He had to take on Webster's classes as well as visit him in prison and console his family, whom he had come to know very well during the ordeal.[32]

In spite of these extra burdens Horsford managed to run the laboratory and carry on his research. He was even optimistic in 1849 and 1850 about the future. In 1849 the school showed a $650 surplus, and in 1850 Horsford could say to James Hall, with whom he shared his moments of hope and despair, "Now we seem to be on the high road to prosperity." By 1849 he already had ideas for inventions, such as condensed milk and a safety lamp, but he was not devoting much time to them. He even gave the condensed milk idea to his assistant, Lieutenant August Dalson, in 1851. He was at this time fairly content with his lot and looking forward to continued usefulness.[33]

In the summer of 1852 Horsford came down with typhoid fever. This and other events of 1852–54 were to lure him away from his established pattern of teaching and research. He recovered after a month in New Hampshire, but the brush with death scared him about what would happen to his wife and two daughters if he should die. Though he was only thirty-four, young deaths were not uncommon; John P. Norton died that September at the age of thirty. Horsford began to take stock of the situation and disliked what he saw—he worked hard all day for his university salary, he was striving hard to provide his family with the comforts they deserved, and yet he had neither a fortune nor a prospect of one. The satisfactions of research and a European reputation began to seem remote and unimportant, as he wrote Mary in September 1854: "Must I sit here and see my family growing up around me, and be forever solicitous about what we shall eat and what we shall drink, or shall I not shake off the incubus of my present rotations [?] and take the place nature offers me—What do you say my beloved? Do we not need comforts and privileges for our children more than we need honors?" A few days later he wrote, "There are many things to be said on both sides, but my health and independence are of more moment than anything in the way of worldly name and place."

Horsford thus decided that he needed to build up a fortune quickly. Fortunately the means were available. By 1853, when he had regained his health, he had begun to work on his patents in earnest. By 1854 he could list several patents on which he was actively engaged—sulphite of lime (also called "anti-chlorine of bleach"), moth apparatus, safety lamps, india rubber, gas burners, lead pipes, lined iron pipes, grindstones, soap, soda fountain, screws, ink, manure, fire annihilators, and yeast powder.[34]

Besides the illness, Horsford had probably damaged his chemical reputation with a series of papers in the *American Journal of Science* and the *Proceedings to the AAAS* in 1851–53 on the chemical nature of corals. James Dwight Dana had been publishing items on the corals he had collected on the Wilkes Expedition, and Horsford obtained a few sample for analysis from Louis Agassiz after the latter's trip to the Florida Keys in 1851. From his analysis (which showed an abundance of carbonate of lime) Horsford went on to speculate about the processes by which corals grew in the sea. His chemistry seems to have been correct for the time, but the problem was terribly complex. Dana rejected his theorizing and pointed out that there were several kinds of corals, parts of which varied in composition, and the surrounding sea water varied in temperature and content. It is hard to judge how Dana, Horsford, and the rest of the scientific community felt about the issue, although A. A. Hayes of Boston thought "that Professor Horsford in his want of chemical knowledge, has assumed an amount of impudence and obstinacy, which is likely to shipwreck his prospects here." Dana's letters to Horsford were polite throughout the dispute, but Horsford never published again in Silliman's *Journal*. Nor did he wish to have his rebuttal published after delivering it to the 1853 AAAS meeting in Cleveland that year.[35]

By 1854 Horsford's attention had shifted so far from the laboratory that he admitted to his wife that the accounts had fallen into arrears, and he was expecting an investigation by the Overseers, but he just did not care. Despite the earlier surplus of $650, the laboratory was now running $500 in debt. The enrollment had dropped somewhat, and the costs had risen. Horsford was further disillusioned by a visit from his former students the Hague boys, who were now successfully building gas works and "making fortunes." There were tremendous opportunities like that outside the laboratory for someone with chemical knowledge. With much less fatigue Horsford could make much more money. He was eager to quit his job. The only deterrent was the dishonor that Mary's father might feel about it. Horsford at this point was facing a definite financial strain. Mary was sick and spending the summer at a watering place in Brattleboro, Vermont. The children were with her sister Phoebe (later Horsford's second wife) at Shelter Island. The cost of Mary's care, Horsford insisted, was less than that of running their household in Cambridge, but they were going to have a long talk about their finances when she returned. He could forego a new coat this year if she could mend his old one, and maybe they could get along with one Irish maid rather than two.[36]

Between March and October 1854 all these problems came to a head, and Horsford nearly resigned. He did not in the end because Charles Loring of the Corporation (and Asa Gray's father-in-law) convinced him that he should stay on, even if he had to give up all attempts at research. He could cut costs by getting a smaller gas heater, perhaps get along without an assistant, and concentrate on his teaching and inventions. Loring was sure the Corporation would be amenable to the change and wrote President Walker a remarkably perceptive letter after the interview. He had been concerned about all the recent criticisms of Horsford in the journals, but concluded, "I do not believe that the scientific world, excepting one or two personal enemies, think that he is not fit as a man of science, for this position. On the contrary I am satisfactorily assured that to displace him on the ground of supposed incompetency in that particular, would be esteemed unreasonable + unjust—by those in whom we are accustomed most to confide—." He thought the Corporation ought to blame itself as much as Horsford for the school's failure to life up to their earlier "jubilant expectations." He was also convinced that the combination of advanced research and elementary laboratory instruction was too much for one man, although

> it is probable that a man of wider experience + more wordly wisdom, + perhaps of more nervous energy,—would have bested the impossibilities, or rescued himself from the dilemma more readily + judiciously—And I incline to think that much of the present trouble is attributable to want of force of character to encounter trouble + overcome it—: Tho I believe he has a very manly fortitude to bear it.

"But," he added, "we should not forget that we are at least equally in fault, in placing him in this condition. We knew his youth + inexperience + that this was his first essay— + perhaps we might have known by more extensive inquiry, the impossibilities we were expecting." Horsford's letter to the Corporation of April 1854 describing the modifications he sought at the laboratory presented his version of the whole seemingly misguided attempt to import Liebig's laboratory into America. (It is reproduced in appendix 4.) What had seemed so desirable and possible only seven years before had proven impossible after all.[37]

The school continued after 1854 with a few modifications. Horsford, although released from part of his duties, had less and less interest. When in 1858 his department's debt reached \$3,000, the Corporation raised the tuition, instituted stricter accounting procedures, and appointed Charles W. Eliot as assistant professor to keep track of the finances. Eliot thought that Horsford had shown "criminal negligence" with the funds, and the two men reportedly feuded for the next thirty years. Horsford finally resigned in 1863 to devote full time to his Rumford Chemical Works in Providence, Rhode Island. His extraordinary knowledge of phosphates yielded big returns there in patents on baking powder and acid phosphate, a medicinal beverage. He was much more of a success in industry than he ever was at the Lawrence Scientific School.[38]

The failure of Liebig's laboratory in America was due to two factors. In spite of the financial support of Abbott Lawrence, pure chemical research on the scale of Liebig's laboratory was too expensive for America in the 1840s and 1850s. Economic differences between Germany and America at that time are often overlooked in attempts to find an American mind that did not like pure research. Horsford had done pure research in Germany and would have continued to do it in America if the rewards had been competitive with those of industry, but they were not. To make Liebig's laboratory succeed would have required a selfless and independently wealthy soul like John Pitkin Norton; this, Horsford was not. He had sought a career in science as a means of rising in status and wealth in order to marry Mary Gardiner. For a while at Giessen in conducive surroundings he thought he would seek fame by research; but back in America, where obstacles to such achievements abounded, and where other more lucrative avenues were open to him, his motivations changed. He gave up research and used his hard-won chemical knowledge in industry, where the large returns provided him with the material things he had been seeking. Unfortunately, Mary, for whose sake he had first taken up research and later abandoned it, was no longer around to enjoy these benefits when they did come, for she died of pneumonia at Thanksgiving 1855.

PART III

Soil Analysis: The Craze and Its Critics

6

John Pitkin Norton and Edinburgh

In the spring of 1844, when the craze over soil analysis erupted and when Eben Horsford was deciding to go to Giessen to study with Liebig, another young American, Horsford's kinsman in fact, was also making plans to go abroad to study agricultural chemistry. But John Pitkin Norton's personality, family background, foreign training, and opinions of Liebig were very different from Horsford's. Norton did not look upon agricultural chemistry as a congenial way to rise in status and fortune, for his branch of the Norton family already had both in abundance. Instead, he found agricultural chemistry a desirable outlet for his considerable reforming energies. The cause of scientific agriculture appealed to his strong desire to serve his fellow men and to his equally strong attachment to the life of the farm. Upon Horsford's withdrawal from agricultural chemistry in 1847, Norton became the sole leader of the movement in America. Yet his leadership demonstrates the increasing complexity of the movement, for he was not a disciple of Liebig. On the contrary, he professed to being decidedly anti-Liebig on most key points. Although he had been introduced to agricultural chemistry by reading Liebig in April 1842, subsequent study with the Sillimans at Yale, Johnston in Edinburgh, and Mulder in Utrecht had indoctrinated him into the faction increasingly opposed to Liebig. Norton, therefore, had no desire to be an American Liebig like Horsford at Harvard. The tradition he started at Yale was the product of a very different personality and a very different foreign experience.

John Pitkin Norton was born on July 19, 1822, in Albany, New York, into a highly respected family. His father, John Treadwell Norton, was the grandson of John Treadwell, governor of Connecticut from 1809 to 1811; and his mother, Mary Hubbard Pitkin, was the daughter of the Honorable Timothy Pitkin, Federalist statesman and historian. She died in 1829, when Norton was only seven years old, and the father married Elizabeth Cogswell, also of Hartford, two years later. Norton's immediate family, therefore, included close ties with several prominent Connecticut families— the Treadwells, Pitkins, Cogswells, and Welds. But his aristocratic background did not keep Norton from a career in applied science as might have been expected.[1] In fact, in a curious way, it rather pushed him into one.

Although the Norton family heritage was distinguished, there had been hard times in John Treadwell Norton's youth, around 1800–1805, when it appears that his father deserted his mother. He was thus forced to give up the idea of attending college and had to seek a trade. He worked in a bookseller's shop in Hudson, New York, but then moved to Albany and entered the hardware business with Erastus Corning and Edward C. Delavan. The company was successful enough for them all to begin investing in railroads, and John T. Norton was for a brief time president and superintendent of the Albany and Schenectady line. With this return to affluence, he moved his family back to the ancestral home in Farmington, Connecticut, in 1835, even though it meant frequent business trips to Albany for him. Each winter the whole family moved back to Albany and shared in the life of the capital with other leading families there— the Olcotts, the Delavans, the Spragues, the Marvins, and Uncle (Dr.) Mason Cogswell. Norton thus grew up both in the city and on the farm and felt at home in either place.[2]

In Farmington John Treadwell Norton took up the role of an English country gentleman and devoted much energy to building up his manor. Like Jerediah Horsford, he also was enthusiastic about scientific agriculture, experimenting with new crops and breeds, subscribing to the *Cultivator,* entering state agricultural contests, and judging at them occasionally. He also helped establish the local lyceum, planned a new female seminary, inspected a nearby asylum, and attended numerous temperance and abolition meetings. This dual Albany/Farmington upbringing and the reforming interests of his father, to whom Norton was very close, contributed a considerable amount to forming his personality and developing his interests.[3]

Young Norton attended local schools in Albany and Farmington and recited to his father at home until 1838, when he enrolled at the Albany Academy, ostensibly to prepare for college. But from the start he studied Euclid, algebra, trigonometry, and surveying rather than the Latin and Greek necessary to enter Yale College. He evidently so disliked the classics already that he did not want to go to college if it required learning more of them. The alternative, which his father arranged, was probably better suited to his present needs and eventual interests than the traditional liberal arts curriculum would have been. Instead of attending college as a regular student, Norton arranged his own special program of lectures and tutors in New York, New Haven, and Boston between 1839 and 1843. This arrangement allowed him to choose subjects that interested him and to try out several possible professional fields before settling down to one. In the early 1840s agricultural chemistry was only just emerging as a subject and as a possible profession, and Norton and Horsford were among the first to come to it. Horsford reached it after several years of teaching, and Norton only after rejecting the other more traditional professions.

Norton spent his first winter away from home in 1839–40 when he went to Brooklyn, New York, to study with tutor Theodore Dwight. There he recited his way through French grammar, surveying, physiology, ancient history, the history of Connecticut, geology, Cuvier's *Animal Kingdom,* Cleaveland's *Mineralogy,* and Silliman's two-volume *Elements of Chemistry,* showing particular interest in the last two, which he had already started at home. In April he returned to Farmington, where he helped plant the crops (oats, rye, hay, corn, beans, potatoes, and turnips), draw the manure, plaster the fields, care for the cattle and sheep, and tend the fruit trees.[4] It was a vigorous year for any young man and a very progressive farm for Connecticut in 1839.

The next winter, 1840–41, when his younger brother Edward was setting off for Yale, Norton went along, boarded nearby, and attended Benjamin Silliman's lectures on chemistry and Denison Olmsted's on natural philosophy. But if Norton had wanted at this point to become a chemist, Silliman's lectures did not inspire him further. In fact, he preferred Olmsted to Silliman, whom he found "diffuse" and "well calculated to be popular" but not as "instructive if closely attended to." Besides, the Olmsteds also came from Farmington, and Norton had collected minerals with the sons. By now mineralogy had become Norton's preponderant interest, and he exchanged specimens with the Olmsteds, the Sillimans, and others as far away as the West Indies. Had James Dwight Dana not been off on the Wilkes Expedition at the time, Norton might well have become a mineralogist in 1840.[5]

When Norton returned to Farmington in January, however, a religious revival was taking place there. The constant round of prayer meetings, temperance meetings, abolition meetings, and Sunday school teaching of the black "Amistad captives," as well as several deaths among young people that year, all had a strong influence on Norton, who soon began to show more interest in his soul and its salvation than in his minerals. He went through a religious crisis during the summer and, realizing that he must soon choose a profession, considered becoming a minister or a missionary. The need for service and sacrifice appealed to him, but he did not know "whether a life of study or one of action will suit me best." Reverend Noah Porter urged him not to make a hasty decision, but to pursue his interest by attending the lectures of Reverend Nathaniel Taylor on theology and moral philosophy at Yale the next winter. Taylor was one of the outstanding "New Light" Congregational theologians of the time.[6]

Norton attended Taylor's lectures in 1841–42 and at first seemed to enjoy them, but later found he could not follow the constant defining and redefining of terms which the students and professors used when trying to catch each other on a heresy. It was all a "confused mass," and the more he tried to make sense of it, "the deeper into the fog" he sank. He was glad enough to escape and take it all on faith.

While in New Haven that year, Norton managed to take several other studies on the side. He attended Silliman's lectures on mineralogy, but since he had already read and used Dana's *System of Mineralogy*, he found them rather elementary. His admiration for Olmsted increased as he finished the course on natural philosophy he had started the year before and also took his lectures on astronomy and meteorology. In addition he found time to translate and recite French for a tutor and to write essays for William Larned, professor of rhetoric, who surprised Norton one day by telling him that he had a gift for writing after all. Norton later made considerable use of this talent in the cause of scientific agriculture. Besides his studies Norton enjoyed talking about minerals with Benjamin Silliman, Jr., and attending church services where sermons on the missionaries in the western colleges always stirred him. But appealing as the life of a missionary was to him, he returned to Farmington in the spring convinced he was not to be a clergyman.[7]

It was at this juncture, in the summer of 1842, that Norton recorded, "I also commenced Liebig's Agricultural Chemistry," which his father may have used the previous winter for a talk on agriculture at the local lyceum. Norton may also have read the Sillimans' review of Liebig's book in the *American Journal of Science* as early as February 1841. But these early encounters with Liebig had no immediate effects. There is no indication that he even finished reading the book, for he left soon after for a mineral trip to the White Mountains in New Hampshire and made no further comments upon it. The conversion to agricultural chemistry was not to be that simple.[8]

The next fall, 1842, his father decided that since the ministry was not to be Norton's career, he must go to Boston to read law with Professor Greenleaf at Harvard. Norton spent the winter there attending the lectures of the kindly professor but showed more enthusiasm in his diary for entomology. He had studied it somewhat at home, but now sought the library's books and the advice of Thaddeus W. Harris, the Harvard librarian and a noted entomologist. Norton even thought for a short while he might like to become one himself. With a friend he attended a few medical lectures, but found the "hardened indifference" of physicians toward their patients enough to make him dislike medicine as a career. He heard a few more missionary sermons that aroused his admiration, commenting on one, "I have scarcely ever been more interested," but he returned to Farmington in February, apparently as disenchanted with the law and medicine as he had been with the ministry a year before.[9]

Once home he began to a make plans for the summer, because this year his father was to let him manage the farm. Norton puzzled over how many men to hire and at what wages and how much gypsum to apply to the fields. The results were not terribly successful, however, despite his best efforts, since there was a drought in Connecticut that year.[10]

In the fall of 1843, the annual problem of Norton's winter study plans arose again. The ministry, law, and medicine having been rejected, his interest in entomology having subsided, the possibility of mineralogy never having been considered, his father, who had

just returned from a horticultural exhibition in Hartford, had a
new suggestion. John should become an agricultural chemist. Norton
was greatly pleased by the idea and went down to Yale to ask the
advice of Professor Silliman immediately.

> This morning after breakfast I saw Prof. Silliman; he was very
> kind + said that he knew just the plan for me. It is to go to
> England + put myself under the instruction of Prof. Johnston
> a friend of his + one of the best chemical agriculturalists now
> living. He is in the University of Durham, + Prof. Silliman
> says he can give me a letter that would ensure a favorable re-
> ception. This plan would be no small trial yet if it is necessary
> I shall do it. I went to Prof. Silliman's house + got two books
> of Prof. Johnston's that will give me some knowledge of his
> system + discoveries.[11]

The possibility of going to Giessen to study with Liebig, with whose
works Norton was more familiar, seems never to have come up.
Though the Sillimans had been enthusiastic about Liebig in 1841,
they had subsequently been even more impressed with Johnstons'
Lectures on the Applications of Chemistry and Geology to Agriculture. They
considered these lectures to be "unquestionably the most important
contribution that has recently been made to popular science" and
felt that Liebig's book, "notwithstanding its originality and the
philosophical beauty of its theories, is apt to make the impression
upon the farmer that he is not at present to expect much from agricultural chemistry but ingenious conjecture." Likewise Asa Gray
felt that Johnston's volume was "unrivalled" for its practical and
scientific views. Specifically, "it embraces a wider field, and enters
into more specific details, than the plan of Professor Liebig's works
permitted; and is, therefore, more directly available to the cultivator
of the soil, whose wants it was especially intended to supply." An
alternative to Liebig and Giessen had, therefore, appeared in the
early 1840s, and if a student wished to learn "practical" agricultural
chemistry, as Norton did, many felt he would be better off going to
Professor Johnston than to Liebig.[12]

   James F. W. Johnston had been one of the small group of British
chemists who had invited Liebig in 1837 to write his report on organic
chemistry for the British Assoication for the Advancement of Science.
Johnston, a graduate of the University of Glasgow, had studied

briefly with Berzelius in 1832–33 and then had joined the faculty of the new University of Durham. He had worked on mineral chemistry, dimorphism, and resins before 1840; but in that year, stimulated by Liebig's book, he had started an even more successful second career as an agricultural chemist and popularizer. He had written a series of talks on the chemistry of soils, manures, plants, and foods for the Durham County Agricultural Society in 1841 and expanded it into his massive *Lectures* (1842–44), which so impressed Gray and Silliman.[13]

Before joining Johnston the next spring (1844), Norton spent the winter in Benjamin Silliman, Jr.'s new private laboratory in New Haven. Norton's few months there were instructive, although the laboratory's deficiencies in equipment and chemicals, the comings and goings of both Sillimans, and the time spent preparing demonstrations for the professor's lectures held him up considerably. However, Norton completed several soil and mineral analyses, one of which on sillimanite was published in the *American Journal of Science*. Norton also began to feel more at home in New Haven, joining the college choir and visiting the professors' homes, where he could talk about minerals and chemistry or chat with the Silliman daughters.[14]

While in New Haven, Norton heard from Professor Silliman that Professor Johnston had just opened a new laboratory in Edinburgh for the Agricultural Chemistry Association, as offshoot of the very active and greatly respected Highland and Agricultural Society. Johnston's duties there were to analyze soils and fertilizers for the member farmers, to visit their farms and offer advice on improvements, to give public lectures in various towns, and to do research on agricultural chemistry. Such support and sponsorship by an agricultural society, or a part of one, was an early step in the institutionalization of agricultural chemistry. For Norton it meant that in his year with Johnston he could observe the latest advances in agricultural chemistry in the field as well as in the laboratory.[15]

That Scotland should have taken the lead in providing this early form of extension work should not be surprising. After the 1790s, when Sir Arthur Young began to popularize scientific agriculture, England and Scotland went through a period of great agricultural reform. Many British farmers were very eager for the latest improvements, and several strong agricultural journals actively supported them.[16] The intensity of interest in guano, the superphosphates,

Liebig's patent manure, agricultural chemistry, and Liebig himself
was initially much greater in Britain than in the United States, where
the availability of cheap fertile lands took off much of the pressure for
improvements. But many of the British problems of the 1840s with
fertilizers, adulterations, and regulations would become issues in
America in the 1850s. Therefore, for Norton to go to Scotland in 1844
was for him to see something of a preview of the problems that would
be coming up in the United States upon his return.

Norton set sail from New York on April 17, 1844, and arrived at
Professor Johnston's in Durham, England, a month later. The
professor was sick at the time but had Norton copy reports and
proofread a new edition of his *Lectures* until he was better. Finally,
on June 21 they went up to the Edinburgh laboratory where Norton
was eager to settle down and start his work.

As might have been expected, Norton experienced much less
culture shock in Edinburgh than Horsford did in Giessen. The
economy of the region was enough like that of New England at the
time for Norton to feel in familiar surroundings. He did not find
Edinburgh quaint or backward as Horsford found Giessen. Since
there were also no language barriers and hardly any religious differences, he had no trouble finding a suitable Presbyterian church
and feeling somewhat at home. His chief difficulty was that, like
Horsford at first, he stuck rigidly to his temperance and sabbatarian
principles, even to the point of inconvenience and embarrassment.
When he suspected Horsford of weakening in his tempeance principles, he sent him a stern letter of warning, and he even lectured a
laboratory assistant on the vices of drinking—only to be laughed at
in return.[17]

In general Norton by no means held Johnston in the same awe
as Horsford did Liebig. Although Johnston's works had been praised
in America as surpassing those of the great Liebig, the Scotsman did
not have the same magnetic appeal as Liebig had. Nor was Norton
as prone to hero worshiping as was Horsford. Although Norton
always valued Johnston's favorable comments, especially when they
were delivered in front of others in the laboratory, he was also aware
of the professor's failings. Johnston was sometimes snappish and
unjust, occasionally made false accusations about persons in the
laboratory, and frequently used tuition-paying students on his own
projects without compensation. Norton recognized these faults and

tried to avoid them, but they later became much more pronounced and led to a break between Norton and Johnston in 1851.[18]

In spite of these weaknesses, Professor Johnston was, in 1844, very eager to advance Norton's career. Even before Norton arrived, the professor had arranged for him to do an intensive study of the oat for the 1845 Highland and Agricultural Society prize competition. Though the oat was important in both the Scottish and American economies, only Hermbstadt, Sprengel, and most recently Boussingault had made reliable single analyses. Norton's project, on the contrary, was to be so extensive that it would take him eighteen months of tedious ash analyses and much help from Johnston's assistant P. F. H. Fromberg. Norton analyzed each part (leaf, stalk, knots, chaff, oat, straw, husk, and grain) of five varieties of the plant as it developed through the growing season from June to September. He showed in hundreds of analyses (he had as many as fifteen going at once) that the sodium chloride and phosphoric acid content dropped off considerably as the plant developed. But his only explanation for these and a great many other variations was to observe that they seemed to arise from "a law infinitely more unerring than any which human wisdom can devise." He hoped, however, that his analyses would show what minerals oats needed, so that soil deficiencies could be corrected with proper fertilizers. He read part of his paper at the meeting of the British Association for the Advancement of Science at Cambridge in June 1845, where it aroused a great deal of interest from Thomas Graham and others, although some criticized his technique as unduly tedious. His analysis of the oat was a model of how each crop should be studied, and he hoped to work on Indian corn when he returned to America. But his study also showed the limitations of agricultural chemistry, which, in collecting all these data, was galloping ahead of plant physiology's ability to explain them.[19]

Norton also managed to do a few other researches while in Edinburgh. He analyzed horn flints for their value as fertilizers and detected one of the first fertilizer frauds in an analysis of "Potter's Artificial Guano." He also became interested in agricultural geology and analyzed a series of seven slates to see what soils they would form on decomposition. Though they all came from an area of twenty-mile radius, they showed very different compositions when pulverized to soil. It was no wonder, therefore, that the soils in the area had shown a great variety of responses to the use of lime, and Norton could cite his study as prime evidence that soil analysis was valuable.[20]

Norton worked very hard in Edinburgh, but by comparison with what he might have learned in eighteen months at Giessen, or what he might have done with several smaller and progressively more difficult projects in Edinburgh, the oat analysis, impressive as it was, was probably too large a project for someone who was still a student and had so much to learn. Though he won the prize and spent his $250 on apparatus, the project tested and retested his patience and perseverance rather than teaching him the latest methods of analysis and new theoretical principles. Norton had come to Edinburgh with what was probably the best chemical training available in the United States at the time, but he too, like Horsford, could have profited from a year in Dr. Will's laboratory in Giessen, learning thoroughly the basic methods of analysis with the "hundred bottles." He would also have benefited from the many lectures available in Giessen, from the work of his fellow students in the laboratory, and, of course, from the daily attentions of the professor. In Edinburgh, by contrast, there were no lectures, because the laboratory was not connected with the university. Norton's fellows in the laboratory were, except for Fromberg, hired assistants of an unreliable sort, and Professor Johnston was often away for extended periods. Norton, therefore, never felt the contagious esprit de corps of the Giessen students or the charismatic appeal of their great professor. Even the BAAS meeting in 1845, where Norton saw Lyon Playfair, Thomas Graham, Sir David Brewster, and Michael Faraday, the great men of British science at the time, failed to give him the exhilarating feeling of being near greatness and struggling to measure up that Horsford found so exciting at Giessen and thought Norton should likewise be experiencing.[21]

Norton was quite satisfied with his training at Edinburgh until the end of his stay, when he, like Horsford, toured the Continent visiting important chemists. In two months he saw Dumas, Payen, and Boussingault in Paris; Nicklès and Persoz in Strassburg; Liebig in Giessen; Erdmann's laboratory in Liepzig; Heinrich Rose, Rammelsberg, and Magnus in Berlin; and Mulder in Utrecht. But it was the week with Horsford in Giessen in January 1846 that convinced him he must supplement his Edinburgh training with a year on the

Continent. He was greatly impressed with Horsford's mastery of the latest tests for nitrogen and his grasp of theoretical principles. Norton now realized that practical agriculture required a thorough grounding in pure organic chemistry, which he ought to obtain before settling down in a professorship in America. But of all the Continental laboratories Norton might have selected, he never considered studying at Giessen, because by January 1846, he had joined the anti-Liebig faction of agricultural chemists.[22]

Although Norton had originally known little of Johnston's works, in his eighteen months in Edinburgh he had been converted to the Mulder-Johnston side of the quarrel that was brewing with Liebig. His diary contains no references as to how Johnston indoctrinated him, but a few incidents show his increasingly anti-Liebig stance. When Horsford wrote him how impressed he was with Liebig, Norton showed the letter to Johnston, and they both had a good laugh. When a fellow student in the younger Silliman's laboratory wrote for advice on European laboratories, Norton commented, "I must not let him go to Liebig." When, as mentioned earlier, Liebig visited Scotland in October 1844, a large banquet was held for him in Glasgow. Norton went and, disgusted by all the adulation poured upon Liebig, sent off to the *Cultivator* some of Johnston's recent "excellent remarks" about scientists who "have launched off into wild theories" and who with only an "imperfect knowledge of the subject, boldly arrogate to themselves the office of teachers, and by erroneous results and conclusions, not only lead others astray, but throw discredit upon the whole science." When later on his tour of the Continent, Norton met Liebig and presented his letter from Johnston, he felt Liebig was "rather ungracious," a first impression Horsford, Gibbs, and Whitney had also had. In the course of his visit at Giessen Norton grew to like Horsford more than before, but he did not give Professor Liebig such a second chance. Norton was already too far entrenched in the enemy camp, and when it came time to choose a continental laboratory to work in, his choice would be Mulder's rather than Liebig's.[23]

Just as Norton had been predisposed to dislike Liebig, he was prepared to like Mulder. Johnston and Mulder were close friends, both having been students of Berzelius, and each had his own reasons for opposing Liebig. There were also close ties between Johnston's laboratory in Edinburgh and Mulder's in Utrecht. Johnston's assistants, first Fromberg and then Voelcker, were students of Mulder. The network of ties spread to include Yale College when Norton arranged in 1845 for Benjamin Silliman, Jr., to edit an American edition of Mulder's text, *The Chemistry of Vegetable and Animal Physiology* (1845), with an introduction by Johnston. There were thus several reasons why Mulder was much more cordial to the visiting Norton than Liebig had been. Norton thought Mulder's laboratory the best on the Continent and was "impressed with his kindness & good feeling as well as great powers." Since Norton had recently been in Giessen, the subject of proteins inevitably came up, and Mulder hastily overcame any of Norton's doubts. "Among other things I spoke of their fancied discovery in Geissen [*sic*] that Proteine did not exist; because the Sulphur could not be separated from it. He showed me by a most conclusive series of experiments that Proteine does exist, without the slightest trace of Sulphur. I was much pleased by my visit."[24] Upon leaving Utrecht, Norton expressed to Mulder his intention to return to spend a year with him. Mulder was "much gratified" and urged him to do so. Norton would be back within the year.

Norton's laboratory experiences in Edinburgh, however, were not as important for his career in America as what he was able to learn outside the laboratory. The main reason that Norton and Silliman had chosen Johnston in the first place had been his interest in practical agriculture, and Norton's experience with him fully justified his selection on this basis. Johnston's visits and lectures to farmers throughout Scotland were major features of Norton's stay in Edinburgh. Horsford did not see any similar extension work in Germany in the 1840s. Norton accompanied Johnston on his lecture tours and farm visits, absorbing much that would later be of use to him in America. He learned not only which farm practices were best, but also how to handle farmers themselves. Johnston was fairly successful with the Scottish farmers, and Norton was always impressed with the response he got from them. He became eager to bring some of their "awakened spirit" back to the United States. Just how to do so remained a problem, however, for, though Norton felt that the "conviction and spirit" of the Agricultural Chemistry Association ought to be copied in America, he suspected its organizational form should not. He was already aware that popular control had its difficulties, having seen some of the internal bickering that would cause the association to disband in 1849. In the United States, he thought, perhaps the reform spirit could be tied to the movement for agricultural colleges, which already had some momentum and which seemed in 1845 on the verge of major state appropriations.[25]

Norton described these excursions and the latest laboratory findings in nineteen monthly letters to the *Cultivator* and sixteen to the *American Agriculturalist* between July 1844 and February 1846. Norton had a touch of the agricultural journalist about him which he used to great advantage in these letters. He had an eye for the key features on a farm and could describe them in simple language. His farm background enabled him to judge a crop and appreciate the innovations of the Scottish farmers—their diagonal drilling, draining, new crop rotations, and fertilizers. Norton's letters also took up other timely and practical topics—the potato disease, guanos and their adulterations, bone dust fertilizers, draining, and agricultural education.

The effect of these letters in the United States was electric. They were published at the same time as Horsford's from Giessen, frequently appearing on the same page, and spelled out the practical advantages of agricultural chemistry and soil analysis to an even larger audience of farmers who might not have read Liebig, Dana, or Johnston themselves. Now one did not have to read them to know that he should have his soils analyzed to increase his crops. Suddenly soil analysts and lecturers on agricultural chemistry were "starting up in the United States in every direction," as Norton noted in December 1844. Immediately the farm journals were flooded with analyses of soils, plants, and fertilizers of all sorts, and their discussions of crop failures and the use of manures revolved more and more around deficiencies in the soil and analyses of the plant.[26]

The Sillimans at Yale were likewise enthusiastic, reporting in December 1844 that Norton's letters were "making something of a sensation" in New Haven. By February 1845 Benjamin Silliman, Jr., who was editing Mulder's textbook, was anxious to add a section on agricultural chemistry to the *American Journal of Science*.[27] By October the Sillimans were so confident of the future benefits of scientific agriculture that they were considering the creation of a professorship of agricultural chemistry at Yale College. But Yale was not alone in planning such a step.

The trustees of Union College had already responded to the

excitement over agricultural chemistry by writing Norton in Edinburgh that they wished to hire him for the next year. President
Eliphalet Nott and Trustee Edward C. Delavan had known him
and his father for years. Although Norton was flattered by Union's
offer, he preferred to go to Yale if it would create a similar position
for him. As soon as he heard from Union he wrote Benjamin Silliman, Jr., to ask what plans they might have at Yale.[28]

Unlike Harvard, which was not using its Bussey agricultural fund
and which had hired an agricultural chemist only to avoid a difficult personality clash, Yale clearly intended to do something about
agricultural chemistry. The problem was how to do it and when,
since, as at Harvard, a new president was to be inaugurated soon.
The matter dragged on and still was not settled when Norton returned from his European tour in April 1846. Eventually, after a few
trips from Farmington to New Haven and a few more months of
uncertainty, Norton, himself wrote the proposal for the creation of
two new professorships, one for Benjamin Silliman, Jr., in "practical
chemistry" and the other for himself in "agricultural chemistry and
vegetable and animal physiology." Benjamin Silliman, Sr., then
presented the petition to the Yale Corporation and had the two
posts created, though without any salary, in August 1846.[29]

Norton was very pleased with the outcome, even though no salary
had been attached, since the Corporation had also authorized a
fund drive to endow his professorship with $20,000. The younger
Silliman also had hopes for a grant from the state legislature when it
met in the spring. But the size, or even the existence, of a salary did
not concern Norton. Earlier in August 1846, before he could have
any definite assurances he even had a job, Norton had felt confident
enough of his future in agricultural chemistry to refuse a generous
offer of a position as an industrial chemist at Abbott Lawrence's
Merrimac Print Works. Norton was set on his career as an agricultural chemist, and with or without a salary he meant to be one.
This freedom from financial considerations was in sharp contrast to
the attitude of Horsford, who was greatly preoccupied with money
problems and steered his career toward areas more lucrative than
agricultural chemistry. For Norton it was enough to know that five
agricultural societies had invited him to speak at their autumn
fairs. Such interest bode well for his future usefulness in America.[30]

Once his future at Yale had been established, there was only one unsettled problem in Norton's life. Miss Elizabeth Marvin, a close friend since childhood days in Albany, whose letters had cheered him greatly in Edinburgh, had at first declined and then postponed a decision on whether to marry him. She had been spending part of the summer near New Haven, so that Norton on his many visits to the Sillimans there had been as concerned about his relationship with Lizzie as about his job prospects at Yale. In the end she waited for him, and they were married a year later in December 1847, a few months after Horsford and Mary Gardiner. Since Norton and his wife came from the same social background and Elizabeth's father accepted him readily, he, unlike Horsford, felt no need to be constantly proving himself to his father-in-law. Instead he graciously accepted gifts of up to $500 from Mr. Marvin, who was a prosperous merchant in Albany.

While the fund drive was in progress and Lizzie was making up her mind, Norton returned to Europe for his much desired stay with Mulder. After landing in Liverpool, in October 1846, he stopped over in Edinburgh for what turned into a stay of several weeks. Unfortunately, by this time Mulder's protein controversy with Liebig had reached major proportions. Professor Johnston immediately conscripted Norton into the fight and had him edit Mulder's polemic against Liebig, *Liebig's Question to Mulder Tested by Morality and Science*. In it Mulder blasted Liebig and his Russian student Nicholas Laskowski (Horsford's friend) for, primarily, the tone in which they had challenged and disproven Mulder's analyses. When the edition was completed and Norton, accompanied by the increasingly disagreeable Johnston, finally reached Utrecht in early November, Mulder was quite deranged by the topic. He came to the laboratory only infrequently, and when he did was barely communicative and very suspicious of everyone, including Norton and his student Fromberg. For two and a half months, until Mulder began to improve in mid-January 1847, Norton was extremely concerned about his crazed behavior and almost regretted having come to Utrecht to study with him. But Mulder eventually improved and came to the laboratory more often, though, even at his best, he was still secretive and suspicious. Then in May 1847, after another cruel blast from Liebig had appeared in the April *Annalen,* Mulder's brother died. Though he was able to give Fromberg his doctoral examination the next week, Mulder did not reappear in the laboratory for almost a month. Under these conditions Norton was left to work almost entirely on his own.[31]

Upon arriving in Utrecht, Norton had been in great haste to start his work, especially after the delays in Edinburgh. He planned to continue his work on the oat by comparing a protein mass, named "avenine" by Johnston, with two other similar but little known proteins, the legumin of almonds and of peas. While Mulder entertained Johnston and proofread the English translation of his tirade against Liebig, Norton started preparing quantities of avenine and legumin on his own. He had already done a great deal of work, when, a month later, Mulder finally began to advise him on how to spend his time in Utrecht. He recommended that Norton give up his comparison of proteins and work on a series of simpler organic substances. Norton readily agreed, but in succeeding days when Mulder did not offer specific suggestions or even come to the laboratory, he continued with his avenine and legumin. A few months later, in April, Norton learned that Mulder was greatly displeased with him for not pursuing other topics, though he had said nothing further about it to him. Mulder's frequent absences and inability to communicate prevented Norton from learning all that he might have at Utrecht. His experience with Mulder shows all the more the value of the careful daily attention that was a feature of Liebig's instruction at Giessen.[32]

Though Mulder had at first criticized Norton for undertaking his protein experiments, he later became quite interested in them, since they could be interpreted to support his side of the argument with Liebig and since they suggested to him a coup de grace. Norton had hoped to show that avenine and the two legumins had a similar composition. In this he was unsuccessful, since the carbon and nitrogen content varied over 2 percent, but his other findings were of interest. Although his tests had shown that avenine and the legumins all contained sulphur, they did not respond to Mulder's usual test for it (when combined with dilute potash and heated, none would discolor silver). Thus, Mulder could take advantage of the confusion and consider Norton's analyses as support for his theory of sulphur-free "proteines" in spite of some of the results. Norton also found that all three substances showed an excess of nitrogen over what should have been expected in a protein. Since Norton used a great deal of ammonia in his preparations, he suspected some form of "ammoniacal combination" to be the source of the extra nitrogen. This prompted Mulder to make the "beautiful discovery" that the sulphur was not in the protein itself but in a "sulphuret of amid" or SNH_2 with the extra nitrogen. He developed a whole series of hypothetical reactions to support this new explanation. Though it now seems that Mulder was grasping in the dark, Norton eagerly added these admittedly incomplete findings to his paper as strong evidence that the Utrecht laboratory was superior to the one at Giessen. Norton had become a full-fledged member of the anti-Liebig camp of organic chemists and in later years would uphold Mulder and denounce Liebig whenever possible.[33]

On his preliminary visit to Utrecht Norton had been greatly impressed with the laboratory facilities there and thought them superior to anything he had seen in Germany including Erdmann's new laboratory at Leipzig. But there were few students at Utrecht. Either Mulder failed to attract them, or the Dutch educational system did not prepare many. Norton liked the one student he did meet in Mulder's laboratory, August Völcker,* who had earned his doctorate at Göttingen with Wöhler in 1847 and who later became a professor of chemistry at the Cirencester Agricultural Academy and the Royal Agricultural Society of England. But Völcker was about to leave for Edinburgh to replace Fromberg as Johnston's assistant. When Völcker left, Norton was quite lonely in Utrecht. Though he found little in Dutch agriculture for Americans to copy and felt he could spend his time more profitably in the laboratory than in excursions among the Dutch farmers, he managed to keep up his former habit of writing monthly letters to the agricultural journals back home. He concentrated on the peculiarities of Dutch life: the dikes, polders, sand dunes, windmills, and Gouda cheese.[34] All in all Norton was glad to return home in June 1847. The year had been a disappointment. Except for aligning him more closely with Mulder, to whom he remained loyal despite the difficulties, it would not be as significant for his later career as would the stay in Edinburgh.

Norton, therefore, returned from his agricultural studies abroad with no desire to be an American Liebig nor to build another Giessen in New Haven. But neither did he plan to copy Mulder's laboratory

---

*Not to be confused with Karl Völckel, who did a guano analysis with Wöhler in 1841 (see chapter 3).

and carry on his battles at Yale. Instead, Norton preferred to popularize agricultural chemistry among the farmers of Connecticut and
to train teachers for the new agricultural colleges. The Edinburgh
model with its stress on extension work was, with some modifications,
better suited to Norton's personality and American conditions in the
1840s and 1850s than the Giessen or Utrecht examples. But it too
would be difficult to implement in America.

7

Norton and the Craze over Soil Analysis

In August 1847, after his second trip to Europe, John Pitkin Norton arrived in New Haven, more embittered than ever against Liebig, but anxious to begin his career as an agricultural chemist in America. Unfortunately, he and his partner Benjamin Silliman, Jr., faced a difficult struggle in trying to run a laboratory at Yale, because they had neither a Rumford fund to pay their salaries nor an Abbott Lawrence to build the laboratory. But despite these unfavorable circumstances, Yale was to become the center of agricultural chemistry in the United States. From 1847 to 1852 Norton fought like a missionary with a cause to spread the gospel of soil analysis wherever he could. He was convinced of its effectiveness in helping farmers and became its outspoken advocate in public speeches, agricultural columns, textbooks, and lectures at Yale. His faith was so strong that the obstacles of farmers' inertia, charlatans' claims, and, later, scientists' criticisms only spurred him on to greater efforts. Unfortunately, his view of soil analysis was as naïvely optimistic and misleading as that of his foe Justus Liebig, and later agricultural chemists would wish that he had not been quite so successful in spreading such a simplistic view of the benefits of soil analysis. At the time, however, Norton was extraordinarily successful, producing in only five years at Yale a laboratory, a tradition, and, most important, a corps of trained disciples ready to carry on after him.

Back home, Norton soon discovered that the state of Connecticut was not a propitious place in which to seek support for agriculture in 1847. The fund drive launched so optimistically the year before had proven unsuccessful and showed that, except for the Nortons and Sillimans, few persons in Connecticut were interested in scientific agriculture after all. Likewise, the legislature refused to support an "agricultural professorship" in 1847 or to subsidize Norton's salary

or provide scholarships in 1848 and 1849. In their debates the legislators showed themselves not merely indifferent to Norton's project
but bitterly opposed both to the idea of "book-farming" and to the
support of a school at Yale or even in New Haven (Hartford and
New Haven being rivals for state patronage). Even the crusading
Norton gave up trying to influence the Connecticut legislature in
1849. Thereafter he was torn between his base at Yale and his desire
to work in New York State, where the prospects for agricultural
reform seemed much more favorable.[1]

Connecticut at this time lacked both an effective agricultural
journal and a statewide agricultural society, two important first
steps in lobbying for agricultural education. With the lack of such
groups, the impetus for the Yale laboratory came not from the
demands of Connecticut farmers but, rather, from the Nortons,
Sillimans, and the Albany *Cultivator*. In a sense they created the
school for the state of Connecticut, and then, as has been generally
the case in the history of agricultural education, tried to create a
demand for it.[2]

In the summer of 1847, then, when Horsford was planning his new
$25,000 laboratory at Harvard, Norton and Benjamin Silliman, Jr.,
made a much more modest beginning at Yale. They agreed to rent
from the college the house recently vacated by former President
Jeremiah Day for $150 per year. The two professors thought this
arrangement would be cheaper and more convenient than crowding
in upon Professor Silliman, Sr., in the "Old Laboratory" also on the
Old Campus. They planned to start as cheaply as possible and to
avoid costly frills such as the fancy heating and ventilating devices
Horsford was planning. Though their building lacked the separate
living quarters that Horsford's had, the Yale Analytical Laboratory
had one advantage over its Harvard counterpart. It had upstairs
rooms which, when rented out to students for $80–$100 each per
year, yielded a fairly large source of income for the laboratory.[3]

Though the Yale laboratory thus had much less overhead than
Horsford's grandiose structure at Harvard, it too faced severe
financial problems in its complete lack of funds for equipment and
maintenance. Norton and Silliman were forced to pay all such costs
themselves. Though they skimped on foreign journals and tried to
buy as much as possible from American suppliers, the expenses
quickly amounted to $2,000.[4] After the initial expenses, however,

they were able to break even with an enrollment that, as at Harvard, averaged around twenty students per year during the 1850s.[5]

The tuition charged at both laboratories was also roughly the same. Norton and Silliman set their tuition at $20 per month or $200 per year (40 weeks), which they considered low. It was not as high as the $30 per month that the younger Silliman had charged Norton at his private laboratory in 1843–44 or the exorbitant $500 per year that Professor Johnston had charged him in 1844–45, but it was equivalent to the $75 per term (20 weeks) that Horsford was charging at Harvard, because it included laboratory equipment and supplies, which Horsford's tuition did not.[6]

Despite the larger laboratory at Harvard and Horsford's superior training at Giessen, the instruction offered in the two laboratories was largely similar. Students in both laboratories used the same basic texts, Will's *Outlines of the Course of Qualitative Analysis Followed in the Giessen Laboratory* (1847) and Fresenius's *Introduction to Chemical Analysis, Quantitative* (1846). Despite his other differences with Liebig, Norton, it seems, recognized the value of these textbooks written by Liebig's students. Both schools also emphasized long hours of daily analyses in the laboratory. Yale offered an advantage to the many beginners who enrolled in these schools in the ready availability of undergraduate lectures on science. For an extra $15 per term, a student at the Yale laboratory could hear Benjamin Silliman, Sr., lecture on elementary chemistry from October through January, or on mineralogy from January through April, or on geology in the summer. He could also hear Denison Olmsted on natural philosophy from December to May or on astronomy and meteorology between January and August, simply by buying the tickets, just as Norton himself had done a few years earlier.

The feature of the program at Yale, one that Norton proudly proclaimed was unequaled elsewhere in the United States, was his series of thirty-three lectures on scientific agriculture delivered from January through March each year. In them he made a complete survey of the subject, covering the organic and inorganic elements, the constituents of plants, the structure and function of their various organs, the "proximate principles" and differing composition of each, the rotation of crops, the formation and composition of the soil, the practices of draining and subsoiling, the use of mineral manures (lime, nitrates, sulphates, phosphates) and animal and vegetable manures (bones, guano, and barnyard manures), the nutritive values of different grains in feeding animals, the feeding of dairy cattle, and the food values of milk and butter. The lectures were taken from Johnston's monumental *Lectures,* which Norton recommended as a text. The lectures were fairly popular, attracting around twenty-five persons, farmers as well as students, in 1848. Norton charged $10 for these lectures and for an extra $25 provided a "complete laboratory course" to supplement them. The program was advertised widely in the agricultural press and set the precedent for John Addison Porter's later attempt to bring farmers to Yale.[7] It was also one force behind the University of Albany project in 1852.

Norton was aware that most of his students, like Horsford's, sought only an elementary training and that many were farm boys with inadequate preparation. But he was also aware that there was a strong demand for his graduates to teach in new agricultural colleges and academies and was eager for his students to have the best education possible. He therefore arranged an extra optional class for them on writing at his home one evening a week. The more highly motivated students took advantage of it and showed decided improvement. Norton also encouraged the older students to teach the younger and suggested that the more needy and enterprising students arrange private classes and lectures on botany or blowpipe analysis. He had attended such private classes himself in New Haven, Boston, and Edinburgh. By 1850 Norton had a good idea of what his curriculum should cover and, simultaneously with Horsford at Harvard, pushed the Yale Corporation to create a degree to be granted upon the successful completion of two years of studies and the passing of three examinations. Since Norton wanted the degree to compete with Harvard's new S.B. and be "something analogous to the German system" but not as advanced as a doctorate, he called it the Bachelor of Philosophy (Ph.B.). He hoped a degree would reward the better students and create some incentive for the others to return for a second year. Although of the school's most outstanding graduates, George J. Brush, William H. Brewer, and William P. Blake, were in the first class in 1852, Norton was fully aware that the training he could offer was not the equivalent of advanced work in Germany. He urged his graduates to study abroad, suggesting that two years at Yale and one year abroad would make an excellent education. A great many students took his advice. In 1854 five graduates of the "Old Lab" were together in Munich studying mineralogy, chemistry, and physics.[8]

Though Norton did not expect his students to do extensive research, he encouraged them to present papers on topics drawn from the laboratory's analysis work at the AAAS meetings in the early 1850s. Many of their projects were analyses of minerals, but several dealt with agricultural topics. In 1850 Jonathan Bunce presented an analysis of anthracite coal ashes, which showed that they contained alkalies and made as effective a manure as the bituminous coal ashes recommended by Johnston. William H. Brewer, in his paper on the "Determinations of Nitrogen in Two Varieties of Indian Corn," disproved recent work by Ebenezer Emmons and J. H. Salisbury of the New York State Agricultural Society and testified to Norton's continuing interest in Indian corn. In 1851 at Albany George W. Weyman followed up Bunce's work with a more precise determination of the value of bituminous coal as a fertilizer. Orange Judd, later editor of the *American Agriculturalist,* presented an "Analysis of the Ash of a Cotton Stalk," a paper which probably grew out of his trip south to recover from tuberculosis. Mason C. Weld, also a future agricultural editor, read a paper on the composition of Indian corn. They were all well-chosen topics and showed quite competent work.[9]

But Norton himself published no researches, and the students noted that he worked more at his desk than in the laboratory. The most he could accomplish was to pursue an occasionally interesting or challenging commercial analysis. He would have liked to have done an extensive series of analyses of Indian corn in the summer of 1849, but when a request for financial support from the Smithsonian was unsuccessful, Norton had Brewer and Weld work on parts of it instead. Norton seemed to experience little unhappiness at not being able to do research at Yale, since he had a different conception of what he should be doing to further chemistry in America.[10]

Both Horsford and Norton, in deciding how to spend their time, had to balance off a set of partially conflicting goals—money, research, and public service. Horsford at Harvard first chose research and later switched to money. But Norton's situation and priorities at Yale were quite different. He was, for the most part, unconcerned about his lack of a salary and was perfectly willing to volunteer his services to the laboratory while continuing to accept $100 per month from his father. Although living well beyond his income in New Haven, he felt no pressure either to earn money or to do research and preferred giving the highest priority to serving the public, especially the farmers.[11]

It had probably not been Norton's idea that the laboratory should have to break even. In his letters to customers about the costs of analyses, he repeatedly expressed the wish that the laboratory would not have to support itself, and he would probably have been willing to seek at least a partial subsidy from his father. But his partner Benjamin Silliman, Jr., was much stricter about the running of the laboratory. He was willing to contribute his services to the venture, but he could not afford to subsidize it and was disappointed that it had not been a source of profit. Since the laboratory could not pay even one professor's salary, let alone two, Silliman left in September 1849 for a more lucrative position at the Louisville Medical School. He was back in the spring and most summers thereafter, but in November 1850 he sold his half of the laboratory to Norton for $1,020, a sum which Norton obtained from his father. Norton was left in full command and able to run the laboratory as he chose.[12]

Norton's ideas of accounting, however, were so unbusinesslike as almost to suggest that he did not want to make a profit even if he could. In fact, he ran the laboratory as a charity or public service. When the laboratory needed new equipment, Norton contributed it, as in 1851 when he spent $270 of a $500 gift from his father-in-law for a new sand bath like those Horsford and Gibbs already had. But when he later came to compute the laboratory's accounts for the term, Norton counted this gift as a regular laboratory "expense," thus cutting down the laboratory's profits from a possible $300 to practically nothing. He seemed to like making gifts to the laboratory, but at the same time to dislike taking the profit it allowed him.[13]

Norton's notions of pricing were also somewhat naïve and un-businesslike, as were the expectations of many of his clients, who requested analyses without realizing how difficult and costly they would be. Sometimes Norton charged what the work had actually cost him, such as $30 for a water analysis which had taken two weeks' work plus chemicals. This was roughly commensurate with the $50 Benjamin Silliman, Jr., charged for another water analysis that had taken 30 days' labor. But in other cases Norton took other factors into consideration in setting his prices. The standard price for testing a stomach for arsenic poisoning was $10 ($2 for chemicals and 3.5 days' labor), but Norton found these cases so "extremely disagreeable to me involving as they do responsibility + often the loss of time in a most vexatious degree" that "if it were not for considerations of duty in assisting the administration of justice I should refuse such business at any price." (Samuel W. Johnson charged a more realistic $25 for the detection of arsenic and $50 for the preparation of the full chemical evidence in 1860.) For analyses of coal Norton charged $20 rather than $8–$10, because he found them such "troublesome work." More frequently he lowered his prices when he found the problem interesting, as with Ebeneezer Emmons's eupyrchroite, or when he feared that his results were not of use to the customer. Unfortunately, such frequent discounts and underpricing did not help to educate the public to the true cost of science, a persistent issue in the battles against "quacks" in the 1850s.[14]

But Nortons' real weakness was for agricultural analyses. He charged James Vick of the *Genesee Farmer* only $5 (cost of chemicals) for an analysis of a fraudulent"prepared guano"since it was "done for a public service" and he thought that "such a shameful imposition ought to be fearlessly exposed." To another farmer, whom he had charged $10 for an analysis of his calcareous manure, he expressed the wish that he could do all analyses for free. Norton felt a special responsibility to do soil analyses. The going rate in the agricultural journals was $5–$10 for "a complete analysis," though a quantitative analysis of a soil took about ten days' work and should therefore cost $25–$30. Even though Norton took a loss on each one, since he had his "hands full now nearly all the time of work that pays twice as well with much less trouble," he encouraged whole groups to send their soils in because "it is an object with me to encourage every advance among practical men + to give them results which are to be depended upon in place of the apologies for analyses which are so often palmed off as accurate & complete." Since he was not in chemistry merely to make money and could guarantee an accurate analysis, Norton felt he had a public duty to help the farmers and to analyze their soils. Such a selfless attitude was rare among chemists of the time (see chapter 9).[15]

Between 1847 and 1852 soil analysis became one of the major activities of the Yale laboratory. In these five years Norton and his students analyzed about 75 soils, many fewer than the 134 that Johnston's laboratory analyzed in Edinburgh in the single year 1844–45 or the 210 of 1846–47. Norton at first adopted Johnston's method of hiring assistants to perform such analyses, but he found his first two, Henry Erni and Henry Wurtz, to be such complainers and troublemakers that he began to appoint his own older students. This arrangement not only got the work done as reliably and efficiently as before, but also boosted student morale, for it gave the older students the feeling that they were running the place. Several of them also came to share Norton's patrician view that public service rather than private profit was the proper goal of the laboratory.[16]

Besides his chemical work at the laboratory, Norton, like Professor Johnston, took on a second career as a popularizer of scientific agriculture, for only by such work could he hope to attract more funds and students to the laboratory. Already well known for his foreign letters, Norton became between 1847 and 1852 a prominent advocate of scientific agriculture. He wrote monthly columns for the *Cultivator* and after 1851 for the *Soil of the South;* prepared an elementary textbook, *Elements of Scientific Agriculture* (1850); and added the American notes to *The Farmer's Guide to Scientific and Practical Agriculture* (1851), a large Scottish compendium on farm life. Norton also ventured forth several times a year to lecture before agricultural societies and their autumn fairs in Connecticut, New York, and western Massachusetts. In all these ways he was eager to play the missionary and exhort farmers to give up their old ways and take up the new.[17]

In his lectures and publications on scientific agriculture, Norton was always eager to criticize Liebig. At the start of practically every speech, Norton would refer to his own farm background in an attempt to dissociate himself from those "eminent philosophers" so lacking in practical experience, who had made "unsupported assertions" and given "free rein to [their] enthusiastic imaginations." Such "mistaken zeal," Norton feared, had done more harm than good to the cause, but he hoped that his audience would give agricultural chemistry a second chance because it was a new field with a lot to offer. Most of its work had been done since 1840, but he did not attribute this achievement in any way to Liebig. Norton had picked up this anti-Liebig bias in Edinburgh and Utrecht, but such frequent though veiled references to Liebig and perhaps other theorists are an indication that their work was well known in America in 1847–52, even if it was less readily accepted now that the initial enthusiasm had worn off and their weaknesses were being exposed.[18]

Though Norton was eager to criticize Liebig and found it politic to do so, in fact his indebtedness to Liebig was considerable. Norton thought he was being anti-Liebig because he disagreed with him on several controversial points—the action of gypsum, the source of nitrogen in plants, the nature of proteins, and the effectiveness of purely mineral or patent manures. In almost all these cases Norton objected more to Liebig's assertive tone than to his actual results, for frequently after criticizing Liebig's explanations as wrong or not *entirely* true, Norton quietly accepted them as the best explanation available, though not the whole story. Most of Norton's views of scientific agriculture were, in fact, little more than an extension of Leibig's ideas in the second and third editions of *Chemistry in Its Applications to Agriculture and Physiology*. Norton even reached the point where he could use one of Liebig's basic contributions, the idea of deficiencies in the soil's constituents, against one of his controversial applications, the patent manures, without seeming to realize it. Despite all his anti-Liebig rhetoric, Norton was, like all agricultural chemists of the 1840s, more indebted to Liebig than he was to Mulder.[19]

Norton's lectures constantly stressed the ability of agricultural chemistry to explain old practices and to suggest new improved ones. He particularly stressed the value of the chemical analysis of soils, which would make possible the use of "special manures" which were cheaper, easier, and, in most cases, more effective than traditional barnyard manures. Soil analysis, the heart of Norton's view of scientific agriculture, was after 1843 most closely associated with Liebig and through him with Sprengel. But, as mentioned in chapter 3, a second school, composed of Berzelius, Mulder, Samuel Dana, and Charles T. Jackson, had developed another version of soil analysis in the 1830s and early 1840s. The first group stressed the role of minerals; the second, the role of the organic acids (crenic, apocrenic, humic, ulmic, and geic). Norton's stress on soil analysis in the late 1840s and early 1850s is not surprising, but his adoption of the Liebig-Sprengel version, rather than that of Mulder, is remarkable and due primarily to Johnston's example.

Norton received his formative training in soil analysis from Pro-

fessor Johnston's *Lectures on Agricultural Chemistry and Geology* and
from work in his laboratory. In his textbook Johnston was quite
eclectic about the two views, presenting data from both Mulder and
Sprengel. But his conclusions show that though theoretically both
organic acids and minerals were necessary to soils, in practice an
agricultural chemist used only the soil's mineral composition. If,
for example, a soil showed a deficiency of potash or phosphates, it
could be easily corrected with gypsum, lime, and other mineral
manures; but the quantity of "organic matter" (and so the organic
acids) was so widely variable in soils that it was unclear what constituted a deficiency or how to remedy it. Liebig's view of soil analysis, therefore, came to predominate even in Edinburgh because
of its practical implications. Although Johnston and Norton had
upheld Mulder's side in the protein controversy, they quietly adopted Liebig's "inorganic" approach to soils and manures. They even
applied it to such "mixed" manures as guano and bones, whose
effects they attributed to nitrogen and phosphates, rather than to
any crenates or apocrenates they might contain. An understanding
of the role of organic matter lay far in the future.[20]

In this early phase of scientific agriculture, in the 1840s and early
1850s, all truths were considered to be basically very simple. Though
Norton might criticize Liebig for his simple theories, he too liked to
present soil analysis as a fairly elementary subject that any layman
could understand. Liebig had aroused the hope in 1843 that a very
precise determination of the mineral composition of a soil would
reveal its fertility. A deficiency in any one of several substances (by
Norton's time it was up to twelve) would cause a lowering of the
fertility of a crop. A deficiency in several would lead to barrenness.
The most fertile soils would have a healthy supply of all the essential
nutrients, although too much of one substance might be unhealthy.
Thus "the question of fertility or barrenness becomes, as a general
rule, very simple, and one which the chemist can determine with
great certainty." As mentioned in chapter 3, Liebig inserted a
"supplementary chapter" of Sprengel's soil analyses in the second
edition of his book and left it to speak for itself. Fertile soils usually
had an abundance of nutrients, but comparisons with the compositions of less fertile soils were not always convincing. In the third
edition, Liebig emphasized even more the idea that soils, manures
and plants must all be analyzed in order for their deficiencies to be

Composition of Soils of Different Degrees of Fertility

	Fertile without manure	Fertile with manure	Barren
Organic matter	97	50	40
Silica (in the sand and clay)	648	833	778
Alumina (in the clay)	57	51	91
Lime	59	18	4
Magnesia	$8\frac{1}{2}$	8	1
Oxide of iron	61	30	81
Oxide of manganese	1	3	$\frac{1}{2}$
Potash	2	trace	trace
Soda (chiefly as common salt)	4		
Chlorine (chiefly as common salt)	2		
Sulphuric acid	2	$\frac{3}{4}$	
Phosphoric acid	$4\frac{1}{2}$	$1\frac{3}{4}$	
Carbonic acid (combined with the lime and magnesia)	40	$4\frac{1}{2}$	
Loss	14		$4\frac{1}{2}$
	1000	1000	1000

SOURCE: James F. W. Johnston, *Catechism of Agricultural Chemistry and Geology* (1846), p. 41.

NOTE: The high percentages of alumina and the lack of phosphorus or sulphur in the "barren" soil indicate an older outdated analysis, a factor that helped the comparison.

noted and corrected. Professor Johnston elaborated on this idea in his *Lectures*, bolstering it with carefully chosen analyses by Sprengel and others.

In his little *Catechism of Agricultural Chemistry and Geology*, Johnston reduced the whole idea to a single chart, which expressed the crux of the theory in three very carefully chosen samples.[21] (See the accompanying table.) Norton used this classic chart in his *Elements* and in at least one lecture and referred to it or its basic principle in practically every lecture he ever gave. In practice the most important ingredients were the lime and the phosphoric acid. Johnston had chosen good examples for his chart, since they do drop off from 5.9 percent to 1.8 percent to 0.4 percent for lime and 0.45 percent to 0.175 percent to zero for phosphoric acid. The percentage difference between fertility and sterility was already quite small by 1844 when Johnston published this edition of the chart. When in 1850 Charles T. Jackson commented in a discussion of soil analysis at the AAAS meeting in New Haven that a difference of only 2 percent separated the fertile from the barren soils, T. Sterry Hunt, a former Yale student and now chemist for the Canadian Geological Survey, responded quite truthfully that it was much smaller than that. It was down to tenths of a percent.

But in Johnston's *Lectures* there were inconsistencies and over-lappings between the categories.[22] For instance, barren soils had from a "trace" to 0.866 percent lime, "fertile with manure" had from 0.038 percent to 0.539 percent, and "fertile," 0.243 percent to 0.987 percent; and likewise with phosphoric acid. Agricultural chemists tried to avoid such comparisons, but when forced to explain them, they would point to "other factors" such as water supply or the size of the particles. But these difficulties were only rarely mentioned; in their efforts to popularize a simple view of scientific agriculture and to interest farmers in having their soils analyzed, Norton and others put the emphasis quite decidedly upon the chemical composition of the soils.

The vie wthat soil analysis was beneficial and worth while remained unquestioned until 1851. As long as any problems or inconsistencies could be ascribed to defective analytical methods, the belief remained strong that the most fertile soils contained the most nutrients. About 1850, however, enough doubts of the value of soil analysis had arisen for Norton to feel that a full-scale defense was necessary. At the AAAS meeting in Albany in August 1851 he delievered a paper "On the Value of Soil Analyses, and the Points to Which Especial Attention Should Be Directed." He started off by acknowledging the fact "that many chemists, and among them some of the highest reputation, have of late been accustomed to speak slightingly of soil analyses, and to intimate that they are of little value. Some have even said that we cannot from analyses tell what constitutes fertility, and what barrenness." He ascribed these criticisms to "erroneous ideas with regard to the connection between the soil and the plant," and to a "deficiency in practical knowledge" especially among those who worked only on small quantities of soils in laboratories.

There was, however, one criticism he thought valid and meant to disprove it. Some mineral chemists, who were used to working with materials of a fixed composition, questioned whether a single analysis of a soil of a greatly variable composition could be accurate.

Norton responded with analyses of three trap* soils and three clay soils. In both cases, all the analyses were shown to be similar enough for similar conclusions as to their nature to be reached. Norton also analyzed another soil that adjoined the trap rocks but was part of a different formation. In spite of its proximity, it showed a strikingly different composition. Norton then went on to "prove" the value of soil analysis by presenting the results that Henry Erni and William Brewer had obtained a year earlier on two soils from Mississippi. One was fertile and the other, from the same formation, was "worn out." A first analysis showed that the fertile soil contained 2.022 percent lime and the worn-out soil 1.80 percent. A further analysis of the portion of the soil soluble in water (whose constituents were therefore accessible to the plant) revealed 0.389 percent lime, whereas the comparable portion of the worn-out soil had only 0.020 percent lime. Norton felt that these results would "sustain in a most decisive manner the value of soil analyses" and went on to point to the chief problems facing this branch of chemistry: (1) the knowledge of the crenates and apocrenates was still 'quite indefinite," and they were looked on "with suspicion"; and (2) new tests for phosphoric acid were desperately needed, for none were very speedy or entirely reliable. He concluded by pointing out to the AAAS members the danger to all of science that arose when a large number of charlatans passed off "cheap, worthless analyses," and he recommended that everyone in the association do all he could to discourage such "false science." The paper, according to Norton's diary, was well received, at least by the old guard. "Pres. Hitchcock considered it one of the most important that had been read. Dr. Hare also arose + agreed with the author in every particular an instance almost unparalleled. I had great reason therefore to be satisfied with its reception."[23]

Though some chemists applauded Norton's defense of orthodoxy in Albany, others were discovering data that would cause its downfall. David A. Wells of the Lawrence Scientific School, who followed Norton at Albany with a paper on "A New Method for Analyzing Soils," had been appointed chemist to the Ohio State Board of Agriculture in May 1851. He had spent the summer analyzing the soils of the extremely fertile Scioto Valley. In August or September

*Of igneous origin, probably derived from basalt.

the Hampden County Agricultural Society of Massachusetts asked him for his opinion on the analysis of soils. Wells decided to compare the soils of western Massachusetts (using Dana's analyses in Hitchcock's *Geological Report*) with those of Ohio. He expected to find chemical deficiencies in the Massachusetts soils, since they were known for their sterility. To his surprise he discovered that the two soils were very similar in composition, with the Massachusetts soils even showing higher percentages of both lime (2 percent versus 0.4 percent) and phosphoric acid (0.6 percent versus 0.04 percent). Wells concluded that analysis would not explain their differences, though the fineness of the Ohio soils and their quantity of organic matter might. Wells wrote a full report for the July 1852 *American Journal of Science,* in which he concluded that organic analyses should be trusted more than mineral analyses of soils and that mineral manures should not be allowed to displace the traditional barnyard manures which contained organic matter. He also thought that anyone who claimed to be able to do a soil analysis for less than $20 should be labeled a quack.[24]

With Wells's paper the craze over soil analysis came to an end. The *Cultivator* saw it and reported in October rather hypocritically, "Our readers are aware that we have always urged the insufficiency of simple analysis to determine the real value and productiveness of soils," and cited Wells's article as "strongly corroborating this view of the subject." In January 1853 chemist James C. Booth read a paper on the "Practical Value of the Analysis of Soils" to the Philadelphia Society for the Promotion of Agriculture, in which he denied that soil tests had any usefulness. His article was republished in the *U.S. Patent Office Report for 1852,* which two years before had contained a lengthy and favorable article on "The Study of Soils" by Daniel Lee, who now appended some remarks to Booth's paper. He admitted:

> Baron Liebig raised the expectations of farmers far above what the infancy of chemical science in its applications to agriculture, and especially in the analysis of soils, would justify.
>
> Now there is a strong tendency to run into the opposite extreme, and as greatly underestimate the value of chemical researches as the distinguished Geisin [*sic*] professor prompted the public to over-estimate their importance. The truth lies between these extremes.[25]

Also in January 1853 T. Sterry Hunt, who a few years before had been making soil analyses for the Canadian Geological Survey and writing Horsford about his problems with the phosphates, now favored leaving such analyses to the charlatans.

> You ask me what predilections I have for Agricultural Chemistry & the line pursued by poor Norton. Very little, for I am a great sceptic as to those things. I look upon them as the charlatanism of our science, and as tending to degrade it, making it a plaything for tyros who analyze soils for 2 dollars, etc.— Science for the millions is a humbug! True science, like true nobility, is essentially aristocratic. Far be it from me however to underrate the many practical benefits which flow from chemistry.[26]

Thus soil analysis had by 1852 become discredited both professionally, by being practiced by quacks, and scientifically, by being disproven by chemists. It is hard to tell whether the professional threat motivated in some way the scientific criticisms, but what had in the 1830s and 1840s been a respected and much proclaimed application of science, especially on the state surveys, was after 1852 dropped by most respectable chemists. After this, agricultural chemistry followed a spearate course from that of the rest of chemistry, and the main thrust for professionalization in later years would come from the mineral chemists. Likewise, in agricultural circles the craze brought sharp criticism and even abuse upon chemists who who still wanted to help farmers.[27]

Norton must have known of Wells's criticisms, and perhaps they motivated his defense before the AAAS; but he revised his paper for the *Cultivator* in August and September and for the *American Journal of Science* in late October without mentioning them. Unfortunately, by July 1852 when Wells's major article appeared, Norton, who may have had his own private doubts about soil analysis, was unable to respond to it.[28]

Throughout his career Norton worked to the utmost for agricultural institutions in both New Haven and Albany. It was a dual existence, as his youth had been, but he felt responsibilities in both areas. Norton spoke at the New York State Agricultural Society meetings, wrote for the *Cultivator,* and visited Albany frequently. In 1851, when Albany's ambitions began to turn in the direction of a major university, its supporters wished to include scientific agriculture in the curriculum and entrust it to Norton. He was greatly flattered and promised to do all he could to help, short of leaving Yale. He became an active leader of the movement and spent months writing letters trying to pin down Benjamin Peirce and Louis Agassiz, who expressed support but eluded him with ever-ready excuses whenever he tried to make them commit themselves further. Finally in January 1852 Norton and James Hall inaugurated the new university with two series of lectures. Norton realized that lecturing in both Albany and New Haven during the same months would be a terrible strain but did not feel he could leave the laboratory and move to Albany for three months. The Albany lectures could not be rescheduled, since for maximum effect they had to coincide with the legislative session there. Norton decided to commute weekly to Albany for the three months, lecturing three times each week in each place. A few weeks after beginning this frantic pace (he hardly had time to answer his mail in each place before leaving for the other), he began to spit up blood. Greatly concerned, he had his illness diagnosed in Albany by his uncle Dr. Mason Cogswell, who thought it a rare heart condition and recommended rest. Continued bleeding forced Norton to withdraw entirely from both the University of Albany lectures and the Yale laboratory in March 1852 and to travel south with his father. The trip seemed to improve him, but an attack of measles en route home set him back considerably. He lingered on during the summer but died in Farmington on September 5, 1852, barely thirty years old. The loss was tragic and struck all his friends very strongly. He left both the young University of Albany and the Yale Analytical Laboratory in a precarious state, for they both had depended quite heavily on his efforts.[29]

At Yale Norton's death caused a crisis, for in only five years he had established a tradition of public service in agricultural chemistry and had attracted many able students to New Haven. Fortunately, though Norton died young, his idealism and personal example were not lost. They had made a strong impression on his students, who in later years would struggle to carry the remnants of the agricultural chemistry movement into a new era.

PART IV

From Liebig to the Agricultural Experiment Station

8

Samuel W. Johnson and the Search for
a New Soil Science, 1852–1870

After Norton's death and the discrediting of soil analysis in 1852, agricultural chemistry both at Yale and elsewhere entered a very difficult period. A science that had formerly attracted widespread excitement now suffered from the hostility and ridicule of many of its former friends in science, agriculture, state government, and even the agricultural press. This severe reaction threatened for a time to undermine any further attempts to apply chemistry to agriculture. But even in the period 1852–70, when the future seemed darkest, a new leader of the movement was emerging, who would guide the field through its difficult years and lead it on to even greater heights in the future.

A farm boy from upstate New York, a student of both Norton and Liebig, and later a professor at Yale, Johnson, more than any other man in America, developed the new rationale for scientific agriculture in the mid-1850s that led it beyond Liebig and soil analysis and into the twentieth century. The new view was both more cautious than its predecessors' in its claims and theories and more ambitious in its scope and demands. In short, Johnson admitted the errors and overexpectations of the past, called for more rather than less science to correct them, and demanded state funding for new agricultural experiment stations in which to attack them systematically. A delicate but determined young man, Johnson worked for twenty years and tried a variety of approaches to convince farmers and legislators of the need for experiment stations. In 1856–59 he led a dramatic campaign in the agricultural press against fertilizer frauds, and in the 1860s he wrote two popular textbooks which stressed once again that agricultural science had moved beyond well-meaning amateurs and laymen and required a new institution that would bridge the gap between theory and practice. If agricultural science was ever to solve the detailed problems that Liebig had left it, such stations were necessary.

Then, in the early 1870s, when the forces of agricultural reform revived across the nation, Johnson, by now forty and the movement's elder statesman, and his student W. O. Atwater led the drive that culminated in the establishment of the nation's first agricultural experiment station in Connecticut in 1875. Later, as director of the station, Johnson fought for funds for expansion and research and oversaw some of the early work on vitamins A and B, hybrid corn, and other wonders of the twentieth century. Thus, with great persistence over several decades, Johnson was able to transform the much-maligned agricultural chemistry of the 1850s into a permanent part of the state and federal governments, and thereby bring Liebig's 1840 vision of a "rational agriculture" very close to reality in the twentieth century.

Samuel W. Johnson was born on July 3, 1830, in Kingsboro, New York, where his father was a prosperous merchant. A few years later his father retired to a large, fertile farm in Deer River, north of Watertown, New York. Here the rather frail and studious youth grew up with his numerous brothers and sisters and attended the local academy. In 1846, his last year at the school, he became so interested in chemistry that his teacher gave him a copy of Fresenius's recently translated textbook on qualitative analysis. A year later Johnson showed his mastery of this and other chemical texts in his first publication, an article in the *Cultivator*, "On Fixing Ammonia." It is not known when Johnson first read the works of Justus Liebig, but, since the family subscribed to the *Cultivator*, he may have started reading Liebig about this time. If not, he learned of the German chemist by 1849, for in a second article in the *Cultivator* Johnson urged farmers to have their sons "study Liebig before Virgil, and Boussingault before Horace."[1]

After graduating from Lowville Academy in 1846, Johnson taught for three years at private schools in New York State. He then decided that he wanted to study chemistry further. He had the choice of Harvard or Yale, and after meeting Norton and comparing the schools' expenses, he chose Yale. He started there in January 1850 and made such rapid progress that by the end of the year

Norton was advising him to go to Germany whenever he could get enough money. Johnson's father could afford to send him and in the end did, but in 1850 he was not yet convinced that his son would be able to earn a living as a chemist. Like Norton's father, Johnson's also thought that the ministry, law, medicine, and farming were the only safe professions. But Horsford, Norton, and O. W. Gibbs were much more optimistic in 1850, perhaps overoptimistic in the light of actual circumstances, that in a few years Johnson could pay off any debts he might incur on a trip abroad. Johnson began to make plans to leave for Europe but broke them off when he got a well-paying position originally offered to Norton at the New York State Normal School in Albany. Johnson then used the summer at Yale to finish up an analysis of houghite for the AAAS meeting at Albany.[2]

After teaching at Albany for one term and spending six months at Glen Haven, New York, taking a water cure for "dyspepsia," Johnson returned to Yale in the fall of 1852 in order to study more before going abroad. Since Norton was ill, Johnson took on his task of contributing regularly to the *Country Gentleman,* the successor to the *Cultivator.* Johnson was glad of the chance both to earn some money and to defend agricultural chemistry. He had hardly begun his series, however, when he found he could afford to leave for Germany after all. His father had finally decided to support his ambition to become a chemist and to provide him with the necessary $1,500 to $2,000. Planning to stay two years, Johnson set off for Germany in May 1853 with Mason Cogswell Weld, a classmate at the Yale Analytical Laboratory and a cousin of Professor Norton. Johnson's long-time ambition had been to study with Liebig, but the master had just left Giessen for Munich where, it was rumored, he did not intend to take students. Friends at Göttingen recommended spending a year at Erdmann's laboratory in Leipzig until Liebig's new laboratory in Munich would open. Erdmann was the editor of the *Journal für Praktische Chemie,* and his laboratory was considered the cleanest and most modern in Europe in the mid-1850s.[3]

Johnson spent his year at Leipzig perfecting his analytical technique and publishing two papers, one, "Chemische Notizen," a collection of four analyses, and the second, "Ueber das zweifach schleimsäure Amyloxyd," a continuation of a study of mucic acid taken up by Malaguti in 1836. But, like Norton in Edinburgh, Johnson's observations outside the laboratory were perhaps more important for his later career than were his researches inside and his short stay at Leipzig brought unexpected advantages.[4]

In the intervening eight years since Horsford and Norton had toured the German schools and laboratories (1846–54), there had been important changes. Liebig's books, so influential abroad, had also had a certain impact in Germany itself. In particular, Julius Adolph Stöckhardt, a former pharmacist, and Emil Theodor Wolff, a mineral chemist from Berlin, had turned to agricultural chemistry in the 1840s and founded in 1851 the world's first agricultural experiment station at Möckern outside Leipzig. The "Versuchsstation" had a modest farm (120 acres), a simple laboratory, and a small governmental subsidy, which was administered by a board of wealthy landowners. Though the station started with poor facilities for research and was committed to routine fertilizer analyses (Stöckhardt perfected the technique), its staff was large and included two well-qualified chemists in Drs. Wolff and Karl Ritthausen. Through their efforts the station was able to rise above its meager surroundings and to do thorough and well-designed experiments. Johnson and another American at Leipzig, Evan Pugh of Pennsylvania (the first president of what later became Pennsylvania State University), visited the station in February 1854 and were greatly impressed with the work of Wolff and Ritthausen. Here they saw a promising combination of the laboratory and the farm that would provide a middle way between the theorizing of a university-based Liebig who did no field experiments and the random experimentation of assorted farmers who scorned theory. They immediately became very enthusiastic about the German agricultural experiment stations and were eager to bring them back to America.[5]

In April 1854 Johnson and Weld moved to Munich to study with Liebig in his new laboratory. They were lucky to obtain places, for he now took only seven students, but they had already had elementary training, and Liebig had a special fondness for Americans.[6]

Johnson's experience with Liebig was rather different from what Horsford's had been several years before. After the excitement of the experiment station outside Leipzig, Johnson may well have found his stay with the Baron anticlimactic. The atmosphere in Munich was not as intensely scientific as at Giessen, for one of Liebig's primary motives in moving had been to give up directing a laboratory. The absence of a large number of chemistry students meant that the strong camaraderie and esprit de corps that had been so much a part of life in Giessen were lacking in Munich. Besides, the university terms were so short in Munich and the laboratory closed on so many Catholic holy days that students found it difficult to complete their researches. A cholera epidemic from August to October 1854 also closed the laboratory for several months. All in all, Munich presented a great many diversions for a weary professor. Liebig, who now lacked the energy for concentrated thought in the evening, went frequently to the theater, the opera, the court, or the Academy. In Munich the professors entertained more frequently and more lavishly than at Giessen, where they had all lived in relative poverty. But Liebig still had the energy to lash out at his opponents on occasion and to come up with new theories to refute them. A student with him in Munich, however, was not as totally immersed in the Liebig faction of these quarrels as had been true at Giessen in the 1840s.[7]

The atmosphere in Munich was probably better suited to Samuel Johnson's personality than the one at Giessen would have been. Johnson was by nature quiet, retiring, and thoughtful rather than effusive and partisan like Horsford. His letters home are subdued and infrequent in comparison with Horsford's, but they record the same round of activities—long days in the laboratory; evenings of reading, writing, and translating; and vacations of touring or more reading. Likewise, an occasional evening or holiday at the Liebig or von Kobell home was practically his only social activity.[8] His friends were the other Yale students in Munich and the radical Englishman Edmund K. Muspratt. But the relative isolation that Johnson encountered in Munich was freer intellectually and more tolerant of critical and independent thought than the enforced good fellowship and intense partisanship of Giessen had been.

By 1854 the heady enthusiasm that had greeted Liebig's ideas had abated, and important experimental work was being completed that cast serious doubt on some of his generalizations. It was a time for more thoughtful reevaluation of what the known facts really were and what they proved rather than for more theorizing and assertions. Johnson, who was at this time slowly evolving his new view of the complexity of agricultural science, needed a quiet year to absorb himself in the latest thought on agricultural problems. Much of what he taught himself in his year in Munich, especially his study of Emil Wolff's work, was critical of Liebig and would have been unthinkable and probably subversive at Giessen in the 1840s. Johnson, however, was detached and mature enough to be able to admire Liebig and to appreciate his accomplishments but, at the same time, to avoid full commitment to his controversial views. Such ambivalence toward Liebig, so unlike Horsford's uncritical admiration and Norton's heightened animosity, was the product of Johnson's personality, the freer spirit of Munich, and the passage of eight years.[9]

Johnson's primary work in the Munich laboratory was an extension of his Leipzig study of mucic acid. He analyzed its hitherto unstudied alkali compounds. He also did some analyses of plants, soils, and water for botanist O. Sendtner, who was trying (unsuccessfully) to determine why some plants that flourished on lime-poor soils contained so much lime. Aside from his laboratory work, which does not seem extensive, Johnson continued his series of articles for the *Country Gentleman* with several thorough and thoughtful review articles on major problems of the time: the practical value of soil and plant analyses, the effects of gypsum, the nature of theory and practice, and the work of Ville and Boussingault on the sources of plant nitrogen. Johnson also translated Liebig's lengthy reply to Lawes and Gilbert, Wolff's cattle feeding experiments at Möckern and parts of his recent agricultural textbook, and, with George J. Brush, prepared some mineralogical tables for professor von Kobell. All in all, it was for Johnson a year of intensive thought on agricultural matters, probably the most important of his life.[10]

While at Yale in 1852–53, Johnson had, as mentioned, started responding to the frequent criticisms of agricultural chemistry in the agricultural press. These criticisms focused on three different, though frequently not separated, targets: (1) science and theories in general, (2) soil analysis, and (3) quacks, humbugs, and professors. Johnson's responses to the first two are important here as part of the development of his new view of soil science. His comments on the third were part of his later battle against the fertilizer frauds in Connecticut (see chapter 9).

The farmer's reaction against agricultural chemistry in the early 1850s revealed once again their empirical or Baconian philosophical bias. Although a few farmers wished to abandon all "science," others seemed to make a distinction between "theory," which they condemned, and the more reliable "facts," "practice," "experience," and "experiments," which they wished to retain, as in "The Quackery of Agricultural Science" of 1853: "Devoted as I am, and always have been to *science,* I would not give one practical experiment for all the 'scientific' theories of Liebig and other chemists put together, for practical farmers' use," and "I would give more for one ounce of good sound science, derived from practical experience, than for ten pounds of that derived from ordinary modern 'scientific analyses and essays.'" Johnson tried to meet these criticisms by a series of articles on "What Is Science?" written at Yale in 1853 and a second series on "Theory and Practice," written abroad in 1855. Although Johnson's idea that "circumstances alter cases" was an early recognition of the statistical nature of proof, his articles were largely ineffective in convincing farmers of the value of science. Readers took little notice of them and continued to either defend or condemn science without referring to Johnson. His attempt to be rational about such an emotional topic was rather a futile one. He would do better when he gave up philosophizing and turned to the issues.[11]

The chief issue was, of course, the value of soil analysis. Any "practical farmer," it was now claimed, could tell more about a soil's fertility than could an analytical chemist. Such a farmer could "at least distinguish between a highly fertile and nearly barren soil," which soil chemistry, it seemed, could not. Similar criticisms of soil analysis persisted all through the 1850s. David A. Wells's article disproving the value of chemical analysis of soils was still being discussed in agricultural journals at least as late as 1858, six years after it had appeared.[12]

Johnson finally faced the issue squarely in July 1854 when he denounced soil analysis entirely and admitted openly that the doctrine had been mistaken. In a masterly article, "On the Practical Value of the Analyses of Soils," which showed the influence of his stay in Leipzig, Johnson confessed that "in the infancy of agricultural science" soil analysis had been found to be useful in determining the needs of soils. But now scholarly opinion (Boussingault, J. A. Stöckhardt, and E. Wolff) held that it was of no practical use. After a few derogatory remarks about the worthlessness of $5 analyses, Johnson dicussed the scientific criticisms of soil tests, paralleling James Booth's 1853 article. Johnson now found proper sampling to be such a difficult problem that, notwithstanding Norton's arguments in 1851, it could not be overcome without the prohibitive cost of taking and testing several samples at once. Even these samples might have impurities, such as bird or dog dung, that would affect the analysis greatly. A second problem Johnson noted was that chemical analysis itself was neither precise enough nor reliable enough. Johnson cited an 1849 analysis of fourteen different soils by assistants of Liebig, Rose, and others in Germany. Their results had varied so greatly, in one case from 0.009 percent to 0.832 percent phosphoric acid, that the tests could be of little value. Furthermore, Johnson did not think chemical analysis could be precise beyond the level of 0.1 percent (despite the above work he cited). This, he pointed out, was not accurate enough to detect an application of 400 pounds of guano on an acre, a dosage that would affect the crop considerably. Nor did Johnson think the chemist could ever precisely determine which elements were present in a soluble state, and therefore available to the crop, and which were not. In addition, physical factors, such as the size of particles, were important, but the chemist could not yet calculate their effect. But Johnson had overstated his criticism of soil analysis, for he had to admit that sometimes analyses had been successful, though he thought such cases were rare. His final opinion was that "a soil-analysis is always interesting, often valuable, rarely economical. It may amuse the amateur, and instruct the philosopher, but for the farmer its value is small, if he has to pay for it."[13] In the 1890s the advocates of soil surveys and soil mapping would modify Johnson's criticisms to argue that, though individual test may be worth little and subject to variation, extensive tests and mapping are very useful.

In a companion piece a few months later, "On the Practical Value of the Analyses of Plants," Johnson remained optimistic that despite the fact "that the analyses of plants *as hitherto interpreted,* to American farmers, are of little practical value, and indeed have been made the basis of false doctrine," new vistas were opening up for agricultural science. Conflicts between theory and practice merely meant that the field of agricultural science included more than chemistry, especially plant anatomy and physiology. Plants were as varied as soils, and only by expanding agricultural science would present problems be solved. Such a view was broad-minded, but it was based more on hope for the future than on present accomplishments.[14]

These two articles foreshadowed the full emergence of Johnson's

new view of agricultural science, toward which he had been groping
for two years. In June 1855, on the eve of his return to the United
States, Johnson unveiled his new rationale in two articles "On the
Agricultural Value of Gypsum," which were a model of how the new
agricultural chemistry should approach the problems that Liebig and
Norton had been unable to master. Although the reasons why
gypsum worked were still unknown, Johnson reviewed current
knowledge of its action in order to "acquire points of departure" to
"guide us through the maze." The crux of the change was that
Johnson did not think, as Liebig and Norton had, that scientific
agriculture was simple and its problems capable of easy solution. He
thought they were complex but soluble by "patient investigation."
Certain points about gypsum were now clear—it helped leguminous
plants most but plants on lime soils least, and it had best effects when
accompanied by frequent gentle rains and a warm moist climate.
Beyond these limited conclusions Johnson could not generalize,
because experiments reported in the agricultural press were so
faulty. Though "a soil is a complex thing," American farmers hardly
ever described the soil they had used in their experiments. Even if
they did, Johnson complained, "we have no logical ground to as-
sume that any of the mentioned causes or circumstances had anything to do with the effect, more than a number of other unnoticed
causes which must have been present and operative." The only hope
was to gain new and more trustworthy information by means of
carefully controlled experiments. There were just too many factors
involved for the random experimentation that farmers had been
doing for years to yield worthwhile results. More rather than less
science was what the farmers should be seeking, particularly rigor-
ous and systematic experimentation with controls and accurate
measurements. They needed an agricultural experiment station with
a staff of trained investigators who could study detailed problems
scientifically. Johnson must have expected his argument to appeal to
farmers who had long wanted to get back to "facts" and "experiments." In time his new view would become the major argument for
the establishment of such experiment stations in the United States.[15]

Johnson had thus evolved a new rationale for agricultural science
even before he returned to the United States in 1855. He had laid
out a plan and a goal toward which he planned to work, but how or
where he might try to implement it was uncertain. Nor could he tell

how long it might take or what obstacles might lie in his path. He
was already too familiar with farmers to think it would be easy,
but the stations abroad were so full of useful results and so obviously
necessary that he did not doubt his eventual triumph. If he could
have foreseen how long it would take, however, and how limited a
victory it would be even then, he might well have given up hope in
1855 and succumbed to one of his recurrent moods of depression.
Neither philanthropists nor state governments would have money for
experiment stations for decades to come.

Johnson's plans for his future were still uncertain in the spring of
1855 when he started his lengthy trip home via Heidelberg, Hohenheim, Cirencester, and Owens College in Manchester, where he
spent two months learning gas analysis from Edward Frankland.
Several possibilities, none of which worked out, seemed open to him.
He could start an agricultural academy either in New York State
with his brother-in-law or in Pennsylvania with his friend Evan
Pugh. He might also succeed his Yale friend William Brewer, who
was leaving for study in Europe, at Ovid Academy in New York
State. Or he could perhaps become an agricultural chemist for the
Commonwealth of Massachusetts or the New York State Agricultural Society. He preferred the last, but in the end events at Yale
created an opening for him there at the last minute, and Johnson
was able to return to Yale to teach agricultural chemistry in 1855.[16]

Shortly after Norton's death in 1852, James Dwight Dana, who
was handling the affairs of the laboratory in the interim, had hired
John Addison Porter, recently of Brown University, as a temporary
replacement. Porter was one of the very few well-trained chemists
available in the country at the time and, at first sight, would seem
to have been an excellent successor to Norton. He was the same age
as Norton, having been born in 1822 in Catskill, New York, and
he had graduated from Yale College in 1842. He had planned to
become a Presbyterian minister like his father, but when he became
disillusioned with theology, like Norton, he had turned to teaching
literature at Delaware College. There in 1844 he had met Eben
Horsford, who was at the college giving his short course on chemistry.
Horsford's enthusiastic personality, his great admiration for Liebig,
and his expectation of financial success in chemistry so impressed
Porter that, when his father died in 1847 and left him the respon-

sibility for eight brothers and sisters, he determined to follow Horsford to Giessen. He stayed two years with Liebig, but he must have lacked Horsford's talent and motivation, for in that time he published only two incomplete researches and wrote only one letter to the *Cultivator*. Upon his return to the United States in 1850, Porter assisted Horsford for a few months at Harvard before being elected to the new Professorship of Chemistry Applied to the Arts at Brown University. Unfortunately, he had hardly set up his laboratory there when a student rebellion broke out. He refused to punish his charges, and when President Francis Wayland threatened to dismiss him, he resigned in February 1852. Porter was thus both qualified and available when Yale suddenly needed a trained agricultural chemist in September 1852.[17]

How Porter managed financially at Yale is not clear. It is hard to see how the laboratory, even with an increase in prices, could have yielded the $1,200 Porter had been earning at Brown. Porter was evidently not pleased with the prospects at Yale and spent much of the period 1852–54 seeking a better-paying position elsewhere.[18]

Despite the financial hardships, Porter managed to carry on the laboratory and be popular with the students, who appreciated his neatness and presence in the laboratory. But Porter did not please Dana and Benjamin Silliman, Jr., so easily. They felt that despite his excellent training and potential, he was more interested in making money than in furthering science. Outside the laboratory Porter was an officer in the new Connecticut State Agricultural Society and gave occasional lectures to farmers, but he seems to have lacked Norton's fervor. Dana and the younger Silliman, who succeeded his father as professor of chemistry in Yale College in 1853, were distressed about Porter's performance and hoped to raise an endowment in order to build up a school around him.[19]

Before they could start their fund drive, Porter married Josephine Sheffield, daughter of a wealthy New Haven railroad magnate, in the summer of 1855. Such a marriage ended Porter's financial worries and enabled him, too, to live on fancy Hillhouse Avenue. But the marriage had advantages for the laboratory as well. It secured the interest of Porter's father-in-law, railroad magnate Joseph Sheffield, who in 1855 gave it $5,000 for endowment. The gift allowed Dana and Silliman to start their expansion sooner than expected and to hire the returning Samuel Johnson in July 1855. They tried to create the position of "assistant professor" of chemistry for him, but the Corporation balked and ruled he could be only an "assistant," something he might have been before studying in Germany. Johnson accepted the post but was unhappy with its poor salary, low status, and janitorial duties. He thought seriously about going to Albany as chemist to the New York State Agricultural Society. The whole episode put even more urgency upon Dana's plans for a major fund drive at the scientific school.[20]

In March 1856 President Theodore Woolsey, the elder Silliman, and the entire scientific school faculty initiated the fund drive with their "Appeal in Behalf of the Yale Scientific School." It and several other articles by Dana, Norton, Porter, and Daniel C. Gilman outlined the glorious future and pressing needs of the school. It was a vision worthy of a German duke, a French emperor, or a state university. The school needed (1) a new laboratory building, (2) endowments for professorships of agricultural chemistry, applied chemistry, and metallurgy, (3) collections of engineering models and agricultural implements, (4) an experimental farm, (5) a maintenance fund for laboratory equipment and assistants, (6) new professorships in architecture, botany, and mining, and (7) a museum of zoology and botany with a fund for a curator's salary. With these added facilities the school could offer a curriculum broadened to include all the sciences that would appeal to the industrial as well as agricultural interests of the state. They optimistically estimated the total cost to be about $150,000.[21]

For this modest sum the professors hoped to create at Yale the American equivalent of Abram Werner's Bergakademie at Freiburg, the Central School of Arts and Manufactures in Paris, and the Royal Polytechnic School at Dresden. But having titillated themselves with this grand idea, the professors immediately admitted that the American model would necessarily be on a greatly reduced scale. Although Germany (especially Saxony), France, and Russia devoted whole schools to engineering, metallurgy, agriculture, and forestry, humble Yale would be pleased to have a single professorship in each of these subjects. But lest even this modest proposal seem overly grand, the fund raisers then tried to show that their scheme was well within the reach of the citizens of Connecticut. Gilman found the annual income of the Royal Prussian Architectural Academy to be about $15,000, or the equivalent of an endowment of $250,000.

This sum was far in excess of what the Yale professors wanted, and yet the Germans gave this much to just one of their many schools.* Surely the people of Connecticut could do as well.[22]

In spite of the professors' efforts to make their plans sound modest, the Yale students abroad thought the proposed plan grandiose with a considerable amount of *'claptrap'* in it.'' Most of the citizens of Connecticut must have agreed, for the fund drive was at first not able to raise more than $30,000. Although this sum was much more than Benjamin Silliman, Jr., and J. P. Norton had been able to raise in 1846–47, it was pitifully inadequate now. Then in 1858, when the drive seemed to have failed, Joseph E. Sheffield, who had given $5,000 more since 1855, returned from Europe and presented the school with a $50,000 laboratory. In 1860, when the laboratory was completed, he added funds for its equipment and maintenance unlike Abbott Lawrence at Harvard thirteen years before. In 1861 Sheffield gave $40,000 more for the endowment of three professorships, making a total gift of $100,000 to the school, which now changed its name to the Sheffield Scientific School to honor him. The Yale Corporation was overwhelmed by his generosity, since his gifts were the largest in the history of the college. Sheffield's gifts changed the scientific school from a poor and dependent relative of Yale College to an affluent and increasingly independent one. After 1860, the scientific school, which had suddenly become so prosperous, attracted even more gifts, most notably $150,000 from George Peabody in 1866 for a museum and further Sheffield gifts bringing his total to $542,700 by 1871. After 1864 the school was also the sole recipient of Connecticut's share of the Morrill Land-Grant income of $8,000–$13,000 per year.[23] The result of all this money at Yale after 1858 was that, at a time when the Lawrence School at Harvard was facing the Horsford scandals and finding itself unable to compete with the new Massachusetts Institute of Technology, the Sheffield School at Yale was able to fulfill many of its early hopes, expand its program into that of a full-scale university,

---

*The professors shrewdly juggled the figures to their advantage in their arguments. When comparing the "whole schools" in Germany to the "single professorship" in the United States, they stressed the large number of professorships abroad. Then, when they came to talk about the modest total budget for such a school, they stressed German costs which reflected the low salaries abroad. Had they computed the total cost of an equal number of professorships in American figures, their sum would have been at least four times as large and perhaps overwhelmed potential contributors.

and become a center of educational innovations. Between 1860 and the opening of the Johns Hopkins University in 1876, the Sheffield School was the leading center of science in the country.

The Yale professors were much luckier with their benefactor than Horsford had been with his at Harvard. Sheffield gave Yale enough money—a full $50,000 for the laboratory plus an endowment for its expenses and a separate $40,000 for professorships—unlike Lawrence who wished to squeeze both laboratory and professorships out of his $50,000. But the Yale professors were also willing to accept lower salaries than were their counterparts at Harvard. Salaries at the Sheffield School reached $2,300 in 1864, still far short of the $3,000 Horsford had thought necessary fifteen years before. But the major difference between the experiences at Harvard and at Yale was that the Yale professors started small and in applied science—agricultural chemistry, applied chemistry, and engineering—and only later in the 1850s, when there was adequate support for it, did they move toward the costly graduate education. They were thus spared the embarrassment of Harvard's premature and unsustained attempt to bring Liebig's laboratory to America.[24]

Yale was also fortunate in this period to obtain the services of William H. Brewer as its new professor of agriculture. Brewer, a farm boy from Ithaca, New York, had studied with John Pitkin Norton at the Yale Analytical Laboratory; taught in Ovid, New York; and studied in Munich (with Liebig and von Kobell), Heidelberg, and Paris. He then returned to a job at Washington College in Pennsylvania where he remained until, distraught over the deaths of his wife and young daughter, he joined J. D. Whitney on the California geological survey in 1860. The passage of the Morrill Land-Grant Act in 1862 created a sudden demand for trained professors of agriculture, and the Yale faculty was lucky to find one as well qualified as its old friend Brewer. Cornell University, founded a few years later in 1867, had an extremely difficult time finding such a professor and tried to tempt Brewer back to his native Ithaca. But they were unsuccessful, for Brewer had found a new home at Yale and had a long and active career in Connecticut public health and agriculture as well. He and Johnson made a strong team in Connecticut agriculture after the Civil War.[25]

Although hired by Yale in 1855, Johnson was not entirely happy there at first and hoped to return soon to his native state of New York as chemist to its state agricultural society. Johnson was eager to go there, since, of all the state agricultural societies in the United States at the time, that of New York was, in membership, leadership, and financial resources, most like the one at Leipzig which had started the world's first agricultural experiment station. The society's leaders—Luther Tucker, B. P. Johnson and Ezra S. Carr—were also enthusiastic about his coming and invited him to address the society in February 1856. In his speech, a manifesto of the new agricultural chemistry, Johnson outlined the great need for field trials and accurate facts, such as could only be obtained at agricultural experiment stations. He also stressed the need for a station or society chemist to analyze fertilizers in order to protect farmers against frauds, as had proven successful in Britain and Germany. He closed by challenging the New Yorkers—Europeans said science could not flourish in a democracy, but New York State had already supported natural history and entomology. What could be worthier than to support agriculture as well by starting a station and hiring a chemist? But Johnson's effort failed, and the society did neither. By the spring of 1856 Johnson was forced to realize that New York agriculture was not as progressive as it had been earlier and that his future lay in Connecticut rather than in New York. Fortunately, the Sillimans finally persuaded the Yale Corporation to elect Johnson Professor of Analytical Chemistry in 1856. In subsequent years this title change as colleagues and assistants came and went, but Johnson taught agricultural and analytical chemistry at Yale for the next forty years.[26]

In his first five years at Yale, before the laboratory was built, Johnson had neither the time nor the facilities to do much research. Horsford had done more in this respect in his first years at Harvard. But shortly after the completion of the new Sheffield laboratory in 1860, Johnson tried out some of the new apparatus in a series of difficult experiments in a new branch of chemistry, spectral analysis. This work, which corrected an error made by Robert Bunsen, one of the founders of the field, in the atomic weights of the new elements cesium and rubidium, was a major triumph for Johnson, his collaborator Oscar D. Allen, and the new laboratory. It was not the first time an American had determined an atomic weight, one of the most delicate and precise problems in analytical chemistry, but it showed that when Americans had the necessary facilities, they could on occasion beat the Germans in their own specialties. The experiments also led, three years later, to Johnson's election to the new National Academy of Sciences, an honor he greatly appreciated.[27]

But this brief and rewarding foray into pure science was only a temporary diversion from Johnson's main scientific achievement at Yale—the undertaking of an ambitious program to update agricultural chemistry since Liebig and to present the new view of the complexity and diversity of agricultural science to his fellow Americans in its full detail. Johnson took time from his duties at Yale in the late 1850s to present the latest researches in Europe to the American farming and scientific communities through a series of review articles, translations, and book reviews in the *Country Gentleman* and the *American Journal of Science*.

At times Johnson resented his role as middleman or schoolmaster and found it a frustrating task to read about the brilliant researches of J. B. Boussingault in Alsace—experiments that he had neither the time nor the farm facilities to perform in Connecticut—and to present them to an American audience which was more interested in perfecting its reaping machines than in understanding theories of plant growth. But generally Johnson was glad of a chance to keep abreast of the latest work in Europe.[28]

At other times Johnson took on the painful professional role of criticizing the recent work of his old professor Justus Liebig. Having moved beyond Liebig to a new view of agricultural chemistry which stressed complexity, patient experimentation, and balanced and limited assessments, Johnson was quite provoked by two of Liebig's latest publications, the *Letters on Modern Agriculture* of 1859 and the *Natural Laws of Husbandry* in 1863. Both books showed that, despite recent work to the contrary, Liebig was still peddling his outmoded ideas as true. His errors had become an embarrassment to other workers in the field and had to be combatted vigorously. Johnson accordingly criticized both publications mercilessly in two series of articles in the *Country Gentleman*. He followed Liebig's reasoning closely, pointing out inconsistencies, outright contradictions, factual errors, and deliberate misrepresentations, and refuted each one in detail. Liebig was, as Johnson put it, "floundering in the dilemma in which his theories have placed him." He was still unaware of the complexity of the problems involved and being by nature assertive and impulsive, he made more of his "glittering generalities" or "broad statements which are almost, but not quite true, and which have already occasioned a large amount of controversy." Frequently, as Johnson pointed out, he relied on logic (and illogic) rather than experimental evidence to support his assertions. Liebig would, typically, say that crops increased *in proportion to* the quantity of mineral fertilizer added. There was certainly some increase, but Lawes and Gilbert had since proven experimentally that it was not in strict proportion and that it had certain limits. Liebig's approach had been very fruitful in 1840 when his keen mind had formulated the problems of agricultural chemistry and outlined areas for experimentation. At that time, clearing away the fuzzy thinking on the humus and focusing on nitrogen and minerals had been a real contribution. But now, twenty years later, there was an abundance of evidence on these very key problems, largely the result of his own stimulus. Unfortunately, Liebig's continued theorizing was frequently contrary to some recently discovered facts or newly developed concept, such as that of "inert nitrogen," which Liebig clearly did not understand. Liebig was no longer leading the field of agricultural chemistry but was lagging seriously behind. More editions of his books would appear in the 1860s and even after his death in 1873 (see appendix 1), but they offered little that was new. Great though his services had been in the 1840s, the field had moved beyond him by 1860.[29]

Although Johnson had resented his role as middleman when he had first returned to the United States, the numerous new developments of the 1850s and the need for textbooks in the 1860s made him more willing to take on this role after the Civil War. His two masterly volumes, *How Crops Grow* of 1868 and *How Crops Feed* of 1870, were tremendously successful, becoming the standard textbooks in agricultural colleges for the next forty years and being translated into Russian, Swedish, Italian, Japanese, and German (by Herman von Liebig). The books grew out of Johnson's courses in agricultural chemistry and plant physiology at the Sheffield School, discussions with Evan Pugh about textbooks, numerous review articles and book reviews, and a series of four lectures on agricultural chemistry at the Smithsonian Institution in 1859. The books were thus not hastily thrown together to meet the new need, but were the product of twelve years of teaching, much thought, and wide reading. Johnson's virtues of thoroughness and objectivity were very evident, since the books were as complete a summary of the state of agricultural chemistry up to 1868–70 as Johnson could make them. Though a projected third volume on fertilizers would have been especially interesting, the two texts were a valuable indication of what had been accomplished in agricultural chemistry in the thirty years since Liebig's book had first appeared.[30]

The books filled a long-felt need for adequate textbooks, but they also served to define the field at a crucial time. The Morrill Land-Grant Act of 1862 had spurred the creation of a large number of agricultural colleges, but few persons knew how to go about teaching a subject like agriculture or to do meaningful research in it. Professors and administrators who were forced to include the subject in their curricula and to do "experiments" to placate hostile legislators and editors (who now claimed they were paying for the schools) were eager to see the subject provided with the maximum amount of intellectual content. Johnson's books provided a feasible model.[31]

The first volume, *How Crops Grow: A Treatise on the Chemical Composition, Structure, and Life of the Plant,* showed the tremendous energy that Liebig's book had unleashed on plant ash analyses. An army of chemists, including Horsford and Norton, had analyzed almost two hundred different plants, some as many as seventy-eight times. From this collected data, Johnson could now list systematically all the elements and their compounds that appeared in plants at all stages of development. Plant chemistry had come a long way since Norton's pioneering study of the oat in 1846. In 1868 Johnson could also begin to determine the range of variation in the composition of well-studied plants. The next step was to separate the "accidental" from the essential constituents. Several experimenters in German agricultural experiment stations had grown plants in artificial soils and solutions carefully controlled to determine which minerals were essential. By 1868 they had found that potash, lime, magnesia, phosphoric acid, and sulphuric acid were "absolutely necessary" to all plants. Silica, on the other hand, the most predominant element in grain ash (30–50 percent), was surprisingly not essential. It was one of the tricks of nature that silica, which was present in all soils, abounded in most plants, and was easily detected by chemists even in Davy's time, should have such a minor role. Recent experiments were showing their worth.[32]

But problems remained. The necessity of soda and chlorine had not been settled despite much experimentation. If they were necessary, only a small amount was required. The idea of "trace elements" or "micronutrients" was emerging, and, as experimentation grew more and more refined in succeeding decades, more and more elements would be found essential. But once an element had been found essential, the agricultural chemist wanted to know its function in the plant. Very little was known about this whole problem in 1868, though a few selected experiments, which had deprived plants of certain minerals, indicated a fruitful line of advance. A vast amount of work had been done in the thirty years since Liebig had pointed to plant minerals as an important area of study, but this work consisted mostly of refining old ideas. No new theories had arisen on the role of minerals in plants, and none were expected. Liebig's ideas on minerals had been made more precise, but on the whole, they were still valid thirty years later.[33]

How Crops Grow also contained sections on plant anatomy and physiology, but they were much more descriptive and less experimental than the preceding section on minerals. One chapter described the cell, whose nucleus and protoplasm had been identified, but about which much remained to be learned. Johnson sensed that cell development might someday be important to plant physiology and thus to agriculture, but for the present it proceeded "according to laws that are hidden from our knowledge" (p. 228). More successful had been the identification since 1840 of the vague "selective power" of the roots "unquestionably" with osmosis, although only a limited amount of experimentation had been done in this area by 1870. However, Johnson's open and interested attitude toward plant physiology was itself a big improvement over Liebig's earlier derogatory tone.

Johnson's second volume, *How Crops Feed,* was much more exciting than its predecessor, for it treated the atmosphere and the soil, two controversial topics that had been investigated intensively since 1840. Researches on the atmosphere had, unlike the work on minerals, revealed enough errors in Liebig's system for chemists to question it seriously and to investigate the organic parts and physical characteristics of the soil, areas which Liebig had ignored. So great was the disaffection with Liebig's views by 1870 that a swing back toward the views of Mulder, Berzelius, and Samuel Dana was taking place.

Liebig's simple and strictly chemical view had been rejected for a more complex and comprehensive one of plant-soil relationships.

Liebig's assertion in 1840 that plants received a large part of their nitrogen from the ammonia in the air had, as mentioned in chapter 3, immediately attracted attention. Shortly thereafter many chemists, including Horsford, undertook detailed determinations of the chemical composition of the atmosphere and the rainwater. Though local conditions varied greatly, there did not seem to be enough ammonia or nitric acid in the atmosphere to supply the plants with nitrogen. The only other possible source of atmospheric nitrogen was free N_2, but experiments by Boussingault in 1855 and Pugh, Gilbert, and Lawes in 1857 had shown that nitrogen did not enter the plant directly. Liebig's theory that the source of the plant's nitrogen was (1) atmospheric and (2) in the form of ammonia was therefore disproven on both accounts, and attention turned in the mid-1850s toward the soil as a possible alternative source of plant nitrogen. Shortly thereafter Boussingault showed, in detailed studies of sunflowers, that the nitrates in the soil were the source of nitrogen in plants, but the process of their formation was too intricate for full elaboration. In fact the chemical analysis of organic processes within the soil had about reached its limits in 1870. As Johnson put it, "Chemical analysis is competent to inform us very accurately as to the ultimate composition of the soil, but as regards its proximate composition or its chemical constitution, there remains a vast and difficult Unknown, which will yield only to a very long and laborious investigation" (p. 371). Johnson could not foresee that Pasteur's work on fermentation in 1859–60 would have an equivalent in soil science in the 1880s and that one of the big "Unknowns" would be microbiological rather than chemical. The discovery of the role of nitrogen-fixing bacteria in legumes by Hermann Hellriegel and Hermann Wilfarth in 1886–88 would open a new era in soil science. Then nitrification, humus formation, and other soil processes that had eluded chemical analysis would be worked out in terms of complex microbial reactions in the early twentieth century.[34]

Johnson was very optimistic, however, in 1870 about the future contribution of "soil physics." Although Humphry Davy and Samuel Dana had treated the subject in an elementary way, and even Liebig had mentioned it in passing, it had long been eclipsed by the excitement over soil chemistry. Topics like soil absorption, capillarity, permeability, cohesiveness, expansion, retention of moisture and gases, and reaction to heat and temperature had all presented great difficulties in experimentation, but now they promised to yield important new concepts of far-reaching importance. For example, J. Thomas Way of England had shown in 1850 that soils were more selective in their absorption of salts than had formerly been thought. They retained more ammonia and potash than other bases and rejected hydrochloric, nitric, and sulphuric acids, leading to a series of displacement reactions within the double silicates in the soil. Way also showed that minerals (in a liquid solution) entered the plant passively by osmosis rather than by the active forces of suction, selection, and excretion that Candolle, Macaire-Princep, and Liebig had been hypothesizing for years. Way's work thus made the soil a dynamic entity unlike the passive storehouse of minerals Liebig had envisioned in 1840. Many reactions were taking place within the soil, breaking down old products and building up new more assimilable ones. For Johnson this meant that the new soil physics, which included for him much that would later be labeled "physical chemistry," could take up where the old soil chemistry had left off—it could now hope to determine in what chemical state the mineral was present in the soil, in what form and under what conditions it could be assimilated by the plant, and what reactions were necessary to bring about the proper changes. Johnson did not talk of "cations," pH, and colloids, but he foresaw that such future "physical" studies not only would be useful in fertilizer applications but would also lead to important new generalizations about soil action. Scientists might now begin to study systematically the problems S. L. Dana had grappled with in 1842.[35]

At the end of his textbook, perhaps carried away by all this new research, Johnson felt able to refute the old concept of worn-out soil had which had so appealed to farmers in the 1830s and 1840s and been one factor behind the craze over soil analysis. Recent experiments in Silesia had shown that the quantity of nitrates in a soil increased rapidly during the growing season despite a loss to vegetation. From this Johnson concluded that the large amounts of inert nitrogen known to be present in the soil had been converted chemically into usable nitrates. If this were generally true, there would be no danger of a nitrogen deficiency in most soils. Likewise, Johnson felt that the idea of the exhaustion of minerals in the soil was a false scare. When the modest quantities of minerals necessary for maximum crop yields were compared with the vast quantities already in the soil breaking down and recombining into assimilable form, it was evident that there was no threat of exhaustion after all. It was a concept that existed only in the works of "speculative writers" and not in agriculture itself.[36]

Unfortunately in his haste to bid Liebig farewell, Johnson overlooked the significance of the growing fertilizer industry. Its flourishing condition in 1870 indicated that, despite Johnson's latest scientific theories, not all American soils were adequately supplied with nitrogen and minerals. Johnson, of all people, should never have made such a miscalculation, for ever since his student days at Yale, he had been carrying on a second career as the leader in the fight against fertilizer frauds in Connecticut.

Justus Liebig in his middle years. From a contemporary print in the possession of Margaret Rossiter.

stus Liebig's laboratory at Giessen. From J. P. Hofmann, *Das Chemische Laboratorium der Ludwigs-iversität zu Giessen* (Heidelberg: C. F. Winter, 1842).

Interior view of Liebig's laboratory at Giessen, showing students at work. From J. P. Hofmann, *Das Chemische Laboratorium der Ludwigs-Universität zu Giessen* (Heidelberg: C. F. Winter, 1842).

Eben Norton Horsford in the late 1840s (*upper left*). From a contemporary print in the possession of Horsford's descendant Andrew Fiske. Reproduced by permission.

John Pitkin Norton, about 1850 (*upper right*). Courtesy of the Library of Congress.

Samuel W. Johnson as a young man (*lower left*). Courtesy of the Library of Congress.

9

Fertilizer Frauds and the Experiment Station

Though Liebig had recommended the use of bones soaked in sulphuric acid or "superphosphates" as early as 1840, and Norton had
frequently recommended them in the late 1840s, the commercial
fertilizer industry was slow in starting in the United States. Americans in the 1840s were experimenting with natural mineral manures
(gypsum, lime, marl, ashes, crushed bones, and New Jersey green-
sand) and organic compounds (guano, muck, and poudrette or
nightsoil) but had not yet taken up artificial or manufactured fertilizers. The delay may have been due to the much publicized failure
of Liebig's patent manure in England, but it was more likely that
soil conditions even on the eastern "worn-out" lands did not yet
require the high percentage of phosphoric acid or nitrogen that
artificial fertilizers were to contain. Where the soils did require
strong fertilizers, guano was effective and not yet blatantly overpriced. Even so, there were frauds. Substances were sold as "guanos"
or "artificial guanos" that were anything from adulterated manures
to combinations of sand and water. If the product looked and smelled
like guano, even the suspicious farmer had no way of being sure of
what he was buying. One such fraud had come to John Pitkin Norton's attention in 1851, but he had been so busy with the University
of Albany project that he did not have time to do more than send
Johnson's analysis of the worthless "prepared guano" to James Vick
of the *Genesee Farmer* and urge him to expose the "shameful imposi-
tion." Norton also felt that there ought to be "some check" upon the
manufacturers of fertilizers, for they might produce unreliable
manures unconsciously. Veins of phosphates were so irregular that
such testing was necessary. But, beyond this, Norton had no plans for
policing the quality of fertilizers. He warned the farmers to beware
of frauds but was not at all explicit about how they were to detect
them.[1]

As more and more farmers near eastern cities started using bone fertilizers, it became profitable to produce "superphosphates" commercially. The first products appeared in 1852. Unfortunately, one of the first to enter the superphosphate business was "Professor" James J. Mapes of Newark, New Jersey, the editor of the *Working Farmer,* who was already well known for his $5 soil analyses and thereby considered a quack by certain persons. Starting in May 1852 he marketed "Mapes' Improved Superphosphate," adding "Mapes' Nitrogenized Superphosphate of Lime" in March 1855 and "Mapes' No. 1 Superphosphate" in October 1855. Instead of pushing the innovation, the editors of the *Country Gentleman* doubted the value of the superphosphate from the start and thought it just another fad that would only hurt the farmers before passing on. They were so skeptical of any quack product that they instructed readers who wanted to try superphosphates to make their own at home rather than purchase Mapes's.[2]

It seems that the reforming editors and chemists may have over-reacted to the fertilizer frauds around them. Although the scientific profession was outraged by such $5 quacks and was for the most part powerless to limit them, the forthcoming campaign against the fertilizer frauds was more venomous and vindictive than the ignorant, blundering, and pioneering fertilizer manufacturers probably deserved. In fact the reformers' angry and suspicious tone may well have arisen as much from their own pent-up hostility toward such quacks as from the actual fertilizer frauds themselves. Denouncing Mapes and others for their quasi-defective fertilizers gave Johnson and his righteous friends a chance to lash out publicly at such rivals while seeming to do it "in the public interest."

Johnson's emphasis on being disinterested and incorruptible was unusual among chemists of the time. Although it was fashionable to denounce quackery, there was not yet an ethical code among scientists or even a clear-cut idea of what constituted quackery. Some chemists (C. T. Jackson, E. N. Horsford, A. A. Hayes, J. C. Booth, and Johnson himself at times) saw no reason why they should not analyze a substance for a fee and "certify" it in an advertisement. They probably thought it a duty to keep the analysis from disreputable chemists. However, there was usually no guarantee that their sample was typical, and many must have been doctored up for them, as the naive Benjamin Silliman, Jr., learned later in a celebrated oil scandal. J. P. Norton, however, had long had strong feelings against such practices.[3]

Whatever his motivation, in February 1853 Samuel W. Johnson, then a twenty-two-year-old student at the Yale Analytical Laboratory, decided to examine the relative merits of the new commercial superphosphates by analyzing the two leading brands, Deburg's "No. 1" and Mapes's "Improved," and comparing them to the current English products. Since he expected the worst, Johnson was surprised to find Mapes' better than Deburg's and "in no respect inferior to the best English samples." Although he reluctantly admitted it a good value at $50 per ton if its present quality were maintained, he still distrusted Mapes's honesty enough to suggest a continuing program of fertilizer analyses for consumer protection: "It should be borne in mind, that the value of these manures may be found to vary greatly at different times, and the farmer can only be fully protected from unprofitable expenditure, by the frequent publication of analyses made upon different samples."[4] Although Johnson had grudgingly approved his product, Mapes was incensed by the tone of the article and retaliated in his own journal by citing the even more favorable analyses of his own consulting chemists, Eben Horsford, A. A. Hayes, and Karl Enderlin, a German student of Liebig who had immigrated to New York. Warfare raged between the *Working Farmer* and the *Country Gentleman* for two years, with each side taking every possible chance to criticize the other. Such a good row was one way to increase interest in both journals and in the disputed superphosphates, but it was only the beginning of a long battle between Mapes and Johnson. On Mapes's side it may be said that users of his superphosphates usually found them effective (although he cited only those who were satisfied); and Johnson's pricing, but not his analyses, was constantly in need of adjustment. Johnson, for his part, could claim that his analyses provided valuable comparative data otherwise unobtainable and rejoice that with fertilizer analysis agricultural chemistry was on safer ground than it had ever been with soil analysis. In fact, fertilizer analysis has proven such a reliable measure of fertilizer effectiveness that its use has continued to the present day and is the government's chief means of inspecting fertilizer quality.[5]

Johnson was not able to pursue Mapes and other quacks immediately, since he left for Germany in the spring of 1853, but upon his return to Yale in 1855, and especially after the collapse of his hopes for a job with the New York State Agricultural Society in 1856, he began to think of continuing his efforts to identify fraudulent fertilizers in Connecticut. Fortunately, by 1856 J. P. Norton's earlier activities had had some effect, and prospects for scientific agriculture in Connecticut were no longer as bleak as they had been in 1847–49. Since then, Norton's friend T. S. Gold, an enthusiast for scientific agriculture, and a former student, Henry A. Dyer, had established the first statewide agricultural society and had founded an agricultural journal, the *Connecticut Homestead,* in Hartford. The new state society enjoyed an annual appropriation from the state legislature, and the *Homestead* was thriving under the editorship of Mason C. Weld, Norton's cousin and Johnson's roommate in Germany. There were signs, then, in 1856 that perhaps Connecticut would outstrip New York in its support of scientific agriculture after all. Johnson, anxious about his low salary at Yale, was eager for the Connecticut society to take the step that New York would not and hire him as its paid agricultural chemist.

In his drive to become chemist for the Connecticut State Agricultural Society, Johnson used different tactics than he had in New York .He did not talk to Connecticut farmers of painstaking research, sophisticated experimentation, or European theories. Instead, with the help of editor Weld, he waged a dramatic and hard-hitting campaign in the *Homestead* against manufacturers of fraudulent fertilizers. Between May and December 1856 he analyzed fourteen different products and presented his results in a series of five articles. All these products had appeared on the market since 1852 and practically all guaranteed marvelous results. Many included in their advertisements an analysis signed by a well-known chemist, presumably as a sign of their honesty and the product's purity and value. The average farmer, however, was so overwhelmed by the number of products and so bewildered by the scientific terminology and deceptive advertisements that he was in a quandary over which to buy, if any.[6]

Johnson's results were spectacular. Using the techniques that J. F. W. Johnston and J. A. Stöckhardt had found effective in Scotland and Germany, Johnson and his students at Yale analyzed each product and then computed its "commercial value" on the basis of current prices for ammonia and phosphoric acid.* In this way Johnson could dramatize in dollars and cents the striking differences between the manufacturers' high prices and the products' actual composition and value. In general Johnson found the whole industry so riddled with fraud that he could agree with editor Joseph Harris that "no manure in this country . . . is worth the money charged for it." Among six superphosphates, all priced at $45 per ton, Johnson found the two best worth $25.22 and $24.32. The worst (Hildreth's) should, he felt, command only $3.80 because it contained no soluble phosphoric acid at all! Mapes's superphosphate, which had merited a comparatively respectable $26.62 per ton in 1853, had dropped off considerably since then, as Johnson had predicted, and was now down to $15.64.[7]

But proving that frauds abounded was only half of Johnson's task; he then went on to make his plea to be elected chemist to the State Agricultural Society. He felt that "the American farmer has a right to ask why he must pay $45 for an inferior or worthless article." In England superphosphates sold for a moderate $26–$30 per ton because British farmers were better informed about frauds and had access to the services of chemists hired by the agricultural societies. If American farmers demanded similar services from their societies, Johnson predicted, "not another ton of any of these superphosphates would find sale among them at the present price. Manufacturers would be compelled to make better articles or to give up the business." The solution to the problem depended on the farmers themselves. They had only to elect a chemist to their state society to remedy this terrible evil.[8]

Dramatic as Johnson's campaign had been, public reaction to it was mixed. Some readers gave his articles high praise, such as, "The information he gives us, is worth more to the farmer, than the subscription he pays for your paper [$2.00] ten times over." Such appreciation undoubtedly pleased Johnson and his students who had

---

*Johnson had difficulty setting accurate prices for ammonia and phosphates and therefore overdramatized the size of the frauds. At first he adopted Stöckhardt's German prices. Later he calculated American equivalents, but in 1874 he admitted that all these prices were still hypothetical, since there was no large chemical industry in the United States from which he could cite actual prices. Nevertheless, Johnson's analyses were probably correct, and gave an accurate evaluation in terms of percentages of ammonia and phosphates of the relative standing of the various products on the market at the time.

worked hard on their thirty-three analyses but had received no payment, not even for chemicals, for Johnson had scrupulously avoided any financial contamination of his ethical purity. But other readers of the *Homestead,* as Weld told Johnson privately, thought it was "impudent" of a twenty-six-year-old chemist to treat "honorable merchants" the way he did. The reformer could not hope to please everyone—he could only hope that his campaign had been effective, and that remained to be determined.[9]

The matter of the creation of a paid post for a chemist was to be discussed at the annual meeting of the State Agricultural Society in January 1857. Weld and Dyer took the precaution of placing Johnson prominently on the program with an address on "Frauds in Commercial Manures." The members, were, however, already aware of the value of his *Homestead* articles and were even willing to create a position that would ensure their continuance, but they balked at paying the $400 salary Weld had requested for it. Some members thought $50 was enough. Weld and others countered that $50 was not at all adequate for all the necessary analyses, and that it would be a "mistaken economy" for the farmers of Connecticut to save this $400 and lose thousands in fertilizer frauds. Eventually, despite "considerable grumbling," the $400 post was created and Johnson elected. But the victory was not secure, and in succeeding issues of the *Homestead* and the society's *Transactions* Weld and Dyer bolstered support for the state chemist by referring frequently to the money-saving value of fraud prevention.[10]

Johnson's goal had been reached, but the campaign, which had stressed the benefits of science in terms of dollars and cents, had not really demonstrated to the farmers the true cost of science. They were eager to have the practical benefits of science if it cost only the price of subscription to a journal, but they were still unaware of how expensive analyses were, especially reliable ones, and were reluctant to pay for it. They were also unaware of the level of professional salaries and distrustful of any professional position whose salary would be fixed in advance of the performance of duties. In spite of Johnson's repeated criticisms of charlatan chemists, the farmers clung to the notion that all chemists were more or less alike except that they thought the overpriced ones were probably the "humbugs." In all fairness to the farmers it is possible to see how they might have been confused. The scientists, here as on other occasions,

were of two minds and strategies. Sometimes they chose to underesti-
mate their costs or lower their fees, as in fund drives and when com-
peting with quacks, as an inducement to benefactors or customers.
Then later they would complain that they were not supported well
enough! At other times they held back and demanded the full
amount, acting outraged that anyone could think science at all
inexpensive. It is no wonder the farmers never knew whether the
scientists were going to sell high or sell low. Either way both sides
ended up feeling cheated and abused.

Since the Connecticut State Agricultural Society, which was
fairly affluent at the time of Johnson's election, was so reluctant to
spend $400 for such a proven and practical application of science as
fertilizer analysis, it is not hard to imagine the fate of any proposal
Johnson might have made for them to spend $8,000 to support
advanced research at an agricultural experiment station. But a step
had been taken. Luther Tucker, who had been fighting farm con-
servatism for twenty years, was glad that Connecticut had been able
to elect the chemist that New York had not and hoped that Johnson's
election would lead to "something good and permanent."[11]

A further test of the effectiveness of Johnson's antifraud campaign
was its ability to root the evil from Connecticut. In this it "proved
efficient beyond the expectations of the warmest friends of the
measure." When Johnson submitted his first report to the society, he
could say, "Since my appointment a year since as chemist to the
Society, it had been difficult to find in all our markets any positive
impositions upon the farmers in the way of fertilizers." His report
was somewhat anticlimactic, since his earlier campaign had frightened away the humbugs before he had had a chance to report on
them officially.

"Prof." Mapes was, however, undaunted, and Johnson exploded
when Mapes's superphosphates reached a new low in 1859. "Of all
the many fraudulent and poor manures that have been from time to
time imposed upon our farmers during the last four years, there is
none so deserving of complete exposure, and sharp rebuke, as that
series of trashy mixtures known as 'Mapes' Superphosphate of Lime.' "
On the whole, however, Johnson found the testing of fertilizers negative and tedious police work and wished to take the more positive
direction of informing Connecticut farmers of cheap alternative
manures. He therefore undertook in 1858, with Henry Dyer's strong

encouragement, an extensive study of the peat and muck deposits throughout the state. Johnson enlisted the help of thirty-five farmers for samples of peat and muck and for answers to a questionnaire about their experience with them both. He also combed the literature for theoretical views on peat and muck, but their action still eluded chemical theory. The final report was a major accomplishment, and when Johnson presented it to the agricultural society in January 1859, Professor John Addison Porter hailed it "as being, together with the previous one, the most valuable contributions to agricultural science ever made on this side of the Atlantic."[12]

Meanwhile, the agricultural society had been facing a series of financial setbacks. In 1857 the annual fair, on whose proceeds the society depended heavily, suffered a loss because the financial panic that year had sharply decreased the number of exhibitors. In 1858 the fair was practically rained out, placing the society $2,000 in debt. It could not afford to pay Johnson immediately for his extensive 1858 report. In spite of this situation, Johnson asked for a salary increase in January 1859, since otherwise "it would be impossible for him to do the same amount of work another year." When it became evident that the society definitely could not afford an increase, and Secretary Dyer took a $200 pay cut from $1,200 to $1,000, Johnson agreed to remain in office but did a much less impressive report for 1859. The fortunes of the society did not improve, however. In 1859 the continuing depression forced the legislature to be economy minded, and it cut the society's annual appropriation from $2,500 to $1,600. Even so, the society was willing to rehire Johnson for his fertilizer analyses at $400, but he again insisted that he could not do the work for that sum. At this point, in January 1860, the position was allowed to fall vacant. Shortly thereafter the society dissolved, and with the coming of the Civil War, Weld enlisted in the Union Army, and the *Homestead,* which had also been in debt since 1857, ceased publication. The movement for agricultural improvement in Connecticut, which had been making such rapid strides in the 1850s, came to a complete halt by 1861.[13]

Had times been more prosperous, the society might well have increased Johnson's salary, making it possible for him to continue his researches on manures. But state funding was generally neither very generous nor very secure. After four years of effort, Johnson was only slightly closer to an experiment station. The state had set a precedent of strong, though indirect, support for fertilizer control, and Johnson had made his first attempt to move beyond fertilizer work to more general problems of agricultural research. He was discovering, however, that it was not as easy a transition in Connecticut as it had seemed at Möckern, where Drs. Wolff and Ritthausen had had time both to do research and to write. For Johnson it was to be a long and frequently disappointing battle.

After the collapse of the movement, Johnson spent the 1860s in researches in the new Sheffield Laboratory at Yale and in writing his two textbooks *How Crops Grow* and *How Crops Feed*. Meanwhile, however, as the Civil War continued, immigration and urbanization were increasing the nation's demand for food products, and Connecticut with its relatively poor land for grain and corn was rapidly losing its remaining markets to western competition. Economic pressures forced Connecticut agriculture back upon its comparative geographical advantage in supplying eastern cities. After 1860 those farms that were not abandoned turned increasingly to such perishable food products as fruits, eggs, and dairy products and to other crops, such as hay, which would not pay the cost of long transportation. The rise of such a specialized commercial agriculture required a more precise knowledge of crops, costs, and methods of cultivation and was a great spur to agricultural reform in Connecticut in the late 1860s.[14]

How aware the state's leaders were of the economic changes underway is debatable, but in July 1866 the legislature established a State Board of Agriculture to "investigate such subjects relating to improvement in agriculture and horticulture in this State as they think proper." The board may have been created at the instigation of T. S. Gold, E. H. Hyde, and Samuel W. Johnson, who had all been active in the old society and were immediately appointed to the new board of twelve. Eight of the other members were chosen by the county agricultural societies, and the twelfth was the governor himself, who was to preside. The driving force behind the board was to be its secretary, the indefatigable T. S. Gold, who for a salary of $700 a year was to travel throughout the state encouraging local farm clubs and spreading useful information among farmers by lectures or otherwise. But the real object of the new board was not so much extension work among farmers as lobbying activities among the legislators. On occasion the board even suggested bills to the legislature's Joint Committee on Agriculture, but the board was not as popular with the committee and the legislature as it might have liked and found its task difficult.[15]

One reason for the board's unpopularity with the legislature may have been that its ties to Yale were farily strong, perhaps stronger than was really politic at the time. When Johnson's term on the board expired in 1868, the governor replaced him with William H. Brewer, also of Yale. These two men and Addison E. Verrill, a zoologist hired by Yale in 1864, were very active in the three-day "Farmers' Conventions" which the Board held in a different part of the state each winter, lecturing on fertilizers, plant diseases, and cattle breeding. The board looked to Yale for ideas for agricultural improvement, and the Yale professors, the recipients of the state's land-grant fund, worked hard to find suitable topics upon which to speak.

The board was, however, very successful in its first round with the legislature, partly because of Samuel Johnson's activities in the 1850s. In January 1869 T. S. Gold reported to the board that he had arranged for Johnson to resume the analyses of commercial fertilizers that he had begun in 1856–59. With the help of Wilbur Olin Atwater, a graduate student at the Sheffield School who would later be more active in the movement for agricultural reform, Johnson analyzed sixteen fertilizers and presented his report in April 1869. Johnson's comments on each product were quite restrained despite some obvious frauds—Baugh's Bone Fertilizer cost $50 per ton but was worth only $13.98, and Wilson's Tobacco Grower (produced by George F. Wilson, Eben Horsford's partner at the Rumford Chemical Works) was priced at $80 per ton but was valued at only $18.71. Mapes's Superphosphate fared rather well this time, being priced at $60 and worth $27.46, which was among the best values at the time. "Prof." James J. Mapes had died in 1866, and his son Charles V. Mapes had apparently changed the company's ways.[16]

But by April 1869 T. S. Gold's ambitions for fertilizer control went beyond the mere publishing of analyses. He thought the time had come for a state fertilizer regulation law, and at the end of Johnson's report Gold recommended adoption of a fair-labeling act for fertilizers such as that recently passed by the state of Maine, which included penalties for fraudulent statements on labels. Connecticut was able, however, with Gold's help, to pass an even stronger fertilizer control bill in July 1869, which included an important enforcement clause:

> SEC. 4. The secretary of the Connecticut board of agriculture is hereby authorized, at his discretion, to procure the analysis of any fertilizer offered for sale in this state, and to prosecute any persons who violate the provisions of this act.[17]

Johnson's fertilizer reports in the 1850s may have been the reason why Connecticut legislators were not as afraid of strong fertilizer regulation as were their counterparts in Maine and Massachusetts; the latter passed an even weaker bill than Maine's in 1869.

Johnson's first report on commercial fertilizers under the new law in June 1870 was, however, unspectacular. He did only six analyses, including two of Wilson's Tobacco Grower, which had performed so poorly in 1869. The product was about 25 percent better now and had an average valuation of $42.34, but most of the increase resulted from a long overdue revision of Johnson's pricing system. The subject of fertilizer control was now attracting such widespread interest that some standardization of prices was necessary. In the last year Mason Weld in New York City, Joseph Harris in Rochester, and Samuel L. Goodale of the Maine Board of Agriculture had all come out with different systems. These published valuations were reprinted far and wide, but the prices of ammonia, phosphoric acid, and potash depended heavily upon transportation costs and were subject to great local variations. Some cautions and more uniformity were necessary to prevent confusion. In the early 1880s the similar need for uniformity of state legislation and for standardization of analytical methods would lead Harvey W. Wiley to establish the Association of Official Analytical Chemists in Washington.[18]

Yet the Connecticut Assembly was not pleased with the board and, despite the passage of the strong law and the revival of Johnson's reports, abruptly abolished it in the summer of 1870. Such legislative proposals were fairly commonly introduced by disgruntled rural districts at this time but usually died in committee or were withdrawn.[19] That this one should slip through showed that despite its recent achievements the cause of scientific agriculture still had strong opposition in Connecticut. Some farmers objected to the cost of publishing reports and holding meetings and were skeptical that anything useful could come of it. Gold, aghast, immediately set to work to have the board reinstated with an even larger appropriation. His lobbying activities were successful, for in July 1871 the legislature reestablished the board with a $2,500 annual appropriation and even closer ties to Yale and to science in its new staff of scientists: Johnson as chemist; Brewer as botanist; Sidney I. Smith, professor of comparative anatomy at Yale, as entomologist; and Dr. Noah Cressy of Middletown as veterinary surgeon. Although the board emerged from its crisis better staffed and funded than before, both the legislature and its Joint Committee on Agriculture had shown themselves divided on agricultural improvement—hostile at times but generous at other times. The reformers would have to pacify the one mood if they were to benefit from the other.[20]

Though Johnson had been unsuccessful in his 1856 attempt to have New York State establish an experiment station, he had not given up the cause and had used every opportunity since then to publicize the importance of such institutions. By 1871 a great many of the leaders of the movement for agricultural reform throughout the nation were aware of the stations and their work. The most effective advertisement for them was Johnson's strong endorsement in the introduction to his textbook *How Crops Grow* in 1868, which stressed that most of the work done on plant minerals had been done at the German agricultural experiment stations(p.24).

But certain other forces were pushing toward more sophisticated agricultural experimentation in the early 1870s. The Morrill Land-Grant Act of 1862 had put agricultural colleges under some pressure to perform experiments by requiring them to include in their annual reports the costs and results of any improvements or experiments they had made. The agricultural press was likewise continually calling for the solution of difficult points in agricultural science. As a result several states (Pennsylvania, Michigan, New Jersey, Massachusetts, Maine, Kansas, Illinois, Minnesota, Wisconsin, and Iowa) undertook various kinds of experiments before 1875. The work usually took place at the state college of agriculture or at an experimental farm; but even when they had the facilities, the administrators lacked the know-how necessary for worthwhile experiments. They readily admitted that their results were frustrating and useless, and in 1870 Ezra S. Carr called for an experiment station in California. But others preferred to band together to exchange ideas and advice before tackling their state legislatures.[21]

The first such meeting was the Convention of Friends of Agricultural Education, which met in Chicago in August 1871 and was attended by administrators of the major land-grant colleges. W. C. Flagg, secretary of the Board of Trustees of Illinois Industrial University and one of the organizers of the meeting, was a Yale graduate and an enthusiast for Johnson's textbooks and agricultural experiment stations. During the discussion of agricultural experiments, Flagg cited Johnson's favorable mention of the stations in his textbook, praised Johnson lavishly as "doing more to advance agricultural interests than any [other] men in the United States," and at the end of the two-day convention called for a resolution urging every state to establish at least one station. He called for a national committee to be formed to "memorialize Congress and the several State Legislatures for the speedy establishment of such stations throughout the country."[22]

The committee met again the next February (1872) as part of a three-day National Agricultural Convention in Washington called by Commissioner Frederick Watts, who was eager to extend federal ties to the state agricultural colleges. At this meeting Wilbur O. Atwater emerged as the driving force behind the movement for agricultural experiment stations when he read a strongly worded report to the convention. Atwater declared that the necessity of establishing such stations "scarcely need be discussed." Agricultural societies, geological commissions, boards of agriculture, and agricultural colleges had all undertaken "spasmodic," "imperfect," and "inadequate" experiments. The time had come to establish stations that would benefit the farmer with systematic experimentation. Cattle feeding and the role of nitrates in the soil were two pressing problems that would yield to such an attack. But experiments were costly, and the stations could not support themselves. The cost "need not be large" since the German stations functioned on $2,000–$5,000 per year, and some research would require only a "few hundreds" of dollars. The convention immediately suggested that Samuel Johnson write a report on the value of such stations. Unfortunately, a publisher could not be found, the report did not appear, and once again the group lost its momentum. Although the convention had publicized the stations and pulled together a national group who were interested in them, it had been unable to take effective action. That would be up to individuals in the various states, as it had been all along.[23]

Atwater went back to his professorship at Eastern Tennessee University but did not forget the experiment stations. He had just returned from two years in Leipzig and Berlin, had visited various stations in Saxony and Prussia, and had come to share Johnson's enthusiasm for them. He used his spare time in Tennessee to think and read more about the stations, and in January 1873 he wrote Johnson that he hoped to get a job soon in Connecticut in order to be close enough to Johnson to work with him on the experiment stations.

> I am very much interested in this Expt. Station business and am anxious to have something done about it. . . . As far as I see—you are the only prominent man who knows how to take hold of the matter—and I want to get in your wake—and am so presuming as to hope that in some way or other I might do something—do the part of organ blower while you play. . . . Of course you won't feel that I am trying to put myself forward in this matter.[24]

Later on, Johnson may well have had his doubts.

Atwater luckily obtained a job at his alma mater, Wesleyan University in Connecticut, in 1873 and began to plan with Johnson how to start a station in Connecticut. Their strategy was to whip up enthusiasm among the various agricultural groups across the state during the winter, converge on the Assembly's agricultural committee in the spring, and then lobby intensively for an appropriation in the summer. Unfortunately events were not to work out according to plan.

Their first effort was a speech on the subject of manures at the December 1873 Farmers' Convention in Meriden. Johnson introduced Atwater—who had earned a Ph.D. at the Sheffield School with a dissertation on Indian corn, studied abroad, and was now teaching chemistry at Wesleyan—by baiting the farmers into expecting more from him.

> He will do a good work there, educating young men in chemistry, but he could do a great deal better work for the State of

Connecticut, if the farmers of this State would take him away from that institution. They could easily find some one to teach them chemistry as well as he can, but there are not in this State, or in this North America, more than three or four men, out of our many millions, who can do more for agriculture in the next twenty or thirty years of activity which are before a young man of his age, than he can, by his previous studies, and by the facilities which he has enjoyed for the study of these matters.[25]

After this introduction, Atwater read his lecture "On Commercial Fertilizers at Home and Abroad," which skillfully appealed to the farmers' interest in financial gain and to their belief in science. The Germans, he reported, had formerly had some fertilizer frauds like the Americans, but the experiment stations had detected them so speedily that the average German fertilizer now had 1.75 times as much nitrogen and 3.1 times as much soluble phosphoric acid as Johnson had found in his most recent report on Connecticut fertilizers. The only way to rid Connecticut of fertilizer frauds, Atwater felt, was to establish an agricultural experiment station within the state. Besides, Atwater added, experiment stations offered more to farmers than fraud protection, for, in fact, "comparatively little of the labor of the German experiment stations is given to the analyses of fertilizers." Rather, "their chief work is the study of the broad and intricate questions of animal and vegetable nutrition, the learning of the laws of animal and vegetable growth."[26] The establishemnt of such a station in Connecticut would be an honor worthy of the illustrious history of the state.

Atwater's audience responded as hoped to his speech. One farmer wished to know the expense of such stations, which Atwater thought cost from $800 to $4,300 per year in Prussia, but would probably cost "considerably more" in the United States, or about $6,000 to start and $3,000 per year to run. Then, after Johnson had made another plea for a station, several men rose to say that the only obstacle to establishing such an experiment station in Connecticut was to convince the other farmers of its necessity. The first step was to form a committee to prepare a report within two days for further discussion.

This committee decided promptly and unanimously that Connecticut ought to have an experiment station "as good as can be found anywhere" and that the legislature ought to support it. They recommended the formation of a permanent committee to spread the idea throughout the state and to bring it before the legislature. The committee, which should consist of eight members, one from each county, should begin immediately and "work until the thing is done."[27]

In the next five months the committee arranged for seventeen meetings with farmers' clubs throughout the state. On each occasion Johnson, Atwater, Gold, Cressy (the veterinarian), and P. M. Augur (state pomologist) gave lectures on the value of agricultural experiment stations. The idea seemed to be popular with the farmers, for, as Gold reported to the board, "Wherever due notice had been given, the attendance was large, and the object of the committee, securing an agricultural Experiment Station in the State, was heartily endorsed."[28]

In addition to all this traveling and speaking, Johnson also managed to prepare his annual report on fertilizers in the spring of 1874. With the help of Edward H. Jenkins, who went on to have a long and distinguished career in agricultural chemistry, Johnson analyzed thirty-one fertilizers; but, finding few outright frauds, he used the report to make one final appeal to the farmers and to the legislature for an experiment station in Connecticut.[29]

Despite all this activity in behalf of the station, it was not popular with the legislature. The board submitted a bill on June 4, 1874, requesting the establishment of an agricultural experiment station with an annual appropriation of $8,000. The Joint Committee on Agriculture, to which it was referred, deferred action and eventually recommended that the bill be held over to the next session. The year 1873 had been a depression year, and $8,000 was a rather large request for a new project. The board might have fared better if it had asked for a smaller amount, but same legislators also objected to the idea of importing a German institution to tell them how to farm.[30] If not handled properly, the idea of importing a foreign institution could be very offensive to many persons, for not everyone was as eager as Edward Everett had been to bring German institutions to America.

Postponement was, however, better than defeat, and there was still hope for next year. Although greatly disappointed, Atwater and Johnson prepared to start over at the next Farmer's Convention in

December 1874. The topic was to be milk and its products, and Atwater could make an effective plea by discussing "Results of Late European Experiments on the Feeding of Cattle." Cattle-feeding researches, along with fertilizer and plant analyses, were the specialties of the German agricultural stations, which were trying to determine how to get the largest amount of work, meat, or milk from a cow on a given amount of fodder. This involved extensive analyses of the protein, carbohydrate, and fat content of all possible cattle foods; studies of the digestive capacities of different animals for different crops; and determinations of efficient daily rations.[31]

Since dairying was a growing industry in Connecticut in the 1870s, the audience was very interested in Atwater's subject. But the mood of the audience was significantly different from the year before. Samuel Johnson, who would have supported Atwater's paper with a plea for more research at an experiment station, was absent; and Orange Judd, the New York agricultural editor who had recently retired to Connecticut, was very much in evidence. Judd had had, he said, little faith in scientific agriculture since 1852 or 1853, when soil analysis and "Prof." Mapes had been shown to be such frauds, but now he had had a change of faith. He now thought that even if Atwater's experiments were not at present readily understandable, they would eventually yield better profits for farmers. Enthusiastic as Judd was, he lacked patience with lengthy scientific and legislative procedures. In Johnson's absence, Judd took command, with rapid and impressive results. His actions were to upset Johnson greatly, but he was to prove a far more effective leader and lobbyist than the professor had ever been.[32]

Judd's impatience and enthusiasm for the station were contagious, and the next day the farmers began to consider possible alternatives to state support. Their discussion brought out some valid fears of governmental control—legislators might demand practical results too soon, or the station might become a political machine. Perhaps a group of private citizens should form a society to support the station. Judd, a wealthy man and recent benefactor of Wesleyan University, then said forcefully that if the state would not support the station, there were those present who would. He was determined to carry the project through.[33]

Atwater was caught in a difficult position. Judd's conception of an experiment station was more utilitarian than Johnson's. Johnson and

Atwater had been stressing fertilizer analyses as a kind of opening wedge to the farmers. They really intended the experiment station to do researches on important points in agricultural science. They were afraid of a station tied to small, private support, which would be expected to produce only practical results, such as Judd seemed to be suggesting.

But Johnson was absent, Judd active, and Brewer sympathetic to Judd's point of view. Before long Judd proposed that they should all make contributions and have a station in operation before spring. Then they could go to the legislature in a better position to ask for their full $8,000. Judd's plan of bypassing the legislature for the present aroused a great deal of support. The members of the committee who had visited the legislature's Joint Committee on Agriculture the previous spring had been very displeased with their hostile reception and the "small" arguments they had encountered. They liked Judd's idea of taking things into their own hands at last:

> We want this question of cattle feed and various other questions settled as soon as possible, and therefore I suggest that without waiting for the Legislature, we make up a little sum here and commence the work at once. Prof. Atwater has some leisure, and he can employ an assistant, and put the thing in operation, under the direction of the Board. This would form a nucleus.[34]

Atwater immediately volunteered his time and $50, and Brewer $50. The next morning Judd had a list ready for those pledging contributions to sign. He expected that with $500–$600 Atwater and Johnson could do "quite respectable work," though "of course we cannot go into the question of feeding of cattle and the thousand other questions that legitimately belong to an experiment station. This is merely a preliminary plan." Despite its faults the plan seemed to satisfy all present. Atwater was pleased, and Judd felt triumphant. After all, the German stations had all been started by societies and later taken over by the government.

The only problem was that the absent Johnson became greatly enraged when he heard of Judd's campaign for private contributions, and throughout the spring he continued to ignore Judd's plan and support the state board's further appeals to the legislature for a full $8,000. There might not have been any real problem, except at the last minute, in early June 1875, Judd again "interfered" by introducing a separate resolution into the Senate offering $1,000 of his own money if the state would grant $700 per quarter for two years "to the college in this state which shall provide the most ample facilities for the establishment of an agricultural experiment station." The two bills were under consideration by the Joint Committee on Agriculture at the same time. Not surprisingly the cheaper one passed in July 1875, and Johnson's bill failed, although it might have failed anyhow. Johnson was depressed and angry at this second betrayal by his old friend Judd. Not only had Judd subverted the board's whole effort, but his offer of Atwater's services and the facilities of Judd Hall, the $100,000 laboratory he had recently donated to Wesleyan, meant that the nation's first experiment station was to be Atwater's at Wesleyan rather than his own at Yale. This was too much to bear.[35]

The moment of success became one of anger, embarrassment, and depression. Johnson was so stung by Judd's action that he advised Atwater to have nothing to do with Judd's schemes. Meanwhile Atwater, embarrassed and confused, had no choice but to carry on Judd's experiment station as best he could for two years. He was also under particular pressure to produce results that would convince a skeptical legislature that the station was worth a full appropriation in 1877. From its very first meeting, the station's Board of Control had to face the perennial problem that the ideal long-range experiments would not appeal to legislators. The board decided on October 12, 1875, "that more abstract scientific investigations would afford not only the proper, but also the most widely and permanently useful field of labor" for an experiment station, but "the need of a fertilizer control system was so pressing and so vital to the interests of a considerable portion of the farmers of the State that it seemed absolutely necessary to turn the first efforts in this direction."[36] It was hoped that this situation would be only temporary. Johnson may have responded later to Atwater's earnest pleas for help and apologies for the misunderstanding, but within a few months he left for an extended tour of Europe. His health was poor, but even more he was despondent. He knew, he wrote his wife from London in April 1876, that things were not always as they seemed, but it certainly seemed "as if there was nothing for me at home but discouragement."[37]

In retrospect it seems that Johnson was unduly frightened of private support. Norton had opposed it after seeing J. F. W. Johnston's difficulties with it, but they may have been due as much to the instability of the group as to the dangers inherent in private support. Certainly state legislatures could be as inconsistent. Besides, private support offered certain advantages; for example, the experiment station at Rothamstead, England, supported entirely by the private funds of philanthropist John Bennet Lawes, did outstanding research, unfettered by the burdens of fertilizer control. Johnson was familiar with Rothamstead and its work as early as the 1850s, since his friend Evan Pugh had been supported lavishly in his work there, but Johnson preferred to model his Connecticut station on the German government-supported ones. In the long run this was probably wise, since after 1887, when federal money was given to the stations, their appropriations far outstripped the ability of any philanthropist. But Johnson was too hasty and too rigid in opposing Judd's private subsidy in 1875. It helped the station get started and besides, as Johnson seemed slow to learn, government money had its problems too.

Atwater accordingly devoted his efforts for the next year and a half to developing a suitable fertilizer control system. Since Wesleyan was providing the laboratory and relieving him of some of his teaching duties, Atwater was able to use most of the state appropriation to hire a chemist and two assistants—Edward H. Jenkins, who had just returned from studies in Leipzig, and Georg Warnecke, formerly an assistant to Professor Knop at Leipzig. The station at Middletown started operation on January 1, 1876, and in its first full year of operation managed to analyze 162 fertilizers. Jenkins and Warnecke also started some seed investigations, which they had both learned from Professor Nobbe at the Tharandt experiment station in Germany, but the fertilizer work left them little time for a thorough study. As expected, the immediate demand for practical results was so great that research had to be squeezed in at considerable sacrifice or given up altogether.[38]

The campaign for an experiment station had been based on the promise that it would reduce fertilizer frauds within the state. It was up to Atwater to prove that the station had fulfilled this promise. If he could do so, and the station became permanent, it might get an appropriation large enough to do research in the future. Fortunately, Atwater was able to prove in January 1877 that such a benefit had taken place. When he compared the cost of nitrogen and phosphoric acid in fertilizers tested before the station was founded with that of those sold in the state after January 1, 1876, he found that the average cost had dropped over half. Nitrogen dropped spectacularly from 59.4c per pound to 24.9c, soluble phosphoric acid from 19.5c to 15.1c per pound, and insoluble phosphoric acid most dramatically of all from 21.1c to 5.6c per pound.[39] Atwater had done his job well despite the difficulties and early embarrassments.

Atwater's achievement put the State Board of Agriculture in a strong position when in January 1877 it submitted its proposal for renewal of the station to the legislature. The bill called for an annual appropriation of $5,000, still less than the original $8,000, and aimed to restore harmony by having Professor Johnson call the first meeting of the station's new Board of Control. To everyone's great delight, the proposal passed and was made into law on March 21, 1877. Judd's strategy of pump-priming, unwelcome as it had been in some quarters, had worked, and the state had taken over full support of the station. Unfortunately, the harmony was short-lived, and this time Judd and Atwater were the ones to feel hurt and stung by their allies.

Within a month of the bill's enactment, the new board elected Johnson the station's director, surprising Atwater, who had assumed that he would continue in office. After all, he had nursed "the puny child" to health and "set it on its feet." But this was not the only blow to the Middletown forces. Brewer, who represented the Sheffield School on the board, offered Johnson and the station a laboratory and an office at the school for five years free of charge. The board promptly accepted the offer and moved the station from Middletown to New Haven. Judd was upset at the change and attempted to fight back for a brief time, but Atwater painfully acquiesced and advised Judd to do so too, for the good of the station. A few days later Atwater wrote a member of the board that, though he had been upset, the decision "is not my funeral you know,"[40] and he went back to his fertilizer studies at Wesleyan. His subsequent career was at least as distingusihed as Johnson's, perhaps more so, for in 1888 he became the first director of both the new Connecticut station at Storrs and the new Office of Experiment Stations in Washington, D.C. From the latter post he coordinated the work of the more than forty experiment stations in existence at that time. In the 1890s he co-invented the Atwater-Rosa calorimeter and carried on extensive studies in human nutrition.

Johnson, for his part, devoted himself to his Yale professorship and the directorship of the New Haven station for the next twenty-four years. He used his fortunate dual position to train many of the experiment station leaders of the next generation, but the first ten years at the station must have been a disappointment to him. State support for fertilizer analyses was, as it turned out, not as easily converted into agricultural research as Johnson had hoped. In fact, the situation had probably worsened by the mid-1880s, for despite the building of a new $25,000 laboratory in suburban New Haven in 1882 and an increase in the annual appropriation to $8,000 in 1884, legislature passed a fertilizer law in 1882 that required even more regulatory work from the station than before. Fertilizer regulation, Johnson felt, was almost too popular for the good of the station. His annual reports throughout the 1880s state that "as usual," "the greater part of the time and labor of the operating force of this Station has been expended . . . in work connected with the collection and analysis of Commercial Fertilizers." In 1887 Johnson complained further of encroachments from the dairy commissioner, who wanted the station to analyze milk and molasses suspected of adulteration. Johnson's resistance was unsuccessful, for once the state had created a station, it wanted to use it for a growing number of related chemical needs. In the face of such heavy burdens, Johnson found it practically impossible to incorporate research into the station program before 1890. Nor could he even find time to work on his third textbook, *How Crops Are Fed,* which had been under way in 1877 but which now fell victim to his administrative duties at the station.[41]

The situation at the Connecticut station was typical of the dilemma of agricultural research (and much other governmental science as well) in the United States in 1880. The fertilizer argument had proven effective in getting state support, but legislators chose to interpret it narrowly as covering only regulatory work and routine testing, tasks that could rapidly consume most of a station's slender budget. Even the scientists were frequently surprised by how much time it took and complained they had no money left for research. But knowing that state legislators were wary of "research," the scientists would typically bid low for a $5,000 appropriation when they really wanted to do work costing $8,000 and then be dismayed when they could not squeeze it all in. They were disappointed that state support had not given them the free hand they had expected. The prospect of doing research while serving the public, which had seemed so natural a combination in Germany, where perhaps fundings and costs were different, faced tight budgetary restrictions in the United States around 1880.[42]

Scientists in other states meanwhile, were fighting for their own experiment stations. By 1880 three more stations had been established in California, North Carolina, and New Jersey, the last two modeled on Johnson's station and stressing fertilizer analysis. By 1886 the stations had spread to eleven more states, with those in the East and South tied strongly to fertilizer control. But here as elsewhere the advocates of stations and research always found state support inadequate.

Dissatisfaction with state funding began to mount during the 1880s, and the station directors and agricultural college administrators began to organize on the national level to work for federal funding for research. Now adept lobbyists, they attended conventions, passed resolutions, made speeches, and formed a committee to visit Congress. After three years of effort (1883–86) a bill was approved by the House Committee on Agriculture in 1886 and passed in 1887. This bill, known as the Hatch Act, allocated $15,000 per year to each experiment station for it to "conduct original researches or verify experiments." After this, and the subsequent passage of the Adams Act of 1906, which increased the amount for each station to $30,000, agricultural research was well supported in the United States.[43]

Many of the stations' glorious achievements—vitamins A and B, hybrid corn, and the Babcock milk test—all date from this later period after 1890. In the future they would thrive and blossom on American soil and form the basis for much of America's wealth and prosperity in the twentieth century, but by 1880 the progression from Liebig to the experiment station, so many years in the making, had been achieved and the transplanting of the first such institutions accomplished.

Conclusion

The years between 1840 and 1880 were a formative period for both science and agriculture in the United States. New fields emerged, old fields were transformed, and new institutions were established which would later develop into the vast "research establishment" of the twentieth century. In particular, the eminent German chemist Justus Liebig attracted great attention to chemistry and agriculture and stimulated lasting changes in these and related areas when in 1840 he held out the promise of guaranteed soil fertility in his epoch-making book *Organic Chemistry in Its Applications to Agriculture and Physiology*. By means of numerous editions and popularizations, Liebig's ideas became widely known in America, and between 1841 and 1852 interest in them reached craze proportions. The name Liebig aroused both positive and negative feelings, but to most Americans it came to personify agricultural chemistry and the progress of modern science.

Even more important and long-lasting for American science and agriculture than Liebig's widespread popular appeal was his influence on a small band of chemists, who went abroad to study with him and others. They returned to the United States ready to improve American science, education, and agriculture by importing European scientific institutions. As a result these few men played a far larger role in the development of science in America between 1840 and 1880 than their numbers would indicate.

By 1840 farmers in New England and New York were already talking of their "worn-out soil," a phenomenon which resulted from the continual cropping of poor soils. Under these worsening conditions, many eastern farmers, traditionally opposed to "book-farming,' turned increasingly to agricultural chemistry to learn how to restore their fields. When Liebig's first book appeared in America in 1841, it had a ready and enthusiastic audience. Farmers and scientists both agreed that it would open a new era for agriculture in America.

Liebig's ideas were the easiest part of his work to import into the United States. His books were rapidly reprinted and widely read. They were discussed in agricultural journals and mentioned in familiar terms into the 1860s. Liebig's ideas had great appeal because they seemed to solve the farmers' worn-out soil problem and predicted optimistically the dawning of a new age of rational agriculture. Rapidly as Liebig's ideas came to America, however, their transit was somewhat selective. His ideas came, criticisms of them by others did not. This deficiency, plus the lack of a strong group of chemists in America able to criticize his ideas, meant that Liebig aroused less controversy in America than he did in Germany and Britain. His image in America was unsullied by such episodes as the Liebig-Mulder controversy, which raged so fiercely in European chemical circles between 1845 and 1847, or the Liebig patent manure fiasco of 1845, which turned practical farmers against him in Britain. Those Americans who did criticize Liebig, such as Samuel L. Dana and John Pitkin Norton, coexisted with Liebig in the popular mind, which was already confused by the rapid succession of Liebig's ammonia and mineral theories on fertilizers between 1841 and 1845.

Several of Liebig's American students took up the multiple duties of institution building in the 1840s and 1850s. In particular, they worked to bring the chemical laboratory and the agricultural experiment station back to the United States, but these institutions were much more difficult to import than anyone had anticipated. Despite the best efforts of several of Liebig's strongest American students, these institutions were only partially successful before 1880. Favorable circumstances at Harvard made the first attempt possible in 1847. A vain and enthusiastic president, a willing philanthropist, and Eben Horsford, a young scholar, brought Liebig's laboratory, or at least the shell of it, speedily to Harvard, but even there high costs and an only modest demand prevented the full implementation of a German research laboratory in the United States in the 1850s. Circumstances were not even this favorable at Yale until 1858 when John A. Porter, another Liebig student, found a benefactor willing to give Yale a modern chemical laboratory also. After the Civil War, when the scale of American philanthropy increased so greatly that gifts for whole universities were not uncommon (Cornell, Johns Hopkins, Stanford, University of Chicago, to name the most prominent), college laboratories became standard gifts for lesser benefactors. But even then they frequently omitted funds for maintenance and assistants, and thus perpetuated Horsford's problem to this day.

The agricultural experiment station took far longer, however, to import into the United States, for Liebig had not at first been aware of its necessity. In fact, his stress on the sureness of his results and the simplicity of the subject obscured the need for systematic agricultural research until the mid-1850s. By then, when some of his American students visited the first agricultural experiment stations in Germany in 1854, such a reaction against Liebig's ineffective ideas and all agricultural chemistry had started in the United States that it was impossible to convince farmers and legislators to support such a station. The chemists had missed their chance. Twenty years later, in 1875, after numerous meetings, campaigns, reports, speeches, much lobbying and some bickering, S. W. Johnson and his friends were able to form the first American station, but with only a fraction of the $8,000 they wanted. Such stations were necessary and popular and spread rapidly throughout the country in the 1880s. Even so, tight budgets and heavy duties long restricted them to routine testing and regulatory activities and kept them from the agricultural research and experiments which their founders had envisioned, and which the Germans had been doing since the 1850s. State governments remained watchful and suspicious of "research" and "theory" for reasons not entirely undeserved by the chemists.

The research spirit of Liebig's laboratory and the German experiment station was the hardest part of German agricultural chemistry to introduce into America. Liebig's students were not able to bring it to America by 1880, for they encountered too many obstacles. Americans, it seemed, were eager to have the form of an institution, to be able to claim that their institution was the equivalent or better than any other elsewhere, but they were reluctant to go beyond this to provide the money for research, pure or applied, which was the heart of the German institutions. Even at Harvard, which had been so ready to build a laboratory better than Liebig's, Horsford soon found that Lawrence was unwilling to support a full-time researcher or to pay the cost of maintenance or assistants. Likewise, Johnson found that he had to make a tremendous fanfare about fertilizer frauds, even to the extent of overdramatizing it sometimes, in order to get $400 from the Connecticut agricultural society for continued police work and the chance to squeeze in some researches on peat or tobacco. Neither approach—the direct appeal to a philanthropist or the indirect appeal to a governmental institution—was very effective before 1880.

At least part of the difficulty in importing the spirit of subsidized research into America from Germany was the economic difference between the two countries at the time. The Americans were not only trying to import a new attitude, but they were facing unfavorable economic conditions. Horsford found that American and German salaries for professional men differed so much that maintaining the large laboratory staff common in Germany was prohibitively expensive. Besides, journals and chemicals, which cost relatively little in Giessen, were far costlier when imported to America. Those Americans trained in Germany who returned to work in the new laboratories and experiment stations faced the disappointment of trying to do research under difficult circumstances. Eventually, however, after a great deal of frustration and some effective appeals to the federal government, these returning students, some of whom were trained by Johnson, managed to introduce the idea of subsidized research into the American experiment stations in the 1890s.

Even though the state governments and American economy exerted pressure against research, a few enclaves, such as the laboratories at Harvard and Yale, were established by 1880. Yet even there, as Horsford's case shows, some personalities were not suited to disinterested research and were attracted to industrial applications. The existence in America of such lucrative opportunities, which had not existed in Germany in the 1850s, and the high cost of research facilities made it especially difficult for Liebig's American students to import a research spirit in chemistry. The problem was all the harder for those who wanted to do research in the public interest, as in agriculture, for it offered its practitioners few monetary rewards, and farmers were particularly tight-fisted and untrusting patrons. Not every personality was suited to such a vocation. It took selfless men like Norton and righteous men like Johnson to earn the farmers' trust, attract students to the field, and procure governmental support to legitimize their role as guardians of the people.

By 1880 the rudiments of a research establishment had come to American chemistry. Then, in succeeding decades, with the development of large-scale philanthropy and the Hatch and Adams Acts, research laboratories would proliferate at the universities, where

Wolcott Gibbs, J. P. Cooke, Ira Remsen, and Charles F. Chandler were already training the chemists of the next generation. Soon and every state would have at least one experiment station with a staff diversifying to bacteriological, biochemical, and, after 1900, genetical researches. In the twentieth century, this whole network of institutions would become the pride of American science and the envy of the world and thereby fulfill the early hopes of those who had fought so hard to bring them to America.

Reference Matter

Appendix 1

LIEBIG'S PUBLISHED BOOKS AND PAMPHLETS ON AGRICULTURE

Since many of Liebig's ideas on agriculture went through important modifications in the 1840s and 1850s, an improvised chronological listing of the various editions of his works seems necessary. Information is taken from the Library of Congress and British Museum catalogs and the Harvard and Yale Union card catalogs. For more information, see Carlo Paolini's *Justus von Liebig: Eine Bibliographie sämtlicher Veröffentlichungen* (Heidelberg:

Carl Winter, 1968), but it is very weak on American editions. One of the largest collections of Liebig's works in the United States is in the UniDel Collection, Morris Library, University of Delaware. Note that after 1842 the word *Organic* was dropped from *Organic Chemistry in Its Application to Agriculture and Physiology*.

Year	Title	Editor/Translator	Edition
1840	Die Organische Chemie in ihrer Anwendung auf Agricultur und Physiologie	—	1st (Braunschweig)
	Organic Chemistry in Its Application to Agriculture and Physiology	Playfair	1st (London)
1841	Organic Chemistry . . .	Playfair, Webster	1st Amer. from 1st London (Cambridge, Mass.)
	Ibid.	Play fair, Webster	2nd Amer. from 1st London (Cambridge, Mass.)
	Die Organische Chemie . . .	—	2nd (Braunschweig)
	Chimie organique appliquée a la physiologie végétale	Gerhardt	1st (Paris)
	Traité de chimie organique		"3e revue et corrigée" (Bruxelles)
1842	Die Organische Chemie . . .	—	4th Auflage (Braunschweig)
	[Organic] Chemistry . . .	Playfair	2nd (London) "with very numerous additions"

Year	Title	Translator/Editor	Edition (Place)
	Ibid.	Playfair, Webster	3rd Amer. from 2nd London (Cambridge, Mass.)
1843	Die [Organische] Chemie . . .	—	5th (Braunschweig) "ungearkeitete und sehr vermehrle Auflage"
	[Organic] Chemistry	Playfair	3rd (London) "revised and enlarged"
	Ibid.	Playfair	"From the last London edition [2nd] much improved" (Philadelphia) (New York)
	Ibid.	Playfair	(New York)
	Ibid.	Playfair, Webster	4th Amer. from 2nd London (Cambridge, Mass.)
	Familiar Letters on Chemistry and Its Relation to Commerce, Physiology, and Agriculture	Gardner	1st (London)
	Ibid.	Gardner	1st Amer (New York: Appleton)
	Ibid.	Gardner	1st Amer. (New York: Winchester)
1844	Chemische Briefe . . .	—	2nd (Braunschweig)
	Familiar Letters . . .	Gardner	2nd series (London)
	Chimie [organique]	Gerhardt	2nd (Paris)
1845	Chemische Briefe . . .	—	2nd (Heidelberg)
	Familiar Letters . . .	Gardner	3rd (London)
	Letters sur la Chimie . . .	Beret-Dupiney & Dubreuil-Helion	2nd (Paris)
	Address to the Agriculturalists of Great Britain, explaining the Principles and use of his artificial manures	—	(Liverpool)
	On Artificial Manures (also in U.S. Pat. Off. Rept., 1845)	—	(London)

Year	Title	Editor/Translator	Edition
1846	Die [Organische] Chemie	—	6th (Braunschweig)
	Uber die Grundsatze der kunstlichen Dungung in A. Petzholdt, Der neu erfundene Patent-Dunger . . .	—	
	Des engrais artificiels		(Paris)
1847	[Organic] Chemistry . . .	Playfair, Gregory	4th ed. (London) "revised and enlarged" 2 vols.
	Ibid.	Playfair, Gregory	"From the last London edition [2nd!] much improved" (Philadelphia)
	Ibid.	Playfair, Gregory	"From the 4th London ed., revised and enlarged" (New York: Wiley & Putnam)
	Chemistry and Its Appl. to Physiol., Ag., and Commerce [really an ed., of Familiar Letters]	Gardner	(New York)
	Letters sur la Chimie . . .	Gerhardt	"Nouvelle edition" (Paris)
	Chemische Untersuchung uber des Fleisch und seine Zubereitung zum Nahrungsmittel	—	(Heidelberg)
1848	Researches on the Chemistry of Food . . .	Gregory	(London)
	Untersuchungen uber einige Ursachen der Saftebewegung in thierischen Organismus	—	(Braunschweig)
	Researches on the Motion of Juices in the Animal Body	Gregory	(London)
1849	Researches on the Chemistry of Food . . .	Gregory, Horsford	(Lowell, Mass.)
	[Organic] Chemistry . . .	Gregory, Playfair	Amer. from 4th London "revised and enlarged"
1850	Complete works	—	1847 Philadelphia ed. with Animal Chemistry & new title page

Year	Title	Author(s)	Place / Edition
	Research on the Motion of Juices . . . together with an acct. of the origin of the potato disease . . .	Gregory, Playfair	(Philadelphia)
1851	Chemische Briefe . . .	—	3rd ed.
	Familiar Letters . . .	Gregory	3rd ed. (London) "revised and much enlarged"
1852	Nouvelles Letters . . .	Gerhardt	(Paris)
	Complete Works . . .		(Philadelphia)
(1853)			
1854	[Organic] Chemistry . . .	Playfair, Gregory	"From the 4th London ed. revised & enlarged" (New York)
1855	Die Grundsatze der Agricultur-Chimie mit Rucksicht auf die in England angestellten Untersuchungen	—	1st ed. (Braunschweig)
	Ibid.	—	2nd enlarged ed. with supplement (Braunschweig)
	Principles of Ag. Chem. with specific reference to late researches made in England	Gregory	(London)
	Ibid.	Gregory	(New York)
	The Relations of Chem. to Ag. and the Ag. Expts. of Mr. J. B. Lawes	S. W. Johnson	(Albany, N. Y.)
1856	Question des engrais	Picard	(Paris)
	Uber Theorie und Praxis in der Landwirtschaft	—	(Braunschweig)
(1857)			
(1858)			
1859	Die [Organische] Chemie . . .	—	4th rev. and enlarged edition (Leipzig), 2 vols.
	Chemische Briefe . . .	—	4th ed (Leipzig)
	Familiar Letters . . .	Blyth	4th ed. (London) enlarged

Year	Title	Editor/Translator	Edition
	Letters on Modern Agriculture	Blyth	(London)
	Ibid., "With addenda, by a practical agri-culturalist. Embracing valuable suggestions, adapted to the wants of American farmers."	Blyth	(New York)
(1860)			
1861	[Organic] Chemistry	Playfair, Gregory	From 4th London ed., revised and enlarged. (New York)
1862	Die [Organische] Chemie . . .	—	7th ed. (Braunschweig), 2 vols.
	Excerpts from above: "Einleitung in die Naturgesetze des Feldbaues"	—	(Braunschweig)
	Die moderne Landwirtschaft als Beispiel der Gemeinnutzkeit der Wissenschaften	—	(Braunschweig)
1863	"Natural Laws of Husbandry" (trans. of "Einleitung in die Naturgesetze". . .)	Blyth	(London)
	Ibid.	Blyth	(New York)
1864	Die [Organische] Chemie . . .		8th (Braunschweig) 2 vols. (Leipzig)
1865	Chemische Briefe . . .	Blyth	(London)
	Letters on the Subject of the Utilization of the Metropolitan Sewage, addressed to the Lord Mayor of London		(London)
(1866)			
1867	"Matiéres fertilisantes d'origine organique ou minerale," in Exposition Universelle de 1867, Rapports du Jury International, vol. 8	—	(Paris)
(1868)			
(1869)			
(1870)			

Year	Title	Editor/Translator	Edition
(1871)			
1872	[Organic] Chemistry	Gregory, Playfair	From 4th London ed., revised and enlarged
(1873)			
(1874)			
(1875)			
(1876)			
(1877)			
1878	Chemische Briefe	—	6th
(1879–1906)			
1907	Justus von Liebig und Emil L. F. Grussefeld Briefwechsel, 1862–66. 22 Briefe Liebigs, zugleich ein Beitrag zur Geschichte der Industrie Kunstlicher Dunger in Deutschland	—	(Leipzig)

Appendix 2

LIEBIG'S FOREIGN STUDENTS AT GIESSEN

The double dates (e.g. 1829–30) are for the winter semester; the single dates (e.g. 1830) are for the summer semester.

Year	Total	New	French	Swiss	British	American	Russian	Other
1829–30	1	1	C. F. Oppérmann	—	—	—	—	—
1830	1	0	(C. F. O.)	—	—	—	—	—
1830–31	0	0	—	—	—	—	—	—
1831	2	2	E. Ehrmann D. Widmann	—	—	—	—	—
1831–32	1	1	J. Gay-Lussac	—	—	—	—	—
1832	1	0	(J. G.-L.)	—	—	—	—	—
1832–33	1	1	—	G. T. Blanchet*	—	—	—	—
1833	0	0	—	—	—	—	—	—
1833–34	0	0	—	—	—	—	—	—
1834	0	0	—	—	—	—	—	—
1834–35	0	0	—	—	—	—	—	—
1835	0	0	—	—	—	—	—	—
1835–36	0	0	—	—	—	—	—	—
1836	2	2	C. Demarcay E. Eckel	—	—	—	—	—
1836–37	4	2	(C. D.) (E. E.) C. F. Gerhardt	—	T. Richardson	—	—	—
1837	5	3	(C. D.)	—	(T. R.) W. Eatwell T. Thomson	—	—	C. Mertzdorff (Belgium)

Year			M. Dollfuss			H. Steiner		A. Woscresensky	J. Thaulow (Norway)
1837–38	3	3	—	—	—	—	—	(A. W.)	(J. T.)
1838	7	4	—	—	(H. S.), P. Plantomour	R. Campbell, W. Macfarlane (W. Mac.), W. Cameron	—	—	E. Hering (?)
1838–39	7	5	—	—	(H. S.), T. Gindroz, R. F. Kocher, F. Schnell, T. Schnell	(W. C.), J. L. Bullock, A. Mitchel, J. Stenhouse	—	—	—
1839	8	3	—	—	(P. P.), (R. F. K.), (F. S.), (T. S.)	(W. C.), M. Detmar, E. A. Pinto, L. Playfair	—	—	—
1839–40	8	5	—	—	(F. S.), (T. S.), F. Chollet	(J. S.), (E. A. P.), (L. P.), R. Smith	—	—	V. Ortigosa (Mexico)
1840	7	2	—	—	(F. C.)	(E. A. P.), (L. P.), (R. S.), T. Thilley	—	C. Rutsch	(V. O.)
1840–41	10	6	M. Dollfuss, C. Marignac	—	F. Wydler, R. Wydler, W. Wydler	(E. A. P.), (T. T.), H. B. Jones, W. Radcliff	—	—	(V. O.)
1841	11	4	(M. D.), L. Jagle	—	(F. W.), (R. W.), (W. W.), T. Schnider	—	—	—	(V. O.)

Year	Total	New	French	Swiss	British	American	Russian	Other
1841–42	15	8	(M. D.) (L. J.) J. A. Hartmann	(F. W.) (R. W.)	(E. A. P.) (W. R.) J. A. Bernays J. Boyd W. Francis	J. L. Smith	F. Ilisch*	(V. O.) A. Hirschmann (Poland) H. Jesovits (Austria)
1842	17	6	(M. D.) (L. J.)	(R. W.) M. F. Gougginsberg	(E. A. P.) (W. R.)	—	(F. I.)	(V. O.) (H. J.)
			(J. A. H.) C. A. Wurtz	J. J. Hofstetter	(J. A. B.) (J. B.) C. J. Dunlope E. Ronalds			M. Iberzabel (Spain)
1842–43	17	9	(M. D.) (L. J.) (J. A. H.)	(M. F. G.) (J. J. H.) H. Reynier R. Schmid C. Stahlein J. Tschudy	(J. B.) W. Bastick C. M. Boyd W. Sullivan	—	(F. I.)	(M. I.) F. Rochleder (Austria) M. Peyrone (Italy)
1843	21	11	(L. J.)	(J. J. H.) (H. R.) (R. S.) (C. S.) (J. T.) J. L. Meyer* F. H. L. Sacc	(J. B.) (W. B.) J. Blake J. B. Blyth J. S. Muspratt F. Muspratt	—	A. Tischo-mandrizky	(F. R.) (M. P.) A. Sobrero (Italy) T. Schlosser (Austria) J. Theyer (Austria) G. W. Bichon (Holland)
1843–44	20	6	(L. J.)	(C. S.)	(W. S.)	—	(F. I.)	(T. S.)

1844	20		(J. L. M.) (F. H. L. S.) A. Ruef	(J. Blake) (J. B. B.) (J. S. M.) (F. S. M.) T. Anderson H. James C. J. Magnay		(A. T.) A. Chodnew	(J. T.) (G. W. B.) G. Kayser (Austria)
	9	(L. J.) H. A. Kochlin	(F. H. L. S.) (A. R.) J. J. F. Archinard F. Bernoulli	(W. S.) (J. B. B.) (J. S. M.) (F. M.) (H. J.) (C. J. M.) J. Allan K. F. O. Glassford A. Williamson F. Wightson	—	(A. C.)	(M. P.) F. Ragsky (Austria) E. Waidele (Austria)
1844–45	17	8	J. E. Hochstetter	(A. R.) (J. J. F. A.)	(J. B. B.) (J. S. M.) (H. J.) (A. J.) (A. W.) (F. W.) B. C. Brodie A. Crum	E. N. Horsford	(F. R.) P. Iljenkow I. Kossow N. Laskowsky	H. M. Golgau (Sweden)
1845	17	6	(J. E. H.) J. K. Meyer	(A. R.)	(H. J.) (A. W.)	(E. N. H.)	(I. K.)	(F. R.) J. Amburger J. Namur (Luxemburg)

Year	Total	New	French	Swiss	British	American	Russian	Other
			F. J. Nickles		(F. W.) (B. C. B.) (A. C.) J. F. Hodges	(E. N. H.)		A. Hessen (H. M. G.)
1845–46	14	6	(J. K. M.) J. M. Laderich	(A. R.)	(H. J.) (A. C.) T. Clunie* A. J. Jamieson R. Maddrell C. Wornum	(E. N. H.)	(N. L.) (J. A.) A. Polunin	(J. N.)
1846	12	7	(J. M. L.) K. Dollfuss	K. Matthieu E. Schulthess	(J. A.) (A. J. J.) (R. M.)	(E. N. H.)	K. E. Glasson	L. Bodgan (Transylvania) F. Janosy (Transylvania) A. von Zeyk (Transylvania)
1846–47	15	10	(K. D.)	(E. S.) K. Fischer J. Papon J. Schilt A. von Planta-Reichenau	(J. A.) (R. M.) J. Crichton J. R. Rogers	W. Gibbs O. Mayer T. J. Summer J. D. Whitney	(K. E. G.)	—
1847	10	5	—	(E. S.) (K. F.) (J. P.)	(J. R. R.) S. Darby* T. Lindsay D. S. Price	(T. J. S.) S. G. Rosengarten	—	A. von Vajna (Transylvania)
1847–48	12	8	—	(J. P.) F. Pfleger	(F. M.) J. H. Gladstone	(T. J. S.) B. W. Bull K. Harris	—	—

					B. H. Paul H. E. Schedel	J. A. Porter		
1848	12	4	G. F. C. Thurneyssen	(J. P.) (F. P.) B. L. Bufard	(S. D.) (D. S. P.) (S. D.) H. Bailey B. Halcrow	K. Wetherill (T. J. S.) (B. W. B.) (K. H.) (J. A. P.) (K. W.)	—	—
1848–49	11	8	E. Haffely	(J. P.) W. Pigott	(B. H.) J. Brown J. Stein	(J. A. P.) K. Johnson F. Lennig	—	T. Sittig (Austria) K. Stammer (Luxemburg)
1849	13	3	(E. H.)	(W. P.) T. Kohler R. Marty	(B. H.) (J. S.) J. Kyd	(J. A. P.) (K. J.) (F. L.)	—	(A. von V.) (T. S.) (K. S.) (A. von V.)
1849–50	8	2	—	(T. K.) (R. M.)	(B. H.) (J. K.) W. Wallace	(K. J.)	—	—
1850	9	6	P. Jagor	J. Ziegler (J. Z.) A. Rohr	(J. K.) L. Cane K. Mackenzie E. Muspratt	(K. J.)	N. Socoloff	
1850–51	7	3	(J. P.)	G. von Tribolet	(E. M.)	(K. J.)	W. L. Faber (N. S.)	—
1851	12	4	(J. P.) J. Risler	(J. Z.) (G. v. T.) (J. Z.)	J. Carnegie J. Krüger (J. Kyd)	(K. J.)	(N. S.)	F. Zedler (Denmark)

Year	Total	New	French	Swiss	British	American	Russian	Other
					(K. M.) (E. M.)			
1851–52	9	5	(J. P.)	H. Sulzer	W. Squire (J. Krüger) (E. M.)	B. Phillips G. Tucker (K. J.)	—	J. Riedl (Prague)
1852	10	5	P. von Clement	(H. S.)	G. Brown A. Fergusson A. Mattiesen (E. M.) (W. S.)	(B. P.)	V. Moschinin (J. R.)	
TOTALS:			23 students (48 semesters)	38 students (85 semesters)	65 students (134 semesters)	16 students (36 semesters)	14 students (26 semesters)	26 students (34 semesters)

*Designation "pharmacy" added to name

( ) Re-enrolled

SOURCES: (1829–50) Taken from "Personalverzeichnis der Universität" and published in Armin Wankmüller, "Auslandische Studierende der Pharmazie und Chemie bei Liebig in Giessen," Tübinger Apothekengeschichtliche Abhandlungen, Heft 15 (Stuttgart: Deutscher Apotheker-Verlag), reprinted from Deutsche Apotheker-Zeitung (vereinigt mit Süddeutsche Apotheker-Zeitung), Zeitschrift für praktische und wissenschaftliche Pharmazie 107 (1967) : 463–66, Appendix. This is the most complete list I have seen, although it is not entirely trustworthy. (1850–52) Private communication to author from W. Leist, Bibl. Rat, Universitätsbibliothek, Giessen, December 10, 1970.

Appendix 3

AMERICAN STUDENTS IN MUNICH, 1852–1872

Winter 1853–54

Name	City	Subject	Note
Brownson, Henry	Boston	Philosophie	(1835–1913) Son of Orestes Brownson, studied with Döllinger at Munich; later soldier, author, and lawyer. *National Cyclopedia of American Biography*, 16: 436.
Fischer, [I.] Davenport	Boston	Naturwissenschaft	(1832–1911) Graduate of R.P.I., studied with Liebig, taught at Annapolis 6 years, analytical chemist in Milwaukee. Private communication from Milwaukee County Historical Society, Dec. 16, 1969.
Brush, George J.	Brooklyn	Philosophie	(1831–1912) Studied at Yale Analytical Laboratory, 1848–50; B. Silliman, Jr.'s assistant in Louisville and abroad, 1850–51; Yale Ph.B., 1852; 1853–55, in Munich with Liebig, von Kobell, and Pettenkoffer and at Freiberg; professor of metallurgy and mineralogy at Sheffield School, 1857–98. *AJS*, 4th ser., 33 (1912): 389–96.
Johnson, Samuel Weld, Mason Cogswell	Kingboro [N.Y.] Hartford	Philosophie Chemie	See chapters 8 and 9. (1829–87) Student at Yale Analytical Laboratory and Silliman's assistant, 1848–53; studied with Liebig and Bunsen; editor of *Homestead*, 1855–60; 1862–63, Colonel in Connecticut Regiment; staff of *American Agriculturalist*; authority on

Weyman, George W.	Pittsburgh	Philosophie	cattle-breeding. *Obituary Records of Graduates of Yale University*, 1888. Student at Yale Analytical Laboratory; subsequently analytical chemist and druggist in Pittsburgh. Private communication from Historical Society of Western Pennsylvania, Dec. 16, 1969.
Summer 1855			
Clarck, Eduard Emerson, Lincoln	Monterey	Chemie Philosophie	(See T.E. Clark, below) (1829–64) Nephew of Geo. B. Emerson; Bowdoin, class of 1849; studied medicine but taught at uncle's private school in Boston. B. K. Emerson, *The Ipswich Emersons, A.D. 1636–1900* (Boston: D. Clapp & Son, 1900), p. 327.
Winter 1856–57			
Brewer, William H.	Ithaca	Chemie	(1828–1910) Studied at Yale Analytical Laboratory, 1848–50; taught in academies and agricultural colleges in N.Y., studied with Liebig in Munich, also at Heidelberg and Paris; on California Geological Survey, 1860–64, and professor of agriculture at Yale after 1864. *AJS* 31 (1911): 71–74.
Clark, T. Edwards	Monterey [Mass.]	Chemie	Graduated University of N.Y., 1849; Agassiz's assistant and Harvard B.S., 1854; Göttingen Ph.D.; professor of chemistry, Williams College, 1858–66; M.D., Columbia, 1866; physician in N.Y.C. Calvin Durfee, *Williams Biog. Annals* (Boston: Lee & Shepard, 1871).

Summer 1859			
Marsh, Edward	New York	Philosophie	———
Winter 1859–60			
Bahlmann, Wilfriedrich	New York	Philosophie	———
Marsh, John Edward	New York	Philosophie	———
Raymond, Rossiter	Brooklyn	Chemie	(1840–1911) Eminent mining engineer; studied with Liebig, with Bunsen, and at Freiberg. *DAB.*
Winter 1860–61			
Brewerton, Henry Feltus	Baltimore	Philosophie	(1838–1913) Son of superintendent of West Point, became military officer who served with distinction in Union Army; retired 1892 as lieutenant colonel. *New York Times,* Nov. 3, 1913, p. 9.
Hobbes, Flint Cl. Joshua	Boston	Philosophie	———
James, Frank	Mobile	Chemie	(1842–1907) Studied with Liebig; blew up federal gunboats in Civil War; fled to Japan until 1877; subsequently physician and microscopist in St. Louis. *National Cyclopedia of American Biography* 12: 226, and *New York Times* May 21, 1907, p. 9.
Olds, Nelson	New York	Philosophie	———
Summer 1861			
Howell, Francis	Philadelphia	Philosophie	———
Patterson, James	Philadelphia	Philosophie	———
Winter 1861–62			
Chapman, Coleman [Jr.]	Louisville	Naturwissenschaft	(1843–1917) For 20 years First Secretary to American Legation in Berlin; later American consul in Rome; trans. German novels. Private communication from Filson Club, Jan. 6, 1970.

Hart, Amos	Guilford [Conn.?]	Philosophie	May have been the Amos W. Hart who wrote digests of patent decisions, 1886–96.
Winter 1864–65			
Baumgartner, Fr. X.	Milwaukee	Chemie	——
Bowman, Amos	Kent Co.	Philosophie	——
Donaldson, Thomas	Baltimore	Naturwissenschaft	——
Winter 1866–67			
Weber, Heinrich	Columbus [Ohio]	Chemie	(1845–1912) Studied with Liebig; chemist on Ohio Geological Survey, 1869–74; professor at University of Illinois, 1874–82; professor of agricultural chemistry at Ohio State, 1884–1912; interested in sorghum and pure food reform. *DAB.*
Summer 1867			
Renouf, Eduard	Lowville [N.Y.]	Chemie	(1846–1922) Studied at Boston grammar schools, Heidelberg, Jena, Munich, and Freiberg (Ph. D., 1870); Volhard's assistant at Munich, 1880–85; professor at Johns Hopkins, 1885–1911. *Who's Who in America*, 1922–23.
Winter 1867–68			
Remsen, Ira	New York	Chemie	(1846–1927) Attended College of City of N.Y.; M. D., Columbia, 1867; studied with Volhard (Liebig's privatdocent) in Munich, Wöhler at Göttingen, Ph. D. 1870; assistant to Fittig at Tübingen 1870–72; professor at Williams College and Johns Hopkins, 1876–1901; president, 1901–13. *DAB.*

Summer 1868			
Minor, Charles	Stanford [Stamford?]	Philosophie	
Beed [Reed?], John	Frankfort	Philosophie	
Winter 1869–70			
Fröbel, Wilhelm	New Orleans	Naturwissenschaft	
Roper, Jourdan	Bowling Green, Va.	Philosophie	(1844–94) Philadelphia lawyer though became totally blind. Obituary in *Philadelphia Evening Bulletin*, Jan. 4, 1894, p. 6.
Summer 1870			
Dyer, Louis	Chicago	Philosophie	(1851–1908) Son of physician-lawyer, educated at Geneva, University of Chicago, Munich, Harvard, Oxford; professor of classics at Harvard, 1881–87; subsequently at Oxford. *DAB*.
Winter 1871–72			
King, Arthur	New York	Philosophie	
Regensburger, Martin	San Francisco	Philosophie	Professor of venereal diseases and dermatology, Univ. of Calif., Berkeley, 1892–1906. Private communication from Calfornia Historical Society, Dec. 19, 1969.

SOURCE: List prepared from Studentenverzeichnisse der Universität Archiv, Munich, in private communication to Margaret Rossiter, by Harald Dickerhoff of Ludwig-Maximilians Univer-sität July 22, 1969.

Appendix 4

Eben Horsford's Letter to the Harvard Corporation
on the State of the Lawrence Scientific School,
April 1854

To The Committee of Conference
on the part of the
President and Fellows of Harvard College:

In submitting a plan for the better organization of the Department of the Rumford Professorship, it seems necessary briefly to review its past and present condition.

Soon after my appointment, now more than seven years since, I laid before the President and Treasurer of the College a plan for a Laboratory for Instruction and Research in Chemistry, contemplating a sum of *fifty thousand dollars.* Twenty thousand dollars or more might, I conceived, be required for the erection and furnishing of a laboratory. The remainder of the sum I proposed to set apart as a *fund the income of which should be devoted to the support of the laboratory.*

As the necessity for the present interview is to be traced to a difference of opinion with regard to this proposition, it will not, I trust, be deemed out of place, if I state the principal reasons which led to the views I entertained.

I had just returned from a residence of two years at Giessen where I had become acquainted with the organization of the laboratory of Prof. Liebig. He had, beside a laboratory, well appointed, and a residence rent-free, the income of the compulsory attendance upon his lectures of a considerable medical class, all the fees of his pupils, a salary of three thousand florins and a nearly equal sum for the support of his laboratory. He was fortunately situated in a town where the expenses of living were very moderate, even for Germany, and the supplies for carrying on a laboratory were near at hand and comparatively cheap. Three thousand florins in Giessen, in view of what they will purchase in supplies either for the laboratory or household, are fully the equivalent of as many dollars in Cambridge.

With all these aids and the income from his published works, Prof. Liebig was living in straitened circumstances.

To carry on his laboratory he had three most competent assistants, a janitor and two servants. In the different branches of chemistry in the University there were five other Professors and Privat-Docents who furnished an aggregate of sixteen courses of lectures annually. There were beside these lectures on chemistry in its various branches, four courses of extended lectures on Physics, which were attended generally by the chemical students.

The students of the laboratory were most of them university men, who had already pursued chemistry, more or less, elsewhere. Liebig gave no elementary instruction—indeed all who entered the laboratory of Prof. Will where most remained a year before joining Prof. Liebig's laboratory, had previously passed through a course of pharmacy with an apothecary, or had listened to courses of illustrated lectures on chemistry and physics. As a consequence, they came to Prof. Liebig's already versed in the principles of experimental chemistry.

From such persons, so qualified, came the students, the progress and the research of Liebig's laboratory.

Admonished by the recollection of all these facilities for carrying forward a laboratory of analytical instruction and research, I foresaw that success in America would depend not alone upon well directed effort, but in great measure upon independent pecuniary support. Beside the appropriate duties of the Rumford Professorship, to wit, investigations in the applications of science to the useful arts, there was required a great amount of instruction in elementary and auxiliary science, in addition to the proper duties of analytical instruction in Chemistry, in order to [guarantee] the success of the laboratory. The successful performance of these varied duties required the cooperation of qualified men.

So far as I am informed, no laboratory for systematic instruction in analysis and experimental investigation has been found self-sustaining. A letter from Professor Hoffmann the Director of the Royal Chemical College London, who was an assistant to Liebig when I was at Giessen, and whose facilities in London were much greater than they have been in Cambridge, states that while the annual income of his laboratory was but about £600, the expenses were £1800. This deficiency was at the outset and is probably less now. The School has passed under the patronage of the Government. Professor Booth of Philadelphia, for a long time the first practical analyst in the country and now the assayer at the mint informs me a few weeks since that taking into account all the receipts for analyses and all the fees from pupils in his laboratory he is entirely satisfied if the income equals the expenditures. The late Professor Norton, who, with Professor Silliman Jr. opened a laboratory for analytical instruction in New Haven, stated to me at the close of the second year, that giving his own and Professor Silliman's services, and taking into account all receipts for analyses and instruction, the total income had exceeded the expenditure of that year by the sum of nineteen dollars. The fees at both the last mentioned institutions are higher than at Cambridge.

Beside the arrangement of a laboratory to meet the wants of a class and to a considerable extent the organization of a system of instruction, there was a serious difficulty to be encountered in the want of suitable apparatus except at prices that would greatly enhance the expense of a chemical education. It became necessary therefore to import these needed supplies and to keep a salesroom of such articles for the use of students: and this must be done by the laboratory, or so indifferently done as to fail of its object.

Such a salesroom in Giessen was owned and conducted by the Janitor of the laboratory, the director of the laboratory having nothing to do with it. But here no janitor could be induced to conduct importations from France and Germany. I had to do it myself in behalf of the laboratory.

It was in the full conviction of the responsibility that rested upon me that I urged the bestowment of a fund for the support of the laboratory. It was however believed, on the other hand, that the number of students able to pay fully for chemical education would be large—large enough to more than meet all the expenses of the laboratory: so much more than enough that the excess would be at least $1500, so that the salary of the Professor would altogether amount to $3000 annually. From there having been no similar establishment in the country, it was not easy to convince others that the expenses of continual chemical experimenting must be very large, as compared with the expenses of most ordinary instruction: and there seemed to be no alternative, in view of the munificence which laid the foundation of the school, but to go forward as cheerfully and enthusiastically as one might, towards the fulfillment of expectations that he felt could not be realized. It may be due to myself to say that from the outset, for the first five years, I devoted my entire energies to daily exhaustion to the duties of the department, and I do not hesitate to affirm that I believe there is no laboratory in the world where the amount of special instruction is equal to that in my own, or where the progress is so rapid. I beg to quote a paragraph from a letter written by one of my students now in a laboratory in Munich, to one of his fellow students still with me. "I work from 8 to 11 daily and on Wednesday and Saturday from 8 till 1. Very inconvenient working so short a time, and consequently don't get along very fast. Laboratory miserable, as all these laboratories here seem compared to our palace of a laboratory at Cambridge. There is no such one in Europe. I have wished myself many a time in our nice clean roomy laboratory. You don't know what a blessing you enjoy in that same laboratory."

I found that the students who came to the laboratory instead of being chiefly college graduates or from the better classes of other institutions and well qualified, as had been expected, were for the most part but indifferently prepared; a large proportion were unacquainted with the elementary principles of the science; many had enjoyed little mental training of any kind; some came who had failed to enter college; and others because their parents did not know where else to send them; and but a small proportion were qualified to profit by the advantages of such a laboratory. The same want of preparation is felt in a greater or less degree in the departments of Zoology and Engineering, but not, it is true with the same results. In the former all are rejected who do not give promise that they will substantially profit by the advantages provided; and the consequence is Professor Agassiz has never more than two or three special students. In the department of engineering the general qualification is better, for the mathematics are taught more or less in all the higher schools; and the number of applications is so great that Prof. Eustis can decline to receive such as are not prepared. I would gladly have elevated the standard of admission, requiring the students to go through elementary preparation elsewhere. But there were two insurmountable objections to this course. There seemed to be no other place where the elementary instruction could be so well obtained; and I could not reject any who might apply, solely because the income was necessary to carry on the laboratory; and further it seemed desirable to have the appearance of success which attends upon numbers.

Of the students so received, a third perhaps came with the intention of remaining but one term, and a third of the remainder find themselves without taste or capacity for the study, or so deficient in general training as to become disheartened in view of the more rapid progress of some of their associates. A still larger proportion, including always the best scholars, find the expenses of tuition, apparatus, supplies and living in Cambridge so high as to shorten their stay, and make their acquisitions but indifferently creditable to the school or serviceable to themselves. Nevertheless in the winter term the number of special students has uniformly been above twenty. It was last term twenty-six. It has once been as high as twenty-nine. The number in the summer term has varied from twelve to twenty. It is now fifteen. It may be proper to add that the number in Liebig's laboratory did not while I was there exceed twenty-five, and for a part of the time was but eighteen; and before Professor Liebig left for Munich it fell to twelve. This laboratory it may not be known, has been founded about thirty years, and during the first ten years of its existence the number of pupils at no time exceeded six. The laboratory now being constructed in Munich for this Great Master, is designed to accommodate but twelve. Each student will have an apartment exclusively to himself.

Professor Liebig gave, as I have before intimated no elementary instruction, but confined himself to a course of lectures, the supervision of his laboratory and to researches conducted by his pupils, assistants and himself. I have been obliged to give all the instruction of whatever kind that is required. Indeed, I shall scarcely overstate the fact when I add that it seems to have been expected by some, that all that was done in Giessen by five eminent men, in the way of elementary instruction, lectures, special instruction and research in chemistry, would be accomplished in Cambridge, whatever might be the character of students presenting themselves, by a single person with a salary of $1500 a year.

Special instruction in chemistry requires that each student shall be a class by himself, and if the numbers of students be large, it leaves the tone of mind too depressed to make lecturing possible, and I was obliged to give it up. In the absence of stated lectures, I have given my time to special instruction at the desk, where alone the arts of manipulation can be taught, to class exercises on the black-board in formulae + calculation, and to the reading + criticism of papers written on assigned themes. The volumes which are herewith submitted are the production of one of my pupils, and represent about a year and half of work.

It is not to be denied that the demand for sound chemistry is less in America than I had anticipated. The applicants for instruction have been numerous enough had they come prepared, and willing to give the requisite time to the acquisition of the science. But aside from the indifferent qualification and training which most brought with them, they brought also, unfortunately, an expectation to master the science in a few months. No measure of effort on the part of an instructor could meet such expectations, under such circumstances.

I was impressed from an early period that no one mind could well perform the two classes of duties which a juncture of circumstances had thrown upon me, to wit, the elementary instruction on the one hand, and instruction of a higher order and experimental investigation on the other.

The prosecution of researches requires time for study and reflection. Processes must be thought out, and experiments elaborated, and there must be the possibility of rest when the mind is overtasked. This relief the constant drilling of elementary instruction does not permit. I need hardly say what would have been the consequences to my colleagues, Professors Agassiz, Gray + Wyman and their departments, had they been required to conduct each twenty special students whatever might have been their qualification through courses of systematic instruction from the most elementary to the highest in their several branches. It would be nothing less than this. First of all there would have been little or no research––one of the glories of our ancient University––, and then the instruction itself would in time from the exhaustion of the officer, have fallen in time to the drilling of a primary school. And it should be remembered too, that as an art to be taught and acquired, chemistry is of vastly more difficult achievement than Zoology, Botany or Comparative Anatomy.

After struggling to no inconsiderable personal detriment with duties too numerous and various and expectations and demands oppressive to a degree, one in another less zealous profession will find it difficult to conceive,—after struggling—till I felt the correctness of my earlier representations fully demonstrated, I conceived the idea a little more than a year since, of securing by my own efforts in industrial investigation, an income that should enable me to employ adequate aid in elementary instruction, and at the same time carry forward research in the legitimate sphere of my professorship. I thought that such time as I might command for two or three years devoted to purely industrial questions would, by securing a tariff on manufactures, bring me an income sufficiently large to relieve myself and the department pecuniarily. Accordingly I employed a competent assistant to aid me in this work and have been able since then to do something in furtherance of the end I had proposed to myself.

The duty and propriety of this course were subjects of conversation with several of my colleagues, and with other gentlemen connected with the University whose opinions I conceived to be safe guides. It was approved without a dissenting voice. My salary of $1500 a year was, I need not say inadequate to the expenses of a family in Cambridge. The income of the laboratory has been at the best but little above its expenditures. Of my immediate colleagues, Professor Eustis has a stated salary equal to my own. The circumstance that the expenses attendant upon instruction in engineering are small, permits a large portion of the fees to go to increase the salary of the Professor. Yet notwithstanding the economy that marks this department, the surplus income has not always amounted to the limit of the professor's salary from fees of pupils, to wit, $1500, to say nothing of the impossibility of providing for the higher wants of the classes in models, apparatus and books. The official position, in point of salary of the head of the department of Zoology and Geology is the same as my own, but it is known to me that in order to carry on his investigations, he has been compelled to earn from without the school from $3500 to $5000 a year. In the mere matter of the collection, since it was purchased by the University, I have seen in his account book the record of expenditures in preserving and increasing the collection to an amount of no less than $3700. It is fortunate for him and doubly fortunate for science that my distinguished colleague has the time for lectures and scientific services elsewhere, which enable him to meet the wants of his family, and without the income from which, it would have been utterly impossible to carry on the brilliant researches which have been the pride of the school and the country.

The necessity of the elementary instruction made it my fortune to be oppressed pecuniarily and professionally. In attempting to do what seemed to be required, I was compelled almost to lose sight of the objects which as a scientific man I had placed before myself.

Such has been the history and such is the present condition of the laboratory.

The plan for the modification of my department which I have for some time entertained, and which has the sanction of Professors Agassiz, Peirce, Gray, Eustis, Jeffries Wyman + Professor Treadwell—to all of whom I have submitted this communication is the following.

To divide the duties of the department assigning the elementary instruction to one officer and the advanced instruction and the duties of the Rumford Professorship to the other.

The upper floor of the laboratory and its appointments might be given to me and the lower floor to the other.

With this arrangement the Rumford Professor would be enabled to fulfil his legitimate duties in the investigation of questions relating to the application of the sciences to the useful arts, duties, which the present organization leave it quite impossible to perform.

This arrangement would provide for a course of lectures to be delivered to undergraduates, as has been the usage by my predecessors, and which the students in chemistry might attend.

It would give to the officer having charge of the more advanced students, time and lessened care for the study and reflection, which would enable him better to conduct his students in research. The number of pupils would be very much less in this department than in the other, and the compensation from this source less, but the deficiency might be met by incidental services to manufacturing interests.

Students might be received into the elementary department at the age of sixteen or perhaps fifteen and some degree of college discipline extended over them. They might at the commencement recite from a text-book and perhaps attend demonstrative lectures for a term, before beginning to receive special instruction.

A second and a third term closing each with an examination as a condition of advancement, would secure a class whose subsequent progress might be relied on. After completing the usual qualitative course and the quantitative course for a term at least, they might, with any others who should present themselves having been elsewhere qualified, pass by examination, to the department of the Rumford Professor.

With some such modification of the department, I feel that the just expectations of its friends and the public, with regard to it, might be fulfilled.

All of which is respectfully
submitted,
[signed]   E. N. Horsford
Rumford Professor
Cambridge, April 26, 1854.

SOURCE: Harvard College Papers 21 (1854): 33–46 in HUA. An earlier draft is in ENHP, R.P.I. Archives, Troy, New York.

Abbreviations Used in References

AJS	*American Journal of Science*
Annalen	*Annalen der Chemie und Pharmacie*
DAB	*Dictionary of American Biography*
ENH	Eben Norton Horsford
ENHP	E. N. Horsford Papers, Rensselaer Polytechnic Institute, Troy, New York
GJBP	George J. Brush Papers, Yale University Archives, New Haven, Connecticut
HUA	Harvard University Archives
JAP	John Addison Porter
JPN	John Pitkin Norton
JPNP	J. P. Norton Papers, Yale University Archives, New Haven, Connecticut
LSS	Lawrence Scientific School
No. Am. Rev.	*North American Review*
QCDC	Quaesita C. Drake Collection, University of Delaware Archives, Newark, Delaware
SSS	Sheffield Scientific School
SWJ	Samuel W. Johnson
SWJT	S. W. Johnson Typescripts, Connecticut Agricultural Experiment Station, New Haven, Connecticut
WCR	W. C. Redfield
WHBP	William H. Brewer Papers, Yale University Archives, New Haven, Connecticut
YAL	Yale Analytical Laboratory
YUA	Yale University Archives

Notes

CHAPTER 1

1 James F. W. Johnston, *Notes on North America*, 1: 356. Soil exhaustion: 1: 162–63, 173, 175, 210–11, 225–27, 259, 356–65; 2: 432, 500.

2 Carl O. Sauer, "Theme of Plant and Animal Destruction in Economic History," in John Leighly, ed., *Land and Life*, p. 151. The extent to which a soil was worn-out or ruined depended as much on competitive and psychological factors as on actual pedological ones. A farmer considered his soil "worn-out" when its yield dropped, for example, from 30–35 bushels per acre to 10–15, a process which Clarence Danhof estimates took from ten to twenty years (*Change in Agriculture*, pp. 253–54). Americans would forsake such a soil as worn-out when it was still fairly fertile by European standards. Fortunately, American soils never became as exhausted as those in certain areas of Ireland and southern Germany where famines were frequent in the 1840s.

3 Avery Craven, *Soil Exhaustion as a Factor in the Agricultural History of Maryland and Virginia, 1606–1860;* Eugene D. Genovese, "Cotton, Slavery, and Soil Exhaustion in the Old South"; Fred A. Shannon, *The Farmer's Last Frontier*, and Edward C. Kirkland, *A History of American Economic Life*, pp. 91–114, discuss the general process.

4 Herman R. Friis, "A Series of Population Maps of the Colonies and the United States, 1625–1790"; Kenneth Lockridge, "Land, Population and the Evolution of New England Society, 1630–1790"; David M. Ellis, "Yankee-Dutch Confrontation in the Albany Area," and "Albany and Troy, Commercial Rivals"; also Charles O. Paullin and John K. Wright, *Atlas of the Historical Geography of the United States*, pl. 76B–G and 77A–C.

5 Cf. Charles B. Hunt, *Physiography of the United States*, chaps. 6 and 11; Harry O. Buckman and Nyle C. Brady, *The Nature and Properties of Soils*, chap. 11; U.S. Dept. of Agriculture, *Soil Survey of Livingston County, New York*, series 1941, no. 15 (August 1956), pp. 101–03.

6 C. Langdon White, Edwin J. Foscue, and Tom L. Mcknight, *Regional Geography of Anglo-America*, pp. 72–76.

7 Russell H. Anderson, "New York Agriculture Meets the West, 1830–1850"; Paullin and Wright, *Atlas*, pl. 143P–S. Eric E. Lampard, *The Rise of the Dairy Industry in Wisconsin*, is an excellent study of this change. Parts of Washington and California were also major areas of production.

8 Paul W. Gates, "Agricultural Change in New York State, 1850–1890." Danhof, *Change in Agriculture*, classifies farmers as (1) innovators, (2) imitators, (3) gradualists, and (4) traditionalists, and identifies Chester County, Pennsylvania; Dutchess County, New York; and Suffolk County, Massachusetts, as the most innovative between 1820 and 1840, and western New York as

the most innovative after 1840 (pp. 256, 238). However, he does not indicate what social characteristics or psychological motivations are correlated with the desire to innovate. The subject merits a study such as James T. Lemon's on the Pennsylvania Dutch, "The Agricultural Practices of National Groups in Eighteenth-Century Southeastern Pennsylvania," and *The Best Poor Man's Country.*

9   See also Margaret W. Rossiter, "The Organization of Agricultural Improvement in the U.S., 1785–1865"; Donald B. Marti, "Early Agricultural Societies in New York" and "The Purposes of Agricultural Education."

10 Whitney R. Cross, *The Burned-over District,* relates the area's emotionalism in 1825–50 to its economic "maturity" but not specifically to fears of worn-out soil.

11 See James M. Hobbins, "Shaping a Provincial Learned Society"; and Robert Silverman and Mark Beach, "A National University for Upstate New York."

12 See M. L. Thompson, "The Second Agricultural Revolution, 1815–1880"; Christabel S. Orwin and Edith H. Whetham, *History of British Agriculture, 1846–1914,* chap. 1; and Rodney C. Loehr, "Arthur Young and American Agriculture."

13 "On the Excrementitious Matter Thrown Off by Plants," *AJS* 28 (1835): 267–68; *Cultivator* 5 (1838): 72.

14 Harry J. Carman, *Jesse Buel,* p. xxxi. Danhof says that by the 1840s agricultural journals in America had the largest circulation in the world (*Change in Agriculture,* p. 57).

CHAPTER 2

1   *AJS* 40 (1841): 177, 182. For more on Benjamin Silliman, Jr.'s lack of caution, see Gerald T. White, *Scientists in Conflict.*
2   *No. Am. Rev.* 51 (1841): 147.
3   *Cultivator* 8 (1841): 73, 75.
4   Herbert S. Klickstein, "Charles Caldwell and the Controversy in America over Liebig's 'Animal Chemistry.'"
5   E.g. Paul W. Gates, *The Farmer's Age,* pp. 358–63.
6   Wyndham D. Miles, "'Sir Humphrey Davie, The Prince of Agricultural Chemists,'" p. 128.
7   See *AJS* 40 (1841): 189.
8   *Cultivator* 5 (1838): 39.
9   The situation in Germany between 1800 and 1840 is quite confusing, but this schema may clarify it somewhat:

	Vitalism	Nutrient Value of Humus	Transmutability of Elements
Thaer (1809–12)	yes	yes	yes
Saussure (1804)	no?	yes/no	no!
Davy (1813)	no	yes/no	no
Berzelius		yes	no

| Sprengel | yes | yes | no? |
| Liebig (1840) | yes/no | no! | no |

What had been a big problem in 1810, the transmutability of air particles into earth particles within the plant (Schrader and Bracconot), was forgotten by 1840. This change allowed Saussure, who had put much energy into fighting transmutability in 1804, to be read in a new light in 1840.

10 Humphry Davy, *Elements of Agricultural Chemistry* (London: Longmans, Hurst et al., 1813), p. 11. Page references in text are to this edition. Best secondary account of Davy's agricultural chemistry is in Stohmann, "Liebig's Beziehungen zur Landwirtschaft," pp. 458–61.

11 See also Davy, *Elements of Agricultural Chemistry*, pp. 154–55.

12 Davy was also unclear as to whether the humus contributed chemical nutrients or a vital principle to the plants (pp. 162, 217–18, 270).

13 The study of fermentation is a major theme in the history of biochemistry. See Joseph Fruton, *Molecules and Life*, pp. 22–86; J. R. Partington, *A History of Chemistry*, 4: 301–10, and Malcolm Dixon, "The History of Enzymes and of Biological Oxidations," in Joseph Needham, ed., *The Chemistry of Life* (Cambridge University Press, 1970), pp. 15–37.

14 *SOIL, Yearbook of Agriculture, 1957*, pp. 67–71, 184–93; Aaron J. Ihde "Edmund Ruffin," p. 412.

15 The Candolle/Macaire-Princep theory of plant excrements is probably one important new addition. It held that the plant, in order to rid itself of nonessential juices which were known to flow downward, must exude them at the roots. Macaire-Princep detected some of these substances and showed that they were poisonous if reabsorbed by the same plant but were sometimes beneficial to different plants. Liebig republished the paper in his *Annalen* and used its arguments as evidence for his own "deficiency" theory (see p. 24), although he later dropped them when other investigators could not duplicate the results.

16 *Cultivator* 6 (1839): 154.

17 Justus Liebig, *Organic Chemistry in Its Applications to Agriculture and Physiology* (London: Taylor and Walton, 1840), p. 14. Page references in text are to this edition.

18 Julius von Sachs, *History of Botany (1530–1860)*, p. 529.

19 Current estimates are that rainfall produces less than 10 kg./hectare of nitrogen, while bacterial effects produce between 56 and 323 kg./hectare annually (C. A. Black, *Soil-Plant Relationships*, pp. 505–06).

20 N. Th. de Saussure, *Recherches chimiques sur la végétation*, pp. 309–27, esp. pp. 321–27.

21 The second half of Liebig's book, his chemical theory of fermentation and putrefaction, went practically unnoticed in America. Most reviewers of the book barely mentioned the second part, which led to important debates in Europe, however. See n. 13.

22 J. J. Berzelius, "Pflanzenchemie," pp. 235–37.

23 Jakob Volhard, *Justus von Liebig*, 1: 57–85; J. B. Morrell, "The Chemist

Breeders"; W. H. Brock, "Liebig's Laboratory Accounts"; H. S. van Klooster, "Liebig and His American Pupils," attributes the laboratory's popularity
to the agricultural chemistry. See appendix 2 for a listing of Liebig's foreign
students at Giessen.

24 Carlo Paoloni, ed., *Justus von Liebig*, p. 74.

25 Partington, *A History of Chemistry*, 4: 278; Robert Rigg, "Outline of an
experimentall Inquiry into a peculiar Property of the Earth"; Volhard,
Justus von Liebig, 1: 43. Another possible precursor is P. E. Jablonski, "Beitrag
zur Lösung der Frage, ob durch den Vegetationsprozess chemisch unzerlegbare Stoffe gebildet werden?", but Liebig does not refer to it.

26 Mack Walker, *Germany and the Emigration, 1816–85*, pp. 47–48, 66–67.

27 Henry R. Kraybill, "Liebig's Influence in the Promotion of Agricultural
Chemical Research," in F.R. Moulton, *Liebig and After Liebig*, pp. 10–18.

28 N. Th. de Saussure, "De l'action de la fermentation sur le mélange des gaz
oxygène et hydrogène," *Bibliothèque Universelle* 13 (1838): 380–401; Justus
Liebig, "Ueber die Erscheinungen der Gährung, Fäulniss und Verwesung
und ihre Ursachen," *Annalen* 30 (1839): 250–87, with a note that it is a
preprint of Liebig's forthcoming *Organic Chemistry*.

Chapter 3

1 *Cultivator* 8 (1841): 201; 9 (1842): 184; but such practices hurt the authors
and editors (Webster to ENH, September 28, 1844, ENHP).

2 *Cultivator*, n.s. 1 (1844): 137–39; *DAB;* Albert L. Demaree, "The Farm
Journals, Their Editors, and Their Public, 1830–1860," 182–88.

3 Liebig, *Organic Chemistry* (1840), pp. 86–89, 193; 61–62, 90–91, 202.

4 *American Agriculturalist* 9 (1850): 251.

5 *Cultivator* 9 (1842): 46; 8 (1841): 75. $CaSO_4$ (gypsum) + $(NH_4)_2CO_3$ (ammonium carbonate) $\rightleftarrows CaCO_3 + (NH_4)_2SO_4$. This is still an important use
of gypsum, although the reaction is reversible. Gypsum is now used as a
source of calcium in the alkali soils of the arid regions of the United States
(*SOIL, 1957*, pp. 195, 235).

6 Edward Hitchcock, *Final Report on the Geology of Massachusetts*.

7 *DAB; Outlines of Mineralogy and Geology of Boston and Its Vicinity* (Boston:
Cummings & Hilliard, University Press, 1818); *AJS* 45 (1868): 424–25; but
cf. Liebig, *Organic Chemistry*, 3rd American edition, appendix, pp. 286–87,
and C. M. Mellor and D. S. L. Cardwell, "Dyes and Dyeing, 1775–1860."
Dana may also have taken offense that Liebig used his discovery of phosphates
as a substitute for cow dung as evidence against humus.

8 Hitchcock, *Geology of Massachusetts*, pp. 26, 55, 121–26.

9 Liebig later complained that many adherents of the humus theory had
incorporated his ideas on ammonia into their still erroneous theories (2nd
London edition, 1842, p. 75n).

10 Samuel L. Dana, *A Muck Manual for Farmers* (Lowell: Daniel Bixby, 1842),
pp. 80–81.

11 Ibid., cf. pp. 60, 116, and 21, 215.

12 *Cultivator* 9 (1842): 90–91.

13 *AJS* 43 (1842): 197; JPN to W. Dickinson, February 14, 1852, YAL Letterpress Book, YUA; editor's preface, in Liebig, *Organic Chemistry,* 3rd American edition.

14 *Cultivator* 9 (1842): 47, 127.

15 Ibid. 10 (1843): 111.

16 Ibid. 9 (1842): 106; n.s. 2 (1845): 185; 10 (1843): 74.

17 Liebig, *Organic Chemistry,* 1st London edition, pp. 62, 90.

18 Cf. *Cultivator,* n.s. 1 (1844): 283.

19 Ibid. 8 (1841): 122. *Charcoal* seems to have been a very vague term at this time. It could mean wood ashes, which would contain alkalies; animal charcoal, which was burned bones and contained phosphates; and charcoal peat or peat charcoal, which, as Samuel W. Johnson showed in 1858, contained ammonia. Any of these substances would make fairly good fertilizers even if charcoal did not have helpful properties of its own.

20 Cf. Liebig, *Organic Chemistry,* 1st American edition, preface and p. 388*n.*

21 *Cultivator* 10 (1843): 74, 197; n.s. 1 (1844): 46.

22 Ibid., n.s. 1 (1844): 142; 10 (1843): 48; n.s. 1 (1844): 381–82; n.s. 2 (1845): 31.

23 Ibid., n.s. 8 (1851): 203–05.

24 Ibid. 10 (1843): 31.

25 Cf. Roy F. Nichols, "Latin American Guano Diplomacy," and Weymouth T. Jordan, "The Peruvian Guano Gospel in the Old South."

26 Liebig, *Organic Chemistry,* 1st London edition, pp. 81–82; [Friedrich Wöhler], "Ueber die Zusammensetzung des Guanos," p. 291; James E. Teschemacher, *Essay on Guano,* pp. 18–19.

27 *Cultivator* 8 (1841): 57; 9 (1842): 92; Liebig, *Organic Chemistry,* 1st London edition, pp. 184–85, 202.

28 Cf. Richard P. Aulie, "Boussingault and the Nitrogen Cycle."

29 Compare, for example, nos. 34 and 35 (pp. 234–35) with nos. 45, 46, and 47 (pp. 241–42), Liebig, *Organic Chemistry,* 2nd London edition.

30 Justus Liebig, *Animal Chemistry,* 1st London edition, pp. 40–41.

31 *Flora* 26 (1843): 21–35; Liebig, *Organic Chemistry,* 3rd London edition, pp. 51, 204–05; ibid., p. 45; cf. Liebig, *Organic Chemistry,* 2nd London edition, pp. 187–92, and 3rd London edition, p. 192. Aulie says Liebig may have misunderstood Boussingault's experiments (Aulie, "Boussingault," p. 151).

32 Liebig, *Organic Chemistry,* 2nd London edition, p. 180, and 3rd London edition, pp. 188 and 212. Liebig also dropped Edward Lukas's experiments on charcoal and rainwater from the third edition, although Lukas had recently shown that plants fared better with phosphatic charcoal (*thierische kohle*) than with the regular pine charcoal (Edward Lukas, "Einiges über die Wirkung der Kohle bei der Vegetation," *Annalen* 39 [1841]: 128).

33 Liebig, *Organic Chemistry,* 2nd London edition, pp. 192–93, and 3rd London edition, p. 192.

34 Charles A. Browne, "Liebig and the Law of the Minimum," implies incorrectly that the law was obvious in the first edition.

35 *Cultivator,* n.s. 4 (1847): 208; Stohmann, "Liebig's Beziehungen zur Land-
    wirtschaft," pp. 470–71; Michael D. Stephens and Gordon W. Roderick,
    "The Muspratts of Liverpool," pp. 295–96; Franz M. Feldhaus, "Liebig als
    Patentinhaber." The whole problem of Liebig's relations with the British
    agriculturalists has not been adequately explored.

36 Liebig, *Organic Chemistry,* 3rd London edition, p. 211.

37 Paoloni, *Justus von Liebig,* lists 51 editions of the *Familiar Letters* in eleven
    languages (pp. 108–13); *Familiar Letters . . .* (New York: D. Appleton &
    Co., 1843), pp. 5, 171. Wyndham Miles has attributed to Liebig the great
    increase in the number of chemical texts printed in the United States in the
    1840s. Of thirty-three editions of fifteen titles published in 1840–49, seventeen
    were of Liebig's volumes ("Books on Chemistry Printed in the United States,
    1775–1900: A Study of Their Origin," *Library Chronicle* 18 [1951–52]: 58–59).

38 *Cultivator,* n.s. 1 (1844): 63–64; *American Agriculturalist* 3 (1844): 127; *Culti-
    vator,* n.s. 1 (1844): 145–46, 148, 160, 187, 215.

CHAPTER 4

1   *Cultivator* 8 (1841): 9. The reference to Dombasle, the obscure proprietor of
    the first French agricultural school, shows the *Cultivator's* close study of the
    agricultural education movement (Alfred C. True, *A History of Agricultural
    Education in the United States,* p. 4).

2   Gould P. Colman, *Education and Agriculture,* chap. 1; and Marti, "Purposes of
    Agricultural Education."

3   For lists of Americans who studied at German universities, see B. A. Hinsdale,
    "Notes on the History of Foreign Influence upon Education in the United
    States"; Daniel B. Shumway, "The American Students of the University
    of Göttingen"; Gustav Toepke, *Die Matrikel der Universität Heidelberg;*
    Benjamin Silliman, Jr., "Memoir of John Lawrence Smith, 1818–1883";
    and Merle Curti and Kendall Birr, *Prelude to Point Four, American Technical
    Missions Overseas* (Madison: University of Wisconsin Press, 1954), pp. 22–24.
    Horsford borrowed $1,778 in 1844 for his trip to Germany (Quaesita C.
    Drake, "Student Life at Giessen in the 1840's," unpublished manuscript,
    QCDC).

4   Through his mother Horsford was related to Andrews Norton, John Pitkin
    Norton, and William A. Norton, but the lack of a complete genealogy leaves
    the exact relationship unclear. Neil A. McNall, *An Agricultural History of the
    Genesee Valley,* pp. 64, 103; William T. Hutchinson, *Cyrus Hall McCormick,*
    p. 165n; *Cultivator,* n.s. 4 (1847): 49; Roswell Ward, *Henry A. Ward,* p. 22;
    Charles L. Jackson, "Eben Norton Horsford," p. 343; *Congressional Globe,*
    32nd Cong., 1st sess., app. (June 24, 1852), pp. 746–48; Lyman Carrier,
    "The United States Agricultural Society"; and A. Hunter Dupree, *Science in
    the Federal Government,* p. 113.

5   ENH Letterbook, October 6, 1845, p. 231, ENHP; James Hall, *Geology of
    New York, Part IV* (Albany: Carroll and Cook, 1843), p. 462. Two maps by
    ENH appear in the annual report for 1840 of the Adirondack Iron and Steel

Company, whose records are contained in the Adirondack Museum, Blue Mountain Lake, New York. I thank Michele Aldrich for this item.

6   John M. Clarke, *James Hall of Albany*, pp. 69–70; Samuel Rezneck, *Education for a Technological Society*, p. 63.

7   Folder 7, QCDC; ENH Letterbook, p. 145, ENHP. Transcripts of ENH's numerous letters home from Giessen, November 1844–November 1846, have been bound together into a Letterbook at ENHP.

8   ENH, *Report on the Phrenological Classification of J. Stanley Grimes.* Horsford was also involved in a daguerreotype business with Samuel F. B. Morse in 1840–43 (S. F. B. Morse to ENH, "Confidential," 1840, and the Thurlow Weed to ENH, 1843, ENHP; but the S. F. B. Morse Papers at the Library of Congress do not mention it). Charles L. Jackson, "Eben Norton Horsford," p. 341; Carleton Mabee, *The American Leonardo* (New York: Knopf, 1943), p. 243n.

9   See Edward Hitchcock, *First Anniversary Address before the Association of American Geologists at Their Second Annual Meeting in Philadelphia, April 5, 1841* (New Haven: B. L. Hamlen, 1841), p. 47; *AJS* 43 (1842): 184.

10 JPN Diary V (March 21, 1844), p. 225, JPNP; *Cultivator*, n.s. 1 (1844): 114, 148, 152–53.

11 ENH to Mary Gardiner, October 23, 1843, ENHP.

12 Folder 8, QCDC.

13 ENH to Samuel Gardiner, October 23, 1843, ENHP. Cf. Robert Seager II, *and Tyler Too*.

14 ENH to Mary Gardiner, October 23, 1843, ENHP. This "diary" is a series of letters that Horsford wrote to Mary in 1844–46 but was forbidden to send.

15 Twenty-three letters of recommendation are in ENHP; J. Hall to Robert Paterson, March 15, 1844; also ENH to W. C. Redfield, February 24, 1844, WCR Papers, Beinecke Rare Book Library, Yale University; Joel Parker to ENH, March 6, 1844, ENHP. Henry was at times friendly to Horsford (ENH to Mary Gardiner, September 26, 1844, ENHP), but at other times cool and distant (ENH to J. Hall, March 27, 1847, Hall Papers). Cf. Nathan Reingold, "Science in the Civil War."

16 ENH to Mary Gardiner, September 26, 1844, ENHP.

17 W. A. Norton to Reverend Ludlow [1844]; John Treadwell Norton to Reverend Ludlow, February 24, 1844, ENHP; JPN Diary V (March 20, 1844), p. 224, JPNP. Horsford and J. T. Norton later disagreed over the relative merits of Edinburgh and Giessen (ENH to J. S. Perry, April 21, 1845, Letterbook, p. 76, ENHP), and were still on bad terms in 1861 when Horsford asked for a loan (ENH to J. T. Norton, draft [1861], ENHP).

18 "Catalogue," July 23, 1844, ENHP.

19 ENH Letterbook, p. 25, ENHP. In 1844–45 Liebig bought a farm in an area outside Giessen known as "Liebig Heights," where he experimented with manures. He did not stick strictly to artificial manures because at one point he purchased several loads of muck. Horsford's corn failed to grow there (*Cultivator*, n.s. 3 [1846]: 170; ENH Letterbook, p. 110; ENH Letterbook, p. 124; Father to ENH, March 6, 1840 [*sic*, 1847], ENHP).

20 ENH Letterbook, p. 281, but cf. p. 366, ENHP, where Horsford said Germans

had titles instead of adequate salaries; JPN Diary VI (October 11, 1844), JPNP, and Liebig to Wöhler, November 7, 1844, in E. Wöhler mit A. W. Hofmann, *Aus Justus Liebig's und Friedrich Wöhler's Briefwechsel*, 1: 245; ENH Letterbook, pp. 128, 240. Animosity toward Liebig was intense in Berlin— cf. ENH Letterbook, p. 240, ENHP.

21 ENH Letterbook, pp. 243–44, 319, ENHP. See also August Vogel, *Zur Geschichte der Liebig'schen Mineraltheorie;* JPN Diary VI (October 11, 1844), JPNP; ENH Letterbook, p. 365; cf. Benjamin Silliman, *A Visit to Europe in 1851*, 2: 294; and Liebig to Wöhler, March 19, 1849, in E. Wöhler mit Hofmann, 1: 333. By the time Liebig left Giessen his enrollments had already dropped off (Liebig to Wöhler, October 21, 1848, in E. Wöhler mit Hofmann 1: 321); ENH Letterbook, pp. 124, 156, ENHP.

22 It was unclear whether Liebig was to visit America or to remain permanently (ENH Letterbook, pp. 41, 130, ENHP). In the 1850s several persons invited Liebig to the United States—the Sillimans in 1851 (Silliman, *A Visit to Europe in 1851*, 2: 295), the backers of the Albany University in 1856 (Clarke, *James Hall of Albany*, pp. 319–20), and James Dwight Dana in 1859 (J. Liebig to Dana, February 5, 1859, Dana Scientific Correspondence, Beinecke Rare Book Library, Yale University)—but he never came. ENH Letterbook, pp. 267, 303, ENHP.

23 Horsford's reaction to German morals was a frequent topic in his letters home (ENH Letterbook, pp. 53–55, 79, 108, 110–12, 270–71, esp. p. 262, ENHP).

24 Cf. Walker, *Germany and the Emigration;* ENH Letterbook, pp. 306, 434, 326, 63, 160, 82, 51, where he exclaimed "And all this in the shadow of Liebig!"; and *Cultivator*, n.s. 2 (1845): 235–36.

25 ENH Letterbook, pp. 124, 161, 164, 288, 247, 325, 341, and 357, ENHP.

26 ENH Letterbook, pp. 38, 44, and O. W. Gibbs to William Channing, November 22, 1846, Gibbs Family Papers, Wisconsin State Historical Society, Madison, Wisconsin.

27 ENH Letterbook, pp. 75, 317, 154, 138, 265, 297, ENHP; and JPN Diary VII (January 9, 1846), JPNP.

28 For accounts of Liebig's laboratory, see chapter 2, n. 23. Amos Eaton started a laboratory school in Troy, New York, in 1824. For differing comparisons of it with Liebig's laboratory see Rezneck, *Education for a Technological Society*, p. 57, and H. S. Van Klooster, "The Beginnings of Laboratory Instruction in the U.S.A.," p. 9.

29 Van Klooster, "Liebig and His American Pupils," p. 497; ENH Letterbook, p. 442, ENHP. There was a great deal of professional jealousy between Berlin and Giessen. Cf. Josiah Dwight Whitney to W. D. Whitney, April, 25, 1846, Berlin; and J. D. Whitney, Jr., to J. D. Whitney, Sr., and J. D. Whitney to W. D. Whitney, both January 26, 1847, W. D. Whitney Collection, YUA; also O. W. Gibbs to Mother, June 25 and July 25, 1846, Berlin; and O. W. Gibbs to George Gibbs, October 27, 1846, and February 22, 1847, Giessen, Gibbs Family Papers, Wisconsin State Historical Society, Madison, Wisconsin); ENH Letterbook, pp. 141, 146, ENHP.

30 ENH Letterbook, pp. 91, 71, ENHP.

31 Ibid., p. 37.

32 Ibid., p. 247; ENH, "Analyse der Asche des Klee's (Trifolium pratense)," *Annalen* 58 (1846): 391; Liebig, *Organic Chemistry*, 4th London edition, p. 262; *Cultivator*, n.s. 3 (1846), 137–39.

33 ENH, "Ammoniakgehalt der Gletscher," *Annalen* 59 (1846): 113–16.

34 *Cultivator* 6 (1839): 69; J.-B. Boussingault, *Economie rurale*, 2: 463–98.

35 ENH Letterbook, p. 309, ENHP; ENH, "Ueber den Werth verschiedener vegetabilischer Nahrungsmittel, hergeleitet aus ihrem Stickstoffgehalt."

36 *Cultivator*, n.s. 2 (1845): 229, criticizes Dumas, Boussingault, and Payen; cf. Stanley L. Becker, "The Emergence of a Trace Nutrient Concept through Animal Feeding Experiments"; Elmer V. McCollum, *A History of Nutrition*, pp. 95–97.

37 ENH to James Hall, July 5, 1846, Hall Papers; ENH Letterbook, pp. 345, 369, ENHP; G. J. Mulder, *Liebig's Question to Mulder Tested by Morality and Science*; E. Rüling, "Bestimmung des Schwefels in den Schwefel- und Stickstoffhaltigen Bestandtheilen des Pflanzen- und Thierorganismus," *Annalen* 58 (1846): 301–15.

38 Partington, *A History of Chemistry*, 4:228–31; ENH, "Ueber Glycocoll (leimzucker) und einige seiner Zersetzungs-producte"; Hubert B. Vickery, "Liebig and Proteins"; Hubert B. Vickery and C. L. A. Schmidt, "The History of the Discovery of the Amino Acids," pp. 195–98 and 300–01; Fruton, *Molecules and Life*, pp. 108–20, discusses later work on amino acids and proteins; Berzelius to Mulder, May 25, 1847, in H. G. Söderbaum, ed., *Jac. Berzelius Bref* (Stockholm: Royal Academy of Sciences of Sweden, 1916), pt. 5, p. 302; only exception was ENH, "On the Relation of the Chemical Constitution of Bodies to Taste."

39 ENH Letterbook, p. 351, ENHP; ENH, "Ueber den elektrischen Leitungswiderstand der Flüssigkeiten"; Partington, *A History of Chemistry*, 4: 669; ENH Letterbook, p. 369, ENHP.

40 ENH Letterbook, pp. 69, 73, ENHP; True, *History of Agricultural Education*, pp. 34–35; James McLachlan, *American Boarding Schools*, pp. 59–63, 87–89, esp. *n*. 51.

CHAPTER 5

1 A. Hunter Dupree, *Asa, Gray*, p. 112; I. B. Cohen, "Harvard and the Scientific Spirit," p. 393.

2 Richard J. Storr, *The Beginnings of Graduate Education in America*, pp. 8, 21, 41, 48.

3 J. W. Webster to ENH, February 3, 1845, and December, 31, 1846, ENHP; cf. JPN Diary V (November 4, 1842), JPNP; Dupree, *Asa Gray*, p. 199.

4 Justus Liebig to Edward Everett, March 27, 1846, copy by ENH in ENHP (trans. in Harvard College Papers, 2nd series, vol. 13, HUA).

5 Harvard College Papers, 13 (January 3, 1846), p. 126; Van Klooster, "Liebig and His American Pupils," p. 495.

6 J. W. Webster to Lewis Norton, February 27, 1846, ENHP; ENH to J. Hall, March 24 and May 1, 1846, Hall Papers; *DAB;* George P. Merrill, *The First One Hundred Years of American Geology,* pp. 167–68, 221, 245–46; Dupree, *Asa Gray,* pp. 144–49.

7 ENH to J. Hall, May 1, 1846, Hall Papers; cf. J. E. Teschemacher to ENH, September 1, 1846, ENHP; J. W. Webster to John Collins Warren, August 20, 1846, vol. 22, John Collins Warren Correspondence, Massachusetts Historical Society; J. W. Webster to ENH, February 27, 1846, ENHP; J. Hall to J. W. Webster, March 14, 1846; Webster also directed the republication of two of Horsford's recent papers and a letter on manures (*AJS* 3 [1847]: 144–45, and *Cultivator,* n.s. 4 [1847]: 201–03).

8 Horsford had over thirty letters of recommendation. Those of Liebig and Bishop Alonzo Potter were the most influential with the Corporation (J. W. Webster to ENH [Febuary 18?, 1847], ENHP). Liebig wrote about Horsford: "Ich weiss niemanden den ich mit grosserer Zuversicht empfehlen konnte. Herr Horsford besitzt nicht blos die tiefsten und gründlichsten Kenntnisse in den genannten Fachern, sondern er ist auch von der Natur begabt mit einem wahrhaft philosophisches Geiste und mit der Fertigkeit [skill, dexterity] und Beharrlichkeit [perseverance] des Characters, welche nothwendig Bedingungen sind um die Grenzen der Wissenschaft zu erweitern und um Burgschaft zu geben eines steten Voranschreitens" (Liebig to Everett, March 27, 1846, ENHP); Harvard College Papers, vol. 13, HUA.

9 Edward Everett, "University Education," *Orations and Speeches on Various Occasions,* 2: 496–97.

10 J. W. Webster to ENH, Febuary 27, 1846; J. E. Teschemacher to ENH, September 1, 1846; J. W. Webster to ENH, April 30 and July 4, 1846, ENHP; ENH to J. Hall, July 5, 1846, Hall Papers; ENH to E. Everett, June 30, 1846 (2 drafts); ENH Letterbook, pp. 320, 376, 405, 407, 426–29, ENHP; J. D. Whitney to J. D. Whitney, Sr., January 26, 1847, Giessen, W. D. Whitney Collection, YUA; W. A. Norton to J. W. Webster, April 6 and May 13, 1846, ENHP.

11 ENH to J. Hall, May 1, September 30 and October 12, 1846, Hall Papers; ENH to E. Everett, n.d. and June 30, 1846 (with insert), ENHP.

12 ENH to J. Hall, January 7 and 8, 1847, Hall Papers. Everett, Walker, and Lowell were the Corporation committee on the scientific school; Harvard Corp. Rec. 8 (January 30, 1847), 337, and (February 13, 1847), 339–40 HUA; ENH to S. S. Gardiner, February 20, 1847, ENHP. The Rogers brothers were bitter, however: James B. Rogers to Henry Rogers, February 6, 1847, William B. Rogers Papers, M.I.T. Archives.

13 Everett to ENH, February 19, 1847, Harvard College Letters I, 160, HUA (copy in ENH Letterbook, p. 467, ENHP); "Treasurer's Report," *Twenty-First Annual Report of the President of the University at Cambridge . . . for the Year 1845–46* (Cambridge: Metcalf & Co., 1847).

14 Margaret Rossiter, "Benjamin Silliman and the Lowell Institute"; George Combe, *Notes on the United States of North America during a Phrenological Visit in*

1838-9-40, 1: app.; JPN Diary VII (August 8, 1846), 251–52, JPNP; "Gentlemen to be particularly invited to Everett's inaugural," March 28, 1846, Harvard College Papers, vol. 13, p. 271, HUA.

15 ENH to Mary Gardiner, May 3 and 8, and June 7, 1846, ENHP. ENH to J. Hall, May 6, 1847, Hall Papers; Abbott Lawrence to S. A. Eliot, June 7, 1847, in Harvard Corp. Rec. 8 (June 7, 1847), 362, HUA. Lawrence was also interested in agriculture (he was recording secretary of the Massachusetts Society for the Promotion of Agriculture in 1844), and his letter indicated he wished to support agricultural chemistry at Harvard: "We inherit, and are forced to cultivate a sterile soil; and what nature has denied, should be, as far as possible supplied by art. We must make better farmers through the application of chemical and agricultural science."

16 ENH to Everett, April 23, 1847, Harvard College Papers, 2nd series, vol. 14, pp. 328–29, HUA; ENH to Mary Gardiner, April 19, 1847, ENHP; ENH Letterbook, p. 282, ENHP; ENH to Mary Gardiner, June 9 and 11, 1847, ENHP.

17 ENH to Everett, April 23, 1847, Harvard College Papers, 2nd series, vol. 14, pp. 328–29, HUA mentions at least fifteen European laboratories.

18 Volhard, *Justus von Liebig,* 1: 62–65; Col. J. J. Abert, "Extension of the Capitol," House Doc. no. 51, 28th Cong., 1st sess., vol. 3 (January 8, 1844), pp. 8–9; ENH Letterbook, p. 441, ENHP; *DAB;* Morrell Wyman to ENH, May 7, 1847, ENHP; *Proceedings of American Academy of Arts and Sciences,* 1: 185, 307–24; ENH to Mary Gardiner, June 11 and 14, 1847, ENHP; untitled, undated [1848?] description of laboratory at home of Andrew Fiske, Shelter Island; Everett to ENH, December 27, 1848, ENHP.

19 ENH to Mary Gardiner, April 16, May 3, and June 4, 1847, ENHP; ENH to Mary Gardiner, [October 5, 1854], ENHP. In the summer and fall of 1854 Mary was taking the water cure at Brattleboro, Vermont, and ENH wrote her daily.

20 ENH to Harvard Corp,. April 26, 1854 (see appendix 4). Ernest Child, *The Tools of the Chemist,* appendix, lists early American chemical suppliers; S. A. Eliot to ENH, September 16, 1848, ENHP; ENH to Harvard Corp., "Statement . . .," August 22, 1848, Harvard College Papers, vol. 16, pp. 124–127; Everett to Lawrence, August 30, 1848, Harvard College Letters, vol. 2, pp. 207–208, HUA; S. A. Eliot to ENH, November 3, 1848, ENHP.

21 See appendix 4; Lawrence Scientific School Faculty Records, I, September 14, 1849, HUA (copy and rough draft in ENHP); also College Letters, vol. 3, HUA; Jared Sparks to Lawrence, September 18, 1849, Harvard College Letters, vol. 3, p. 75, HUA. The high tuition of $75 per semester did deter some students (E. A. Osborne, p. 20; L. Wetherell to ENH, October 3, 1848, WHBP, YUA); A. Lawrence to S. A. Eliot, September 20, 1849, Harvard Corp. Rec. 9 (October 3, 1849), 115–16, HUA (copy in ENHP). In 1862 the Corporation abolished the LSS faculty's dependence on student fees (Harvard Corp. Rec. 9 [May 31, 1862], 270, HUA).

22 There is a table of enrollment figures, 1849–60, taken from the course cata-

logues at HUA, in Margaret W. Rossiter, "Justus Liebig and the Americans: A Study in the Transit of Science," Ph.D. dissertation, Yale University, 1971, p. 159.

23 In 1855 Horsford compiled a list of the occupations of the school's graduates: 23 physicians, 18 practicing chemists, 17 engineers, 13 merchants, 10 college professors, 7 schoolteachers, 5 farmers, 5 lawyers, 4 clergymen, 3 cotton printers, 3 geologists, 2 surgeons, 2 ironmasters, 1 each of glass manufacturer, mining engineer, Patent Office examiner, drug examiner, and secretary of board of agriculture (ENH to Committee of Overseers Visiting LSS, October 31, 1855, in Reports to the Overseers, Instruction Series I [1855–56], pp. 328–31, HUA [draft in ENHP]). Many former students wrote Horsford of the lack of jobs for chemists in the 1850s. Only the pluckier ones found them. Horsford wrote the preface for the American edition of Will's text (Boston: James Munroe and Co., 1847). Daniel Breed, a former student, translated and dedicated the third edition to Horsford (1855). Horsford was thus instrumental in introducing a basic German text into America.

24 John H. Clifford, "Report of the Committee of Overseers to Visit the Lawrence Scientific School," 1856, in Reports to the Overseers, Instruction Series, 2: 510, HUA (draft in ENHP); ENH to J. Hall, November 7, 1853, Hall Papers.

25 James Booth to ENH, April 25, 1854, ENHP. His fees were high ($250/yr.), but his laboratory "barely self-sustaining." He hoped Horsford had other income, for "it is very certain that chemical science does not fairly remunerate her votaries in this country." See appendix 4; Edgar F. Smith, "Charles Mayer Wetherill," p. 1222.

26 ENH Letterbook, p. 296, and J. Liebig to ENH, April 22 [1847], ENHP; J. M. Fessenden to ENH, December 18, 1854, and [J. M. Fessenden], "Statement of the income and expenses of the Zoological + Geological, the Engineering and the Chemical Departments of the Lawrence Scientific School for the year commencing September 1st, 1854," ENHP (copy in Reports to the Overseers, Instruction Series, 1: 152, HUA); a draft of ENH's response is in ENHP. These items reveal that the engineering department of the school was by far the most prosperous, earning $4,700 after expenses, chemistry next with $1,800, and the geology last with a deficit of $100. (See also appendix 4.) Salaries are in the Treasurer's Report appended to the President's Report for 1854–55; cf. O. W. Gibbs to George Gibbs, January 26, 1847, Gibbs Family Collection, Wisconsin State Historical Society.

27 T. S. Hunt to ENH, February 21, 1848, ENHP; ENH experimented with artificial manures in 1853, with unknown results (ENH, "Directions for Use," May 1, 1853, and C. Flint to ENH, August 29, September 7 and 9, 1853, ENHP), and analyzed fertilizers for "Prof." J. J. Mapes (Mapes to ENH, January 5 and March 18, 1853, ENHP).

28 (Lowell, Mass.: Daniel Bixby and Co., 1848); ibid., p. vi, quoting J. Liebig to ENH, January 6, 1848; ibid., p. v; John Dean, "On the Value of the Different Kinds of Prepared Vegetable Food."

29 S. L. Dana, trans., L. Tanquerel des Planches, *Lead Diseases* (1848); "Report

of the Commissioners . . . to Examine the Sources . . . of Pure Water"
(1845); "Report of the Consulting Physicians of the City of Boston . . ."
(1848); "Report of the Water Commissioners on . . . Water Pipes" (1848);
ENH, "Service Pipes for Water," and Martin Boyè, "On the Composition of
the Schuylkill Water," pp. 127, 130–31, for criticisms of ENH; ENH to J.
Hall, December 14, 1848, Hall Papers. See also Nelson M. Blake, *Water for
the Cities*, chap. 12.

30 ENH, "On the Moisture, Ammonia, and Organic Matter of the Atmosphere," "On Ammonia in Atmospheric Air," "Notiz über den Ammoniakgehalt der Atmosphäre," and "Ammonia in the Atmosphere"; ENH
to Mary Horsford, June 22 and July 8, 1849, ENHP; A. A. Hayes, "On the
Assumed Existence of Ammonia in the General Atmosphere."

31 ENH, "Connection between the Atomic Weights and the Physical and
Chemical Properties of Barium . . ."; Partington, *A History of Chemistry*, 4:
884; J. P. Cooke, "The Numerical Relation between the Atomic Weights,
with some thoughts on the Classification of the Chemical Elements," *AJS*,
2nd series, 17 (1854): 387–407.

32 ENH to Mary Gardiner, April 19 and 23–24, June 7, 1847, ENHP; Rossiter,
"Benjamin Silliman"; ENH to J. Hall, December 21, 1847, Hall Papers;
ENH to Mary Horsford, February 14 [1848], ENHP; see also Robert Sullivan, *The Disappearance of Dr. Parkman*, and Helen Thomson, *Murder at Harvard*.

33 ENH to Mary Horsford, July 8 and 11, 1849, ENHP; ENH to J. Hall,
January 18, 1850, Hall Papers, and ENH to Mary Horsford, August 31,
1850, ENHP; ENH, "Results of Some Experiments on the Explosions of
Burning Fluids"; numerous letters from J. R. Nichols to ENH, 1852–55,
ENHP, and joint patent (U.S. #13,729), October 1855; ENH, "Der Geschi-
chte der Condensirten Milch," pp. 539–40.

34 ENH to Mary Horsford, September 18 and 22, 1853, ENHP; list of inventions in ENH to Mary Horsford, [October 10–12, 1854], ENHP; cf. Josiah
Quincy to ENH, "Confidential," April 24, 1854, ENHP.

35 ENH, "Solidification of Rocks of Florida Reefs" (1851), and "Solidification
of the Rocks of the Florida Reefs, and the Sources of Lime in the Growth of
Corals" (1852); James D. Dana, "On Some Modern Calcareous Rock
Formations"; ENH, "On the Solidification of the Coral Reefs of Florida,
and the Sources of Carbonate of Lime in the Growth of Corals"; A. A. Hayes
to J. D. Dana, January 16, 1854, Dana Scientific Correspondence, Beinecke
Rare Book Library, Yale University; J. D. Dana to ENH, November (or September) 15, 1852, also January 25, June 3, 1852, and n.d., ENHP; see
Jérôme Nicklès, "On the Permeability of Metals to Mercury," for more criticisms; ENH to S. F. Baird, March 18, 1854, and ENH to H. L. Smith,
April 28, 1854, ENHP; and John D. Holmfeld, "From Amateurs to Professionals in American Science."

36 ENH to Mary Horsford, September 18 (2), 22, 25, [26], [29], October 2, 5,
1854, ENHP.

37 ENH to Mary Horsford, October [7] and 8, 1854; Charles G. Loring to J.

Walker, October 7, 1854, Harvard College Papers, vol. 21, pp. 340–42, HUA.

38   Corp. Rec. 10 (September 25, 1858), 85–87, HUA; Folder 10, QCDC.

CHAPTER 6

1   The idea that pure science flourishes in an aristocratic society and applied science in a democracy dates back to Alexis de Tocqueville, *Democracy in America,* vol. 2, bk. 2, chap. 10. See Richard Shryock, "American Indifference to Basic Science during the Nineteenth Century," and Nathan Reingold, "American Indifference to Basic Research," for subsequent modifications and criticisms.

2   Noah Porter, "In Memoriam, John Treadwell Norton," p. 451; Frank Walker Stevens, *The Beginnings of the New York Central Railroad,* p. 114.

3   JPN Diaries I–V (1838–44), passim, JPNP; Horatio T. Strother, *The Underground Railroad in Connecticut,* pp. 60–61, 167.

4   Dwight was the nephew of Yale's President Timothy Dwight and a newspaperman and author in New York City (*DAB*); JPN Diary I (November 16, 1838, and May 29, 1839) and passim, JPNP.

5   JPN Diary III (December 21, 1840) and passim, JPNP.

6   The "Amistad captives" were a group of slaves who had mutinied on their passage to America in 1839 and were temporarily in Farmington pending legal proceedings in Washington, D.C.; JPN Diary III (August 29, 1841) and IV (October 17–18, 1841), JPNP. See also Sidney Earl Mead, *Nathaniel William Taylor, 1786–1858.*

7   JPN Diary IV (December 23, 1841; February 8, 6, and 20, 1842), JPNP.

8   JPN Diary IV (August 4, 1842, Dec. 20, 1841); and III (February 1, 1841), JPNP.

9   JPN Diary V (November 19, 1842, February 2, 1843, and October 30, 1842), JPNP.

10   JPN Diary V (November 3, 1843), JPNP.

11   JPN Diary V (October 12–13, 1843), JPNP.

12   *AJS* 42 (1842): 189, 191; 43 (1842): 197; also Asa Gray, "The Chemistry of Vegetation," p. 157.

13   *Quarterly Journal of the Chemical Society* 9 (1857): 157–58.

14   *AJS* 46 (1844): 382; 48 (1845): 219.

15   See also H. C. Knoblauch et al., *State Agricultural Experiment Stations,* pp. 5–11, and Ernest M. Law, "The Agricultural Experiment Station Movement in Connecticut, 1840–1900," chap. 1.

16   Thompson, "The Second Agricultural Revolution."

17   JPN Diary VI (January 3, 16, 20, 1845, and December 3, 1844); VII (June 29 and September 14, 1845), JPNP.

18   JPN Diary VI, passim, and VII (November 9, 1846); J. F. W. Johnston to JPN, May 4, 1849, JPNP. Norton assisted Johnston greatly on his tour of the United States in 1849–50 and was shocked at the professor's ungrateful comments in his *Notes on North America* (1851). Johnston also accused Norton

of forsaking research for money. Norton was aghast, responded to Johnston, and reviewed the book severely. See JPN to Henry Stephens, September 4, 1851; JPN Diary IX (October 3, December 9 and 17, 1851); JPN to J. F. W. Johnston, December 9, 1851, JPNP; *Cultivator* 9 (1852): 44–45, 70–72.

19 JPN, "On the Analysis of the Oat," pp. 228, 327–28; JPN Diary VII (June 23, 1845), JPNP; *American Agriculturalist* 5 (1846), 18.

20 *Cultivator,* n.s. 1 (1844): 364; ibid., 2 (1845): 233.

21 JPN Diary VII (Jan. 11, 1846), JPNP; ENH to JPN, Giessen, Aug. 27, 1846, Houghton Library, Harvard University.

22 JPN Diary VII (January 10, 14, and February 3, 1845).

23 JPN Diary VI (January 3 and 15, 1845; October 11, 1844), JPNP; Volhard, *Justus von Liebig,* 1: 165–72; "Dinner in Honor of Prof. Liebig"; *Cultivator,* n.s. 2 (1845): 16; JPN Diary VII (January 9, 1846), JPNP; J. D. Whitney to W. D. Whitney, January 26, 1847, W. D. Whitney Collection, YUA; JPN Diary VII (January 8–14, 1846), JPNP, and ENH Letterbook, pp. 280, 290, ENHP.

24 Berzelius had criticized Liebig's works on agriculture and physiology, and Liebig opposed Berzelius's dualistic theory for organic compounds. Mulder was fighting Liebig over proteins, and Johnston presumably objected to Liebig's assertive and arrogant tone in agricultural matters. *The Chemistry of Vegetable and Animal Physiology* (New York: Wiley & Putnam, 1845), p. 504; JPN Diary VII (February 2, 1846), JPNP.

25 The speaker's "style" was important, especially if he came from the city or a university and was telling farmers how to farm. It was said of William H. Brewer, later at Yale, that his rough manner and farm humor were more valuable assets to the Sheffield Scientific School than his German training. Norton learned one thing a farm lecturer must never do. Johnston inadvertently at one lecture pointed out the poor practices of one farm he had seen. The farmer was present and was greatly enraged. JPN Diary VII (September 3, 1845), JPNP; *Cultivator,* n.s. 2 (1845): 121; JPN Diary VI (January 13, 1845), JPNP.

26 JPN Diary VI (December 19, 1844), JPNP. Soil analysts who appeared in the *Cultivator* and *American Agriculturalist* between 1844 and 1854 included C. H. Raymond, Charles Whittlesey, M. A. Randall, D. Jay Browne, C. T. Jackson, D. P. Gardner, J. R. Chilton, C. U. Shepard, J. J. Mapes, James Booth, Thomas Antisell, Lewis Beck, Ebenezer Emmons, J. P. Norton, J. H. Salisbury, S. D. Martin, Robert Peter, Benjamin Silliman, Jr., B. Kirkland, and David Wells. Many of their analyses had been undertaken for state surveys and then widely cited as advertisements for commercial analyses.

27 JPN Diary VI (January 1 and February 15, 1845).

28 JPN Diary VII (October 16 and 30, 1845); Stanley M. Guralnick, "Science and the American College," p. 220; JPN Diary I (1838), passim, JPNP; Alice Felt Tyler, *Freedom's Ferment,* chap. 13.

29 [JPN], "Proposals for Establishing a Chair of Agricultural Chemistry and Vegetable and Animal Physiology in Yale College," Sheffield Scientific School Papers, YUA, also published in John F. Fulton and Elizabeth H.

Thomson, *Benjamin Silliman*, p. 208; see also Louis I. Kuslan, "The Founding of the Yale School of Applied Chemistry."

30 JPN Diary VII (May 30 and June 1, 1846); VIII (September 14, 1846), JPNP. It is unclear whether he knew his father had initiated the drive with the offer of $5,000, provided the rest could be raised; JPN Diary VII (May 17 and June 21, 1847; August 8 and September 7, 1846), JPNP.

31 When Norton had visited Mulder early in February 1846, he had found him in good spirits, although he knew his work was being challenged in Giessen. Apparently Mulder had not received the January issue of the *Annalen*, in which Liebig criticized him strongly ("Ueber den Schwefelgehalt des sticks- toffhaltigen Bestandtheils der Erbsen"). This salvo was followed by Lask- owski's paper in the April issue, "Ueber die Proteintheorie," and three articles in the May issue (Dr. E. Rüling, "Bestimmung des Schwefels in den Schwefel- und Stickstoffhaltigen Bestandtheilen des Pflanzen- und Thierorganismus"; Walther, "Schwefelgehalt des Caseins"; and Francois Verdeil, "Schwefel- bestimmung einiger organischer Körper"), all of which contained the Giessen school's experimental data. Mulder responded by writing to Liebig demand- ing that he retract what he had said about protein. Liebig replied that Mulder was a fool and that he would give him fourteen days to retract *his* letter or else he would expose him and it further (ENH Letterbook, p. 345, ENHP). Mulder then sent such a deranged reply that Liebig did not answer (ENH Letterbook, p. 369, ENHP). Frustrated at getting no response and desirous of vindicating publicly his side of the issue, Mulder then resorted to publish- ing a lengthy pamphlet, *Liebig's Question to Mulder Tested by Morality and Science*. JPN Diary VIII (February 22 and April 29, 1847), JPNP; Liebig, "Zur Characteristik des Herrn Prof. Mulder in Utrecht." The whole con- troversy is discussed in Joseph Fruton, *Molecules and Life*, pp. 95–101.

32 JPN, "On the Analysis of the Oat," p. 329n; JPN Diary VIII (December 8, 1846, April 24 and June 8, 1847), JPNP.

33 JPN, "An Account of Some Researches on the Protein Bodies of Peas and Almonds, and a Body of a Somewhat Similar Nature Existing in Oats," pp. 24–25; Th. Fleitmann, "Ueber die Existenz eines schwefelfreien Proteins"; JPN Diary VIII (February 8, 1847), JPNP; August Voelcker, "On the Percentage of Nitrogen as an Index to the Nutritive Value of Food," *Notices and Abstracts of Communications to the British Association for the Advancement of Science, 1850*, pp. 64–65, reprinted in *AJS* 10 (1850): 403–04.

34 *Cultivator*, n.s. 4 (January–October 1847), and *American Agriculturalist* 5–6 (December 1846–October 1847).

CHAPTER 7

1 Kuslan, "Yale School of Applied Chemistry," pp. 444–47; Law, "Agricul- tural Experiment Station Movement," pp. 38–41; JPN, "Address," *Trans- actions of New Haven County Agricultural Society*, pp. 26–28; *Cultivator*, n.s. 7 (1850): 296–97, and 8 (1851): 74–76, 309–10.

2 Cf. Dirk J. Struik, *Yankee Science in the Making*, p. 430.

3   JPN and B. Silliman, Jr., to President of Yale College [1847], SSS Papers,
    YUA; *Catalogues of the Officers and Students in Yale College,* 1847–60.

4   B. Silliman, Jr., and JPN to Prudential Committee, April 10, 1848, SSS
    Papers; B. Silliman, Jr., receipt to JPN, November 6, 1850, Invoice Book,
    JPNP; B. Silliman, Jr., and JPN to Prudential Committee, August 1852,
    SSS Papers; John T. Norton to President T. D. Woolsey, January 12, 1853,
    SSS Papers, all YUA.

5   There is a table of enrollment figures, 1847–64, taken from *Catalogues of the
    Officers and Students in Yale College, 1847–64,* YUA, in Margaret W. Rossiter,
    "Justus Liebig and the Americans: A Study in the Transit of Science," Ph.D.
    dissertation, Yale University, 1971, p. 226.

6   JPN to John Whitman, October 15, 1849, YAL Letterpress Book, YUA;
    JPN Diary V (October 13, 1843), JPNP; JPN to R. B. Howland, July 27,
    1848, and JPN to J. H. Sharon, October 8, 1851, YAL Letterpress Book;
    Elizabeth A. Osborne, ed., *From the Letter-files of S. W. Johnson,* p. 21.

7   JPN to Rollin S. Jones, August 9, 1849, JPN to R. B. Howland, July 27,
    1848, and JPN to J. H. Sharon, October 8, 1851, YAL Letterpress Book;
    lecture notes are in JPNP; W. H. Brewer attended the course in 1849 and
    1850, and his notes are in the William H. Brewer Papers, YUA; *Cultivator,*
    n.s. 6 (1849): 195; 4 (1847): 324–25; 5 (1848): 258, 261; 6 (1849): 34, 38,
    296; 7 (1850): 381, 406; 8 (1851): 217; *American Agriculturalist* 6 (1847):
    326, 359, 383; 7 (1848): 263, and 10 (1851): 39, 310–11.

8   YAL Letterpress Book, passim, esp. JPN to Mrs. F. H. Green, October 30,
    1850, and JPN to W. P. Blake, April 9, 1851; JPN to Prudential Committee,
    December 10, 1850, and JPN to President, Corporation, and Fellows of Yale
    College [July 1851], SSS Papers; JPN to R. B. Howland, July 27, 1848,
    YAL Letterpress Book, all YUA. The letters of these students—G. J. Brush,
    S. W. Johnson, Mason C. Weld, George W. Weyman, and Ogden Rood—in
    the Brewer, Brush and Weld Family Collections in YUA provide much more
    detail of life in the Yale Analytical Laboratory and in several German
    laboratories during the 1850s than can be provided here.

9   Henry Erni of Yale also presented a paper to the AAAS in 1850 on work he
    had left unfinished in Zurich when he left hurriedly in 1848, "Some Experi-
    ments upon the Cause of Fermentation."

10 G. J. Brush to W. H. Brewer, October 19, 1851, and G. W. Weyman to
    Brewer [June 1851], WHBP, and J. E. Willet to G. J. Brush, August 21,
    1860, GJBP; JPN to Joseph Henry, December 5, 1848, and J. Henry to JPN,
    July 3, 1849, JPNP. Eventually in 1857 the Patent Office hired C. T. Jackson
    for a few analyses (*U.S. Patent Office Report for 1857,* vol. 4, pp. 160–64), but the
    first thorough study of maize in the United States was by W. O. Atwater in
    1869. JPN did an extensive analysis of eupyrchroite (apatite) for Ebenezer
    Emmons in 1851, however (JPN to E. Emmons, August 5, 1851, YAL
    Letterpress Book; cf. *AJS* 12 [July 1851]: 73–74).

11 JPN also earned about $150 per year from his speeches and writings and
    received large gifts from his relatives (JPN Diary IX (1851), passim; JPN
    to J. F. W. Johnston, December 9, 1851; E. H. Pease to JPN, March 18,

1851; Messrs. Blackwood to JPN, November 1, 1849, and JPN to Messrs. Blackwood, September 4, 1851, JPNP). Norton lived quite elegantly in a stylish "asymmetrical Italian villa" on Hillhouse Avenue (now #52) in New Haven.

12 JPN to E. Stabler, April 24, 1849, and JPN to W. R. Holt, August 5, 1851, YAL Letterpress Book; JPN to W. H. Brewer, January 23, 1851, WHBP; B. Silliman, Jr., and JPN to Prudential Committee, August 1851, SSS Papers; see also JPN to O. W. Gibbs, June 7, 1849, and B. Silliman, Jr., to H. Erni, July 20, 1849, YAL Letterpress Book; B. Silliman, Jr., receipt to JPN, November 6, 1850, Invoice Book, JPNP; see B. Silliman, Jr., to JPN, September 19, 1850, JPNP for a different view (all in YUA).

13 JPN, "A Description of a New Sand Bath"; Mason Weld to W. H. Brewer, October 18, 1850, WHBP; JPN Diary IX (January 7, February 12, and April 14, 1851), JPNP.

14 JPN to G. W. Merchant, November 21, 1850; B. Silliman, Jr., to J. C. Cotton, January 1, 1849; B. Silliman, Jr., to C. L. Covell, March 7, 1848; JPN to Messrs. Booth, Beach, and Beardsley, January 24 [1851], YAL Letterpress Book; List of prices [1860], SWJT; JPN to A. W. Hart, December 24, 1849; JPN to J. Lewis, December 26, 1848, YAL Letterpress Book, YUA.

15 JPN to James Vick, October 7, 1851; JPN to E. Stabler, April 24, 1849, YAL Letterpress Book; *American Agriculturalist* 10 (1851): 312–14 (Antisell); *Cultivator,* n.s. 7 (1850): 184, and 8 (1841): 60 (Salisbury); JPN to F. L. Olmsted, March 7, 1850, YAL Letterpress Book, YUA.

16 *Cultivator,* n.s. 2 (1845): 121; *American Agriculturalist* 6 (1847): 138; JPN Diary IX (March 21, 27, and April 14, 1851), JPNP; cf. Charles E. Rosenberg, "Science and Social Values in Nineteenth-Century America."

17 JPN also published an American edition of Johnston's *Catechism of Agricultural Chemistry and Geology* (Albany: E. H. Pease, 1846), which did not sell well even though New York State adopted it for its schools (E. H. Pease to JPN, January 28, 1850, and March 18, 1851, JPNP).

18 *Cultivator,* n.s. 8 (1851): 33; JPN, *Transactions of the New Haven County Agricultural Society for 1849,* pp. 28–30.

19 Gypsum: JPN to J. S. Skinner, December 11, 1848, JPNP; JPN, *Elements,* p. 115; *Cultivator* n.s. 9 (1852): 72. Nitrogen: JPN, "American Appendix," in Henry Stephens, *Farmer's Guide,* 2: 69–70. Proteins: The Liebig-Mulder dispute never really took hold in the United States, although JPN mentioned it in his Yale lectures (nos. 11 and 12, JPNP), and A. Voelcker tried to have the *AJS* take it up (see A. Voelcker "To the editors of . . ." [1847], and trans. of Mulder's "Remarks," JPNP). On mineral manures: JPN, *An Address Delivered at the Annual Show of the New York State Agricultural Society at Buffalo, September 6, 1848,* pp. 18–22; and *Cultivator,* n.s. 8 (1851): 392–93.

20 Johnston, *Lectures on Agricultural Chemistry and Geology,* 2nd ed. (Edinburgh: William Blackwood and Sons, 1847), pp. 519–28, 529; JPN Yale Lecture Notes #5, 14–19, JPNP and WHBP, YUA.

21 JPN, *An Address Delivered at the Annual Meeting of the New York State Agricultural Society, at Albany, January 19, 1848,* pp. 3, 9, 21; JPN, "Lecture to Connecticut

Legislature, 1848," n.p., JPNP; JPN, "Address," appended to *Transactions of the Hampden County Society for the year 1851,* p. 8.

22 JPN, *Elements,* p. 60; JPN, *Address at N.Y.S. Agricultural Society, January 19, 1848,* p. 5; discussion following T. S. Hunt, "On the Determination of Phosphoric Acid," p. 338; Johnston, *Lectures,* 2nd ed. (1847), pp. 519–28.

23 *AJS* 40 (1841): 189, and 45 (1843): 337–40; *Proc. AAAS* 6 (1851): 199–206; original data in YAL Analyses Book, April 1850, pp. 42–45, and JPN to B. Silliman, Jr., June 5, 1850, YAL Letterpress Book; JPN Diary IX (August 20, 1851), JPNP, which also praises A. D. Bache's address about quackery. The detection of the phosphates was still a problem in the 1860s (*AJS* 31 [1861]: 281–83).

24 *Proc. AAAS* 6 (1851): 206, 215 (titles only); David A. Wells, "Communication," pp. 19–22; idem. "Notes and Observations on the Analyses and Characters of the Soil of the Scioto Valley, Ohio," pp. 18–19.

25 *Cultivator,* n.s. 9 (1852): 345; James C. Booth, "Practical Value of Soil Analysis," pp. 49–53; Daniel Lee, "Remarks on the Foregoing Communication," *Report of the Commissioner of Patents for Year 1852,* Pt. II, *Agriculture* (Washington, 1853), p. 54.

26 T. S. Hunt to ENH, April 16, 1850, and January 11, 1853, ENHP.

27 Eugene W. Hilgard, "The Objects and Interpretation of Soil Analysis," p. 197; S. W. Johnson, "Agricultural Chemistry—Soil Analysis"; Eugene W. Hilgard, "On Soil Analyses and Their Utility."

28 Wells and JPN corresponded (JPN Diary IX [September 19, 1851], JPNP) and may have met at the Hampden County fair in September 1851 (Wells, "Communication," and JPN, "Address," both in *Transactions of Hampden County Agricultural Society for 1851,* appendix); *Cultivator,* n.s. 8 (1851): 332–33, 362–63; incomplete MS, "Observations on Soil Analysis," in JPNP was probably meant for *AJS* (JPN Diary IX [October 23 and 29, 1851], JPNP); *Country Gentleman* 6 (July 6, 1854): 5.

29 JPN Diary IX (May 16, 1851); Silverman and Beach, "National University for Upstate New York"; JPN Diary IX (October 14–15, 1851) and X (March 1, 1852), JPNP; Mason F. Cogswell to ENH, April 12, 1852, ENHP. Norton's disease was more likely pulmonary tuberculosis with perhaps a secondary tuberculosis of the larynx. The heart condition may have been real, but it does not explain the symptoms recorded in his diary (JPN Diary X [February–August 1852]) (interview with Dr. George Rosen, Professor of the History of Medicine, Yale University, May 3, 1971).

CHAPTER 8

1 Osborne, *Letterfiles,* pp. 9–10; *Cultivator,* n.s. 4 (1847): 240–41; cf. USDA, *SOIL,* p. 235; *Cultivator,* n.s. 6 (1849): 188.

2 One of these academies, the Flushing Institute on Long Island, is important historically as the successor of the Round Hill School in Northampton (McLachlan, *American Boarding Schools,* chap. 4); Osborne, *Letter-files* pp. 26, 29; O. W. Gibbs fragment, n.d., SWJT, p. 21; Obsorne, *Letter-files* pp. 30–31;

JPN to Professor Perkins, June 30, 1851, JPNP; *Proc. AAAS,* 6 (1851): 243–46, and *AJS* 12 (1851): 361–66.

3   SWJ to W. H. Brewer, August 4 and September 25, 1852, and June 30, 1863, WHBP; Osborne, *Letter-files* p. 38; SWJ fragment, n.d., SWJT, p. 41; Mason C. Weld to W. H. Brewer, August 12, 1853, WHBP, YUA.

4   *Journal für Praktische Chemie,* 62 (1854): 261–64; and 64 (1855): 157–59.

5   August Vogel, *Justus Freiherr von Liebig als Begründer der Agrikultur-Chemie,* and Johann Pohl, *Dr. Justus von Liebig und die landwirtschaftliche Lehre.* But Liebig's full impact on German agriculture has yet to be studied adequately. E. Pugh to SWJ, February 22–30 [*sic*], [1855], SWJT; *Country Gentleman* 3 (1854): 261–62.

6   Typescript of WHB's Diary, March 5, 1857, p. 227, WHBP.

7   W. H. Brewer to G. J. Brush, February 2, 1857, GJBP; WHB Diary, October 1856–May 1857, passim, WHBP; E. K. Muspratt, *My Life and Work,* esp. pp. 42–47, 68, 79.

8   Professor Franz von Kobell was a leading mineralogist with whom George Brush was studying.

9   SWJ was also much more tolerant than ENH about German morals (SWJ to W. H. Brewer, January 1854, WHBP).

10   *Annalen* 94 (1855): 224–30; and 95 (1855): 226–42; (Ville) *Country Gentleman* 3 (1854): 373–74; 4 (1854): 213–14; (Wolff) *Country Gentleman* 4 (1854): 69–70, 101–02, 149, 229–30; Justus Liebig, *The Relations of Chemistry;* G. J. Brush, *Manual of Determinative Mineralogy* (New York: John Wiley & Sons, 1875).

11   *Country Gentleman* 1 (1853): 121, 248–49, 265–66, 283; and 5 (1855): 284, 300–01; defend: *Country Gentleman* 3 (1854): 86, 151; condemn: ibid., p. 8. Results of scientific researches still appeared in agricultural journals throughout the 1850s, but they were preceded by apologies that they were not "mere theory" or by boasts that they contained new "facts," as see *Country Gentleman* 6 (1855): 170–71, and 10 (1857), 201–02.

12   *Country Gentleman* 1 (1853): 321; 12 (1858): 157, 410.

13   Ibid. 6 (1854): 5–6; *Cultivator,* n.s. 9 (1852): 411.

14   *Country Gentleman* 4 (1854): 293–94 (his italics).

15   Ibid. 5 (1855): 374, and 6 (1855): 26–27. Some farmers were also demanding more sophisticated experimentation in the mid-1850s: see ibid. 2 (1853): 69; 6 (1855): 393–94; and 8 (1856): 139.

16   Ibid. 6 (1855): 138, and (Hohenheim) ibid. 5 (1855): 333, but cf. typescript of WHB Diary, October 18, 1856, pp. 170–71 and May 31, 1857, pp. 260–2, WHBP; Osborne, *Letter-files,* pp. 66, 83; C. L. Flint to SWJ, December 4, 1854, SWJT.

17   Norton and Dana preferred O. W. Gibbs, but he was not available (JPN to J. D. Dana, July 29, 1852, Dana Scientific Correspondence, Beinecke Library, Yale University; see also JPN to O. W. Gibbs, June 7, 1849, YAL Letterpress Book, and O. W. Gibbs to JPN, June 21, 1849, JPNP); Folder #9, QCDC; *In Memoriam, Professor John Addison Porter,* pp. 4–5, 9; *AJS* 9 (1850): 20 and

20 23; *Cultivator* 6 (1849): 329–30; Sanford Howard to ENH, July 7, 1847, ENHP; Walter C. Bronson, *The History of Brown University,* pp. 286–88, 295–97, and Donald Fleming, *Science and Technology in Providence,* pp. 38–41; W. A. Norton to ENH, February 14, 1852, ENHP; W. A. Norton to T. D. Woolsey, February 19, 1852, Woolsey Papers, YUA; JPN to ENH, January 31, February 14, and July 16, 1852, ENHP; JAP to ENH, September 8, 1852, ENHP.

18 JAP to ENH, October 15, 1852, ENHP; Yale Corp. Rec., 1 (May 10, 1854); Osborne, *Letter-files* p. 90.

19 G. J. Brush to WHB, October 17, 1852; H. Horton to WHB, July 11, 1854; W. J. Craw to WHB, October 11, 1852, and February 17, 1853; M. C. Weld to WHB, November 16, 1852, all in WHBP; *Homestead* 1 (1855): 50, and JAP to J. H. Frazier, June 26, 1855, "Misc. Mss.," YUA.

20 On site of present #38 Hillhouse Ave.; Yale Corp. Rec., 1 (July 24, 1855); J. D. Dana to G. J. Brush, numerous letters 1855, GJBP; Osborne, *Letter-files* p. 90; G. J. Brush to SWJ, December 6, 1855, SWJT; SWJ's father was highly critical (J. C. Easton to Sarah and SWJ, May 12, 1856, SWJT); G. J. Brush to SWJ, December 5, 1855, SWJT.

21 James D. Dana, *Proposed Plan for a Complete Organization of the School of Science* and *Science and Scientific Schools;* Daniel C. Gilman, "Scientific Education, the Want of Connecticut" and "Scientific Schools in Europe"; W. A. Norton, "Plan of Reorganization of the School of Engineering Connected with Yale College," S.S.S. Pamphlets, YUA; John A. Porter, "Plan for an Agricultural School." The experimental farm never came into being. Such farms were popular for a time but were costly to run and no more useful for experiments than small test plots. In the 1870s, therefore, the Yale forces were anxious to avoid such a farm.

22 Gilman, "Scientific Schools in Europe," p. 320.

23 G. J. Brush to SWJ, October 4, 1856, SWJT; D. C. Gilman Memorandum, SSS Papers, YUA; L. Tucker to SWJ, November 19, 1856, SWJT; D. C. Gilman, "Collector's Book . . . 1854," in Yale Misc. Mss., "S," YUA; Yale Corp. Rec., 2 (July 26, 1859; July 24, 1860; and July 23, 1861); "A Preliminary Roll of the SSS, 1846–69," p. 33.

24 Yale Corp. Rec., 2 (July 26, 1864).

25 G. C. Caldwell to SWJ, November 14, 1869, SWJT.

26 E. S. Carr to SWJ, October 1 and 11, 1855; B. P. Johnson to SWJ, January 10, 1856, and L. Tucker to SWJ, January 10, 1856, all in SWJT; (J. H. Salisbury and E. S. Carr had been unsalaried chemists at the society since 1849). SWJ, "On the Relations that Exist between Science and Agriculture"; Yale Corp. Rec., 1 (July 29, 1856); B. Silliman, Sr., to President Woolsey, and B. Silliman, Jr., to President Woolsey, both July 26, 1856, SSS Papers, YUA; see also J. T. Norton to J. D. Dana, January 11, 1858, Dana Scientific Correspondence, Beinecke Rare Book Library, Yale University.

27 O. D. Allen, "Observations on Cesium and Rubidium," *AJS* 34 (1862): 367–73; SWJ and O. D. Allen, "On the Equivalent and Spectrum of Caesi-

um," *AJS* 35 (1863): 94–98; SWJ, "On Caesium Separation from Rubidium," *AJS* 36 (1863): 413–15; G. F. Becker, "Atomic Weight Determinations"; SWJ to sister Lizzie, January 29, 1866, SWJT.

28 *Country Gentleman* 10 (August 20 and 27, 1857): 122–23, 138.

29 Ibid. 14 (1859): 137–38, 153–54, 201–02, 361–62, 377–78; 22 (1863): 185–86, 218, 235, 250, 346–47, 361–62; also *AJS* 37 (1864): 135–36. See also Max von Pettenkofer, *Dr. Justus Freiherrn von Liebig zum Gedächtniss,* p. 15.

30 Hubert B. Vickery, "Samuel W. Johnson and *How Crops Grow,*" p. 7; E. Pugh to SWJ, October 18, 1859, and June 8, 1861, SWJT; SWJ, "Lectures on Agricultural Chemistry."

31 The widespread agricultural chemistry craze of the 1840s must have influenced Justin Morrill and his Land-Grant Act, but the actual links are elusive. D. C. Gilman wrote Justin Morrill in 1858 that the Sheffield professors supported his bill (D. C. Gilman to J. Morrill, March 22, 1858, Gilman Papers, YUA), but neither Johnson nor any other agricultural chemist I have come across took any steps to bring about the bill's passage. They mentioned it only after it had passed and federal money suddenly became available for their projects. Paul Gates, "The Morrill Act and Early Agricultural Science," discusses the possible effect of the Yale program on Morrill's thinking, but interest in agricultural science was generally widespread enough for Morrill to have come upon it independently. See also Margaret Rossiter, "Organization of Agricultural Improvement," for a general discussion.

32 Still correct today (USDA, *SOIL,* p. 80). See also W. O. James, "Julius Sachs and the Nineteenth-Century Renaissance of Botany."

33 Burton E. Livingston, "Mineral Requirements of Plants as Indicated by Means of Solution Cultures," in Forest Ray Moulton, *Liebig and after Liebig,* pp. 83–111.

34 E. Pugh to SWJ, numerous letters, 1857, SWJT; Richard Aulie, "Boussingault and the Nitrogen Cycle"; P. E. Brown, "The Beginnings and Development of Soil Microbiology in the United States."

35 Liebig, *Organic Chemistry,* 3rd London edition, pp. 136–38; SWJ, *How Crops Feed,* chaps. 4 and 6; *Country Gentleman* 4 (1854): 6; SWJ, "Essay on the Physical Properties of Soils as Affecting Fertility," "On Some Points of Agricultural Science," which he later termed "historic" (*How Crops Feed,* p. 375), and "Agricultural Chemistry—Soil Analysis."

36 *How Crops Feed,* pp. 283–89, 371–75.

CHAPTER 9

1 Liebig, *Organic Chemistry,* 1st London edition, pp. 184–86; but it was known earlier in the United States (*Cultivator* 5 [1838]: 141). The name "superphosphate," which lent itself well to fraudulent advertisers, is the technical term for this mixture of calcium phosphate and sulphate:

$$Ca_3(PO_4)_2 + 2H_2SO_4 + 4H_2O = Ca(H_2PO_4)_2 + 2(CaSO_4 \cdot 2H_2O)$$

John Bennet Lawes of England patented the first superphosphate there in 1842. See E. John Russell, "Rothamstead and Its Experiment Station," and

USDA and TVA, *Superphosphate;* $45–50 per ton was considered cheap for guano in the United States, and $60 per ton expensive; 400 1bs. per acre was the usual dosage; JPN to A. Savage, March 19, 1851; JPN to James Vick, October 7, 1851 (2), and December 11, 1851; JPN to Messrs. Choulton, Merle, and Sanford, June 24, 30, and July 7, 1851, and SWJ to same, June 26, 1851, all in YAL Letterpress Book; SWJ analyses, June 27, 1851, in YAL Analysis Notebook, YUA; *Cultivator,* n.s. 7 (1850): 138.

2 Biographies of Mapes consider him an upstanding citizen: Carl R. Woodward, "James J. Mapes and His School," in *The Development of Agriculture in New Jersey* and Brooke Hindle, "The Underside of the Learned Society in New York, 1754–1854"; *Country Gentleman* 1 (1853): 323. As late as 1855 the *Country Gentleman* refused to accept evidence that the superphosphates were worthwhile (6 [1855]: 394).

3 See Gerald White, *Scientists in Conflict,* for a full account of Benjamin Silliman, Jr.'s later discomfiture.

4 *Country Gentleman* 1 (1853): 130–31.

5 *Working Farmer* 5 (1853): 30–31; J. J. Mapes to ENH, January 5 and March 18, 1853, ENHP.

6 The campaign may have hurt the *Homestead* financially, although there is no direct evidence of this. For a related example, see Harvey W. Wiley, *An Autobiography,* pp. 207–209; *Homestead* 1 (1856): 562–64, 581–82, 613–15, 677–80, and 2 (1856): 219–20, also 1 (1856): 709–11, and 2 (1856): 83.

7 Joseph Harris to SWJ, July 13, 1856, SWJT.

8 The Royal Agricultural Society of England had a distinguished series of consulting chemists in Lyon Playfair, J. T. Way, and J. A. Voelcker. See James A. Scott Watson, *The History of the Royal Agricultural Society of England,* pp. 118–12; *Homestead* 1 (1856): 679.

9 *Homestead* 1 (1856): 744. Weld omitted unfavorable letters. SWJ to Messrs. James Lee & Co., June 13, 1856, and M. C. Weld to SWJ, July 25, 1856, SWJT.

10 Dyer favored fertilizer analysis strongly (*Transactions, Connecticut State Agricultural Society for 1854,* pp. 88–91); M. C. Weld to SWJ, January 12, 1856 [1857], SWJT; *Homestead* 2 (1857): 268, 297–98; Dyer, *Transactions, Connecticut State Agricultural Society 1858,* pp. 23–25.

11 Balance on hand, January 1857, $2533.90 (Treasurer's Report, *Transactions, Connecticut State Agricutural Society, 1856,* p. 164); L. Tucker to SWJ, January 19, 1857, SWJT.

12 *Transactions, Connecticut State Agricultural Society, 1857,* pp. 23, 40; *1859,* p. 41; *1858,* pp. 98–104, 31. Muck is now used on dry soils for water retention rather than for its chemical nutrients (USDA, *SOIL,* p. 244).

13 *Transactions, Connecticut State Agricultural Society, 1859,* pp. 29, 31, 28.

14 The Connecticut River Valley, however, had a boom in tobacco during the Civil War: Shannon, *The Farmer's Last Frontier,* chap. 11, "Specialized Agriculture and Eastern Adjustments," esp. "Connecticut as a Case Study."

15 The board's unpopularity is a constant theme in Orange Judd's letters to W. O. Atwater, 1875–77, W. O. Atwater Papers, Wesleyan University.

16   Best biographies of Atwater are: Edward C. Schneider, "Wilbur Olin At-
     water," and Leonard A. Maynard, "Wilbur O. Atwater"; *Third Annual
     Report, Connecticut Board of Agriculture, 1868–69,* pp. 208–28.

17   Gold and Weld were active in the Massachusetts campaign (*Sixteenth Annual
     Report, Secretary of the Massachusetts Board of Agriculture, 1868,* pp. 93–107, and
     discussion; "An Act To Prevent the Manufacture and Sale of Adulterated
     Commercial Fertilizers," in *Acts and Resolves Passed by the General Court of
     Massachusetts, 1869*); "An Act To Prevent Fraud in the Sale of Commercial
     Manures," in *Acts and Resolves of the Forty-Eighth Legislature of the State of Maine,
     1869,* pp. 34–35; "An Act To Prevent Fraud in the Manufacture and Sale of
     Fertilizers" *Public Acts Passed by the General Assembly of the State of Connecticut,
     1869,* p. 302).

18   *Fourth Annual Report, Connecticut Board of Agriculture, 1869–70,* pp. 362–80;
     Oscar E. Anderson, Jr., *The Health of a Nation,* p. 68.

19   There were two such attempts in Massachusetts in 1868 and 1869.

20   *Fourth Annual Report, Connecticut Board of Agriculture, 1869–70,* pp. 421–23.

21   A. C. True, *A History of Agricultural Experimentation and Research in the United
     States,* pp. 67–82.

22   "Proceedings of the Convention of Friends of Agricultural Education, August
     24–25, 1871," pp. 42, 78, 137.

23   *Proceedings of the National Agricultural Convention, 1872,* pp. 61–68.

24   W. O. Atwater to SWJ, January 7, 1873, SWJT.

25   W. O. Atwater to SWJ, July 8, 1873, SWJT; *AJS* 48 (1869): 352–60; *Seventh
     Annual Report, Connecticut Board of Agriculture, 1873–74,* p. 45.

26   Ibid., p. 64.

27   Ibid., pp. 239–40.

28   *Eighth Annual Report, Connecticut Board of Agriculture, 1874–75,* p. 8.

29   *Seventh Annual Report, Connecticut Board of Agriculture, 1873–74,* pp. 346–67.

30   Law, "Agricultural Experiment Station Movement," p. 98.

31   *Eighth Annual Report, Connecticut Board of Agriculture, 1874–75,* pp. 131–80.
     See Becker, "Emergence of a Trace Nutrient Concept."

32   *Eighth Annual Report. Connecticut Board of Agriculture, 1874–75,* pp. 186–88.

33   Ibid., pp. 239–76.

34   Ibid., p. 268.

35   Judd insisted that he had not introduced his bill until Johnson's had failed
     (O. Judd to W. O. Atwater, July 2, 3, 6, and 8, 1875, Atwater Papers, and W.
     O. Atwater to SWJ, July 22, 1875, SWJT), but he must have been acting
     on rumor. He introduced his bill on June 4, 1875 (*Journal of the Senate for
     1875,* p. 174), but the Joint Committee did not recommend the rejection of the
     board's bill until July 1, 1875 (*Journal of the House of Representatives,* p. 312).

36   *Ninth Annual Report, Connecticut Board of Agriculture, 1875–76,* p. 361.

37   W. O. Atwater to SWJ, Oct. 7, 1875, and SWJ to wife, April 15, 1876,
     SWJT. For SWJ's depressions and dyspepsia see also G. J. Brush to W. H.
     Brewer, May 23, 1861, and December 28, 1863, WHBP.

38   *Tenth Annual Report, Connecticut Board of Agriculture, 1876–77,* p. 353; also
     Atwater's correspondence, 1875–77, Wesleyan University.

39 *Tenth Annual Report Connecticut Board of Agriculture, 1876–77,* pp. 361–62.

40 W. O. Atwater to O. Judd, April 14, 20, 27, and May 3, 1877, and W. O. Atwater to Mr. Wells, April 17, 1877, Atwater Papers, Wesleyan University.

41 The station's new site was the former Eli Whitney estate one mile from Yale on what is now Huntington Street, New Haven; *Annual Report of the Connecticut Agricultural Experiment Station for 1887,* pp. 9, 10. SWJ to Eugene W. Hilgard, April 1, 1882, Eugene W. Hilgard Papers, Bancroft Library, University of California, Berkeley. Several other Johnson letters in this collection show how burdened SWJ was after 1877.

42 Dupree, *Science in the Federal Government,* pp. 160–61.

43 See C. Rosenberg, "The Adams Act" and "Science, Technology, and Economic Growth," for a discussion of the psychosocial factors involved.

Bibliography

MANUSCRIPTS

Fortunately, voluminous materials are available on all three of the main figures in this study, Eben Horsford, John P. Norton, and Samuel W. Johnson. Much of it has been acquired recently, and very little has been used before.

There are two major collections of material on the life of Eben Horsford. The most accessible at present is housed in the Archives of the Rensselaer Polytechnic Institute in Troy, New York. The collection contains about fifteen cubic feet of Horsford correspondence for the years 1840–60 and several more feet of related material. Professor Samuel Rezneck obtained the collection in 1965 from Mrs. Augustus H. Fiske, the wife of a grandson of Horsford. The collection is of special interest for the view it offers of industrial chemistry in America in the 1850s.

Mrs. Fiske's stepson, Andrew Fiske, has the other large Horsford collection at the family home, Sylvester Manor on Shelter Island, Long Island, New York. Andrew Fiske is full of interesting anecdotes about the family and the Rumford Chemical Works, which Horsford founded and for which Fiske worked in the 1930s. Since his collection is uncatalogued, I am uncertain just how large it is and what it contains. But it probably has Horsford's Giessen lecture notes, his diaries, and other personal material for the period before 1850, when the collections at RPI become quite full.

Besides these two collections, there are several others that also have useful material on Horsford. John Clayton, Jr., of the University of Delaware Archives was able to acquire the Quaesita C. Drake Collection that provided some helpful references. Quaesita Drake, a University of Delaware Professor of Chemistry Emerita, was writing a biography of Horsford in 1955 but dropped it when H. S. Van Klooster's article on Liebig's American students, primarily Horsford, appeared in 1956. The collection is made up of two Hollinger boxes of her notes. The Rhode Island Historical Society and the Providence Public Library also have a few items of interest on Horsford.

The letters of Oliver Wolcott Gibbs in the Gibbs Family Collection at the Wisconsin State Historical Society in Madison offered useful supplementary material. Many of the Americans who studied in Europe cherished their letters home more than any letters they wrote before or after their trip abroad. Gibbs material before the 1860s is quite scarce except for this set of twenty-six long letters from Berlin, Giessen, and Paris in 1845–47. They provide a valuable comparison of another American's reaction to Liebig in 1845–46.

Likewise, Josiah Dwight Whitney's letters from Berlin and Giessen in 1844–47 have been preserved in the William D. Whitney Collection in the Yale University Archives. Whitney was Gibbs's companion and an acquaintance of Horsford.

The James Hall Papers at the New York Historical Library in Albany contain a large number of letters from Horsford to Hall from the 1840s through the 1860s. They complement the letters from Hall to Horsford at RPI. Since the two men kept each other informed about events in Albany and Cambridge and were frequently rather outspoken, they provide valuable material on the politics of American science. The fifty-four letters before 1854 were the most useful.

The collections at the Harvard University Archives in Widener Libary were voluminous but, in comparison with Horsford's letters, quite disappointing. The most important series of papers were the Corporation Records, the College Letters and Papers, the Reports of Visiting Committees to the Overseers, the L.S.S. Faculty Records, the published President's Reports (with the Treasurer's Statement), and the catalogues.

The only extant letter between J. P. Norton and Horsford when in Europe is at the Houghton Library of Harvard University. The Edward Everett Papers and the John Collins Warren Correspondence at the Massachusetts Historical Society in Boston also had related material on John W. Webster. The William Barton Rogers Papers at the Massachusetts Institute of Technology Archives also had occasional items of interest.

The manuscript material on John Pitkin Norton is mostly located at the Yale University Archives. The recently acquired John Pitkin Norton Papers are the most important. Its six cubic feet contain ten volumes of diaries from 1838–47 and 1851–52. Those covering Norton's first years at the Yale Analytical Laboratory, 1847–50, which would be especially interesting, are unfortunately missing. Besides the diaries, the collection includes three letterbooks, one volume of letters received, an invoice book, a copy book, and drafts of Norton's American notes to Stephens's *Farmer's Guide* (1851), his Yale College lecture notes (thirty-three notebooks), and assorted other published and unpublished lectures. Most of the collection is of the period 1848–52.

The vast William H. Brewer Papers also in the Yale University Archives were of great value. Brewer was closely associated with Norton, the Yale Analytical Laboratory, Johnson, and Connecticut agriculture for about fifty years. Although he did not play a central role in transmitting Liebig's influence to America, he collected material about those who did and was himself an amateur historian of agricultural improvement. The collection has recently been catalogued and comprises over sixty Hollinger boxes.

The George Brush Family Papers, also in the Yale University Archives, were an additional source of information on the Yale Analytical Laboratory. Brush was the confidant of James Dwight Dana and Benjamin Silliman, Jr., and was greatly concerned about the laboratory, even before becoming a professor there in 1855. His letters thus provide one of the best sources on the YAL in the 1850s.

Other material at the Yale University Archives was also of use. The Yale Analytical Laboratory Letterpress Book has about three hundred letters of the period 1847 to 1852 and, together with two notebooks of analytical data, gives a picture of the work being done in the laboratory. But there is nothing comparable for the period after 1852. The Sheffield Scientific School Collection is disappointing. Only one folder of one box covers the pre-1860 period. It contains drafts of official letters from Norton and Silliman, Jr., to governing boards about degrees and finances which are only moderately informative. Other administrative material includes the S.S.S. Pamphlet Collection (fund-raising literature), the Yale Treasurer's Reports, college catalogues, and the Yale Corporation Records (in Woodbridge Hall). Russell H. Chittenden has been through most of these documents in his two-volume *History of the Sheffield Scientific School of Yale University, 1846–1922* (New Haven: Yale University Press, 1928).

There were occasional items in the T. D. Woolsey Papers, the Gilman Family Papers, and the Miscellaneous Manuscripts at the Yale University Archives in Sterling Memorial Library and in the James Dwight Dana Scientific Correspondence and Silliman Family Papers in the Beinecke Rare Book Library at Yale.

The chief manuscript repository for Samuel W. Johnson is the Department of Biochemistry, Connecticut Agricultural Experiment Station, Huntington Street, New Haven. Their collection runs to about 2,000 pages of typescript of diaries, incoming correspondence, and letters home over the period 1848–1909. The letters from Wilbur O. Atwater, Edward H. Jenkins, and Evan Pugh were of primary interest to this study. Large as the collection is, it can hardly be complete, since often whole months pass without a single letter. Johnson's daughter published many of the letters, especially the early ones, in Elizabeth A. Osborne, *From the Letter-Files of Samuel W. Johnson* (New Haven: Yale University Press, 1913), but she often made significant omissions without indication. What she did with the original letters after 1913 is a mystery.

Other useful collections on Johnson are the Lewis Weld Family Papers in the Yale University Archives and the Eugene W. Hilgard Papers at the Bancroft Libarary, University of California, Berkeley. Mason Weld was Johnson's roommate in Germany in 1853–55, and his more than twenty letters home cast additional light on Johnson's rather withdrawn personality. Hilgard was a prominent soil chemist to whom Johnson wrote sporadically from 1877 to 1890.

The Wilbur Olin Atwater Papers in the Wesleyan University Archives, Middletown, Connecticut, are also an important source for material on Johnson and the founding of the Connecticut Agricultural Experiment Station. The two boxes of pre-1878 material form only a small part of the large collection.

SERIALS

American Academy of Arts and Sciences. *Proceedings*. Boston, 1846–60.
American Agriculturalist. New York City, 1843–51.
American Association for the Advancement of Science. *Proceedings*. 1848–60.
American Journal of Science. New Haven, 1840–60.
Connecticut Agricultural Experiment Station. *Annual Report*. 1877–90.
Connecticut General Assembly. *Journal of the House of Representatives*. 1865–80.
———. *Journal of the Senate*. 1865–80.
———. *Public Acts Passed by the General Assembly of the State of Connecticut. 1865–80*.
Connecticut State Agricultural Society. *Transactions*. 1854–59.
Connecticut State Board of Agriculture. *Annual Report*. 1866–86.
Country Gentleman. Albany, 1853–58.
Cultivator. Albany, 1834–52.
Homestead. Hartford, 1855–61.
New York State Agricultural Society. *Transactions*. 1841–57.
Nordamerikanischer Monatsbericht für Natur- und Heilkunde. Philadelphia, 1850–52.
Soil of the South. Columbus, Ga., 1851–52.
U.S. Patent Office. *Report from the Commissioner of Patents*. 1837–60.

OTHER PRINTED WORKS

Anderson, Oscar E., Jr. *The Health of a Nation: Harvey W. Wiley and the Fight for Pure Food*. Chicago: University of Chicago Press, 1958.
Anderson, Russell H. "New York Agriculture Meets the West, 1830–1850," *Wisconsin Magazine of History* 16 (1932–33): 163–98, 285–96.

Appeal in Behalf of the Yale Scientific School. New Haven, 1856. In Yale University Archives.

Atwater, Wilbur O. "Agricultural Experiment Stations in Europe." *Report of the Commissioner of Agriculture for the Year 1875,* pp. 517–24.

———. "On the Proximate Composition of Several Varieties of American Maize." *American Journal of Science* 48 (1869), 352–60.

———. "Reminiscences of Thirty Years of Agricultural Science in Connecticut." *Report of the Connecticut Board of Agriculture for 1903,* pp. 216–33.

Aulie, Richard P. "Boussingault and the Nitrogen Cycle." Ph.D. dissertation, Yale University, 1968.

———. "Boussingault and the Nitrogen Cycle." *Proceedings of the American Philosophical Society,* 114 (1970): 453–79.

Bagley, William C. *Soil Exhaustion and the Civil War.* Washington, D.C.: American Council on Public Affairs, 1942.

Bartow, Virginia. "Chemical Genealogy." *Journal of Chemical Education* 16 (1939): 236–38.

Basalla, George. "The Spread of Western Science." *Science* 156 (May 5, 1967): 611–22.

Bear, Firman E. *Soils in Relation to Crop Growth.* New York: Reinhold Publishing Co., 1965.

Beardsley, Edward H. *The Rise of the American Chemistry Profession, 1850–1900.* University of Florida Monographs, no. 23, Social Sciences. Gainesville, Fla.: University of Florida Press, 1964.

Becker, George F. "Atomic Weight Determinations: A Digest of the Investigations Published since 1814." *Smithsonian Miscellaneous Collections* 27(1883).

Becker, Stanley L. "The Emergence of a Trace Nutrient Concept through Animal Feeding Experiments." Ph.D. dissertation, University of Wisconsin, 1968.

Bell, Whitfield J., Jr. "Philadelphia Medical Students in Europe, 1750–1800." *Pennsylvania Magazine of History and Biography* 67 (1943): 1–29.

Ben-David, Joseph. *The Scientist's Role in Society: A Comparative Study.* Englewood Cliffs, N. J.: Prentice-Hall, 1971.

Berzelius, J. J. *Jac. Berzelius Bref.* Edited by H. G. Söderbaum. Stockholm: Royal Academy of Sciences of Sweden, 1916.

———. "Pflanzenchemie." *Jahresbericht über die Fortschritte der Chemie und Mineralogie* 21 (1842): 235–7.

———. *Traité de Chimie.* Translated by Mme. Esslinger. Vols. 5–6. Paris: Firmin Didot Frères, 1831–32.

Bidwell, Percy W. "Rural Economy in New England at the Beginning of the Nineteenth Century." *Transactions of the Connecticut Academy of Arts and Sciences* 20 (1916): 241–399.

Bidwell, Percy W., and John I. Falconer. *History of Agriculture in the Northern United States, 1620–1860.* Washington, D.C.: Carnegie Institution, 1925.

Bigelow, Jacob. *Elements of Technology, Taken Chiefly from a Course of Lectures Delivered at Cambridge, on the Applications of the Sciences to the Useful Arts.* Boston: Hilliard, Gray, Little and Wilkins, 1829.

——. *The Useful Arts, Considered in Connexion with the Applications of Science.* Boston: Marsh, Capen, Lyon, and Webb, 1840.

Biographical Dictionary of the American Congress, 1774–1961. Washington, D.C.: Government Printing Office, 1961.

Bishop, Lottie G. "The Buildings of Yale University." *Bulletin of Yale University,* series 61, no. 3 (February 1, 1965).

Black, C. A. *Soil-Plant Relationships.* 2nd ed. New York: John Wiley & Sons, 1968.

Black, John D. *The Rural Economy of New England: A Regional Study.* Cambridge: Harvard University Press, 1950.

Blake, Nelson M. *Water for the Cities.* Syracuse: Syracuse University Press, 1956.

Bliss, A. D. "Men and Machines in Early Harvard Science." *Journal of Chemical Education* 17 (1940): 353–60.

Bloom, Jacqueline. "Evan Pugh: The Education of a Scientist, 1828–1859." M. A. thesis, Department of History, Pennsylvania State University, June 1960.

Bogert, Marston Taylor. "Charles Frederic Chandler." *National Academy of Sciences Biographical Memoirs* 14 (1931): 125–81.

Bolton, Henry Carrington. *A Select Bibliography of Chemistry, 1492–1892.* Smithsonian Miscellaneous Collections, no. 850. Washington, D.C.: Smithsonian Institution, 1893.

Bonner, Thomas N. *American Doctors and German Universities: A Chapter in International Intellectual Relations, 1870–1914.* Lincoln, Nebr.: University of Nebraska Press, 1962.

Booth, James C. "Practical Value of Soil Analysis." *Report of the Commissioner of Patents for the Year 1852.* Part II. *Agriculture* (Washington, D.C., 1853), pp. 49–53, with remarks by Daniel Lee, pp. 54–56.

Boussingault, J.–B. *Economie Rurale.* 2 vols. Paris: Bechet Jeune, 1844.

Bowers, Douglas, ed. *A List of References for the History of Agriculture in the United States, 1790–1840.* Davis, Calif.: Agricultural History Center, University of California, 1969.

Boyè, Martin. "On the Composition of the Schuylkill Water." *Proceedings of the American Association for the Advancement of Science* 1 (1848): 123–32.

Bradford, William. *History of Plymouth Plantation, 1620–1647.* 2 vols. Boston: Massachusetts Historical Society, 1912.

Brewer, William H. "Determinations of Nitrogen in Two Varieties of Indian Corn." *Proceedings of the American Association for the Advancement of Science* 4 (1850), 386–89.

Brock, W. H. "Liebig's Laboratory Accounts." *Ambix* 19 (1972): 47–58.

Bronson, Walter C. *The History of Brown University: 1764–1914.* Providence: Brown University Press, 1914.

Brown, P. E. "The Beginnings and Development of Soil Microbiology in the United States." *Soil Science* 40 (1935): 49–58.

Brown, Ralph H. *Historical Geography of the United States.* New York: Harcourt, Brace and Co., 1948.

Browne, Charles A. "Agricultural Chemistry." *Journal of the American Chemical Society* 48 (1926): 127–201.

———. "Bernhard Tollens (1841–1918) and Some American Students of His School of Agricultural Chemistry." *Journal of Chemical Education* 19 (1942): 253–59.

———. "Emerson and Chemistry." *Journal of Chemical Education* 5 (1928): 269–79 and 391–402. (incl. C. T. Jackson and S. L. Dana).

———. "European Laboratory Experiences of an Early American Agricultural Chemist—Dr. Evan Pugh (1828–1864)." *Journal of Chemical Education* 7 (1930): 499–517.

———. "The History of Chemical Education in America between the Years 1820 and 1870." *Journal of Chemical Education* 9 (1932); 696–728.

———. "The Role of Refugees in the History of American Science." *Science* 91 (1940): 203–08.

———. *A Source Book of Agricultural Chemistry.* Waltham, Mass.: Chronica Botanica Co., 1944.

Browne, Charles A., and Eva Armstrong. "History of Chemistry in America." *Journal of Chemical Education* 19 (1942): 379–81.

Browne, Daniel J. "Progress and Public Encouragement of Agriculture in Russia, Prussia, and the United States." *Report of the Commissioner of Patents for the Year 1857, Agriculture,* pp. 1–50.

Buckman, Harry O., and Nyle C. Brady. *The Nature and Properties of Soils.* 7th ed. New York: Macmillan Co., 1969.

Bunce, Jonathan B. "Analyses Relative to the Economical Value of Anthracite Coal Ashes." *Proceedings of the American Association for Advancement of Science* 4 (1850): 213–15.

Carman, Harry J. *Jesse Buel, Agricultural Reformer.* New York: Columbia University Press, 1947.

Carrier, Lyman. "The United States Agricultural Society, 1852–1860: Its Relation to the Origin of the United States Department of Agriculture and Land Grant Colleges." *Agricultural History* 11 (1937): 278–88.

Carriere, Justus, ed. *Berzelius und Liebig, Ihre Briefe von 1831–1845.* Munich and Leipzig: J. F. Lehman, 1893.

Carstensen, Vernon. "The Genesis of an Agricultural Experiment Station." *Agricultural History* 34 (1960): 13–20.

Chambers, Jonathan D., and Gordon E. Mingay. *The Agricultural Revolution, 1750–1880.* New York: Schocken Books, 1966.

Child, Ernest. *The Tools of the Chemist.* New York: Reinhold Co., 1940.

Chittenden, Russell H. *History of the Sheffield Scientific School of Yale University, 1846–1922.* 2 vols. New Haven: Yale University Press, 1928.

Clark, Andrew H. "Suggestions for the Geographical Study of Agricultural Change in the United States, 1790–1840." *Agricultural History* 46 (January 1972): 155–72.

Clarke, John M. *James Hall of Albany, Geologist and Paleontologist, 1811–1898.* Albany, 1921.

Cohen, I. B. "Harvard and the Scientific Spirit." *Harvard Alumni Bulletin* 50 (February 7, 1948): 393–98.

Cole, Arthur H. "Agricultural Crazes: A Neglected Chapter in American Economic History." *American Economic Review* 16 (1926): 622–39.

Colman, Gould P. *Education and Agriculture: A History of the New York State College of Agriculture at Cornell University.* Ithaca, N. Y.: Cornell University Press, 1963.

Colman, Henry. *Reports on the Agriculture of Massachusetts.* 4 vols. Boston: Dutton & Wentworth, 1838–41.

———. Review of Liebig's "Organic Chemistry in Its Applications. . . ." *North American Review* 51 (1841): 147–69.

———. Review of 2nd edition, ibid., 54 (1842), 476–83.

Combe, George. *Notes on the United States of North America during a Phrenological Visit in 1838–9–40.* 2 vols. Philadelphia: Carey & Hart, 1841.

Conant, James Bryant. *Pasteur's Study of Fermentation.* Harvard Case Study in Experimental Science, no. 6. Cambridge: Harvard University Press, 1952.

Coulter, E. Merle. *Daniel Lee, Agriculturalist, His Life North and South.* Athens, Ga.: University of Georgia Press, 1972.

Craven, Avery O. *Edmund Ruffin, Southerner, A Study in Secession.* 1932. Reprint. Hamden, Conn. Archon Books, 1964.

———. "John Taylor and Southern Agriculture." *Journal of Southern History* 4 (1938): 137–47.

———. *Soil Exhaustion as a Factor in the Agricultural History of Virginia and Maryland, 1606–1860.* University of Illinois Studies in the Social Sciences, vol. 13. Urbana, Ill.: University of Illinois Press, 1925. The pioneer study of soil exhaustion.

Cross, Whitney R. *The Burned-over District: The Social and Intellectual History of Enthusiastic Religion in Western New York, 1800–1850.* Ithaca, N.Y.: Cornell University Press, 1950; reprinted New York: Harper Torchbook, 1965.

Dana, James. *Memoir of the Late Hon. Samuel Dana.* Cambridge, Mass.: John Wilson and Son, 1877.

Dana, James D. "On Coral Reefs and Islands, Part Eighth." *American Journal of Science,* 2nd series, 14 (1852): 76–84.

———. "On Some Modern Calcareous Rock Formations." *American Journal of Science,* 2nd series, 14 (1852): 410–18.

———. *Proposed Plan for a Complete Organization of the School of Science, Connected with Yale College.* New Haven, 1856.

———. *Science and Scientific Schools: An Address before the Alumni of Yale College.* New Haven: S. Babcock, 1856.

Dana, Samuel L. *An Essay on Manures.* New York: C. M. Saxton, 1850.

———. *A Muck Manual for Farmers.* Lowell, Mass.: Daniel Bixby, 1842.

———. *A Muck Manual for Farmers.* 4th ed. New York: Orange Judd, 1865. Contains an autobiographical preface.

Danhof, Clarence H. "American Evaluations of European Agriculture." *Journal of Economic History, Supplement* 9 (1949): 61–71.

———. *Change in Agriculture: The Northern United States 1820–1870.* Cambridge: Harvard University Press, 1969.

Davies, John D. *Phrenology, Fad and Science, A 19th-Century American Crusade.* New Haven: Yale University Press, 1955.

Davy, Sir Humphry. *Elements of Agricultural Chemistry in a Course of Lectures for the Board of Agriculture.* London: Longman, Hurst, Rees, Orme, and Brown, 1813.

Dean, John. "On the Value of the Different Kinds of Prepared Vegetable Food." *Proceedings of the American Academy of Arts and Sciences* 3 (April 25, 1854): 109–27.

Demaree, Albert L. *The American Agricultural Press, 1819–1860.* New York: Columbia University Press, 1941. Very useful.

———. "The Farm Journals, Their Editors, and Their Public, 1830–1860." *Agricultural History* 15 (1941): 182–88.

"Dinner in Honor of Professor Liebig." *American Quarterly Journal of Agriculture* 1 (1843): 364–68.

Dupree, A. Hunter. *Asa Gray, 1810–1888.* Cambridge: Harvard University Press, 1959.

———. *Science in the Federal Government.* Cambridge: Harvard University Press, 1957; reprinted as Harper Torchbook, 1964.

Ellis, David M. "Albany and Troy, Commercial Rivals." *New York History* 24 (1943): 484–511.

———. *Landlords and Famers in the Hudson-Mohawk Region, 1790–1850.* Ithaca, N. Y.: Cornell University Press, 1946.

———. "Rivalry between the New York Central and the Erie Canal." *New York History* 29 (1948): 268–300.

———. "Yankee-Dutch Confrontation in the Albany Area." *New England Quarterly* 45 (June 1972): 262–70.

Ellis, David M., James A. Frost, Harold C. Syrett, and Harry J. Carman. *A History of New York State.* Rev. ed. Ithaca, N. Y.: Cornell University Press, 1967.

Erni, Henry. "An Account of Some Experiments upon the Cause of Fermentation." *Proceedings of the American Association for the Advancement of Science* 4 (1850): 143–46.

Everett, Edward. "University Education." In *Orations and Speeches on Various Occasions,* 2: 493–518. 7th ed. Boston: Little, Brown and Co., 1865.

Farber, Eduard. "History of Phosphorus." *Smithsonian Institution Contributions from the Museum of History and Technology* 40 (U.S.N.M. Bulletin 240). Washington, D.C.: U.S. Government Printing Office, 1965.

Farnam, Henry W. "Joseph Earl Sheffield, the Father of the Sheffield Scientific School." *New Haven Colony Historical Society Transactions* 7 (1907): 65–119.

Feldhaus, Franz M. "Liebig als Patentinhaber." *Chemiker-Zeitung* 52 (1928): 377.

Fisher, George P. *Life of Benjamin Silliman, M.D., LL.D.* 2 vols. New York: Charles Scribner & Co., 1866.

Fisher, Irving. "Samuel W. Johnson." In *Bibliography of the Present Officers of Yale University,* pp. 76–84, n.p., 1893.

Fleitmann, Th. "Ueber die Existenz eines schwefelfreien Proteins." *Annalen der Chemie* 61 (1847): 121–26.

Fleming, Donald. *Science and Technology in Providence, 1760–1914.* Providence: Brown University Press, 1952.

Franz, Günther, ed. *Universität Hohenheim–Landwirtschaftliche Hochschule, 1818–1968.* Stuttgart: Ulmer, 1968.

Fresenius, C. Remigius. *Manual of Qualitative Chemical Analysis.* Edited by Samuel W. Johnson. New York: John Wiley & Son, 1864.

Friis, Herman R. "A Series of Population Maps of the Colonies and the United States, 1625–1790." *Geographical Review* 30 (1940): 463–70.

Frothingham, Paul Revere. *Edward Everett, Orator and Statesman.* Boston: Houghton Mifflin Co., 1925.

Fruton, Joseph S. *Molecules and Life: Historical Essays on the Interplay of Chemistry and Biology.* New York: John Wiley & Sons, 1972.

Fulton, John F., and Elizabeth H. Thomson. *Benjamin Silliman, 1779–1864: Pathfinder in American Science.* New York: Henry Schuman, 1947.

Galston, Arthur W. *The Life of the Green Plant.* 2nd ed. Englewood Cliffs, N. J.: Prentice-Hall, 1964.

Gardiner, Curtiss C., ed. *Lion Gardiner and His Descendants.* St. Louis: A. Whipple, 1890.

Gates, Paul W. "Agricultural Change in New York State, 1850–1890." *New York History* 50 (1969): 115–41.

———. *Agriculture and the Civil War.* New York: Alfred A. Knopf, 1965.

———. *The Farmer's Age: Agriculture, 1815–1860.* Vol. 3 of *The Economic History of the United States.* New York: Harper & Row, 1960.

———. "The Morrill Act and Early Agricultural Science." *Michigan History* 46 (December 1962), 289–302. Discusses Norton's activities at Yale.

———. "Problems in Agricultural History, 1790–1840." *Agricultural History* 46 (January 1972): 33–58.

Genovese, Eugene D. "Cotton, Slavery, and Soil Exhaustion in the Old South." *Cotton History Review* 2 (1961): 3–17.

Gilman, Daniel C. "Scientific Education, the Want of Connecticut." In *Transactions of the Connecticut State Agricultural Society for the Year 1855,* pp. 216–24, Hartford: Case, Tiffany & Co., 1856.

———. "Scientific Schools in Europe." *American Journal of Education* 1 (1856): 315–28.

———. *The Sheffield Scientific School of Yale University: A Semi-Centennial Historical Discourse, Oct. 28, 1897.* New Haven, 1897.

Good, H. G. "On the Early History of Liebig's Laboratory." *Journal of Chemical Education* 13 (1936): 557–62.

Gougher, Ronald L. "Comparison of English and American Views of the German University, 1840–65; A Bibliography." *History of Education Quarterly* 9 (1969): 477–91.

Graham, Gerald S. "The Gypsum Trade of the Maritime Provinces: Its Relation to American Diplomacy and Agriculture in the Early Nineteenth Century." *Agricultural History* 12 (1938): 209–23.

[Gray, Asa.] "The Chemistry of Vegetation." *North American Review* 60 (1845): 156–95.

Grossman, H. "Justus von Liebig und die Englander, eine zeitgemässe Betrachtung." *Chemiker-Zeitung* 41 (1917): 429–31.

Guralnick, Stanley M. "Science and the American College: 1828–1860." Ph.D. dissertation, University of Pennsylvania, 1969.

Hamerow, Theodore S. *Restoration, Revolution, Reaction: Economics and Politics in Germany, 1815–1871*. Princeton: Princeton University Press, 1958.

Harding, T. Swann. *Two Blades of Grass: A History of the Scientific Development in the U.S. Department of Agriculture*. Norman: University of Oklahoma Press, 1947.

Hart, Helen. "Nicolas Théodore de Saussure." *Plant Physiology* 5 (1930): 425–29.

Hart, James Morgan. *German Universities: A Narrative of Personal Experience*. New York: G.P. Putnam's Sons, 1874.

Hawker, Lilian E., A. H. Linton, B. F. Folkes, and M. J. Carlile. *An Introduction to the Biology of Micro-organisms*. London: Edward Arnold, 1960.

Hayes, A. A. "On the Assumed Existence of Ammonia in the General Atmosphere." *Proceedings of the American Association for the Advancement of Science* 4 (1850): 207–13.

Haynes, William. *American Chemical Industry, Background and Beginnings*. Vol. 1. New York: D. Van Nostrand Co., 1954.

Hedrick, Ulysses P. *A History of Agriculture in the State of New York*. Albany: New York State Agricultural Society, 1933.

Herbst, Jurgen. *The German Historical School in American Scholarship: A Study in the Transfer of Culture*. Ithaca, N. Y.: Cornell University Press, 1965.

Higbee, Edward. *American Agriculture: Geography, Resources, Conservation*. New York: John Wiley & Sons, 1958.

Hilgard, Eugene W. "The Objects and Interpretation of Soil Analysis." *American Journal of Science*, 3rd ser., 22 (1881): 183–97.

———. "On Soil Analyses and Their Utility." *American Journal of Science*, 3rd series, 4(1882): 434–35

Hill, Hamilton Andrews. *Memoir of Abbott Lawrence*. Boston: privately printed, 1883.

Hill, Robert W. "John Pitkin Norton's Visit to England, 1844." *Agricultural History* 8 (1934): 219–22. Publishes a letter from Norton to Theodore Dwight, Jr.

Hindle, Brooke. "The Underside of the Learned Society in New York, 1754–1854." (In a forthcoming volume edited by Alexandra Oleson and Sanborn Brown. Baltimore: Johns Hopkins University Press.)

Hinsdale, B. A. "Notes on the History of Foreign Influence upon Education in the United States." In *Report of the Commissioner of Education for the Year 1897–98*, part 1, pp. 591–629.

Hitchcock, Edward. *Final Report on the Geology of Massachusetts*. Amherst: J. S. & C. Adams, 1841.

Hobbins, James M. "Shaping a Provincial Learned Society: The Early History of the Albany Institute." (See Hindle entry, above.)

Hofmann, A. W. *The Life-Work of Liebig: The Faraday Lecture for 1875.* London: Macmillan and Co., 1876.

Hofmann, J. P. *Das Chemische Laboratorium der Ludwigs-Universität zu Giessen.* Heidelberg: C. F. Winter, 1842.

Hofstadter, Richard. *Anti-intellectualism in American Life.* New York: Alfred A. Knopf, 1962.

Holmes, Frederic L. "Elementary Analysis and the Origins of Physiological Chemistry." *Isis* 54 (1963): 50–81.

———. "Justus Liebig." *Dictionary of Scientific Biography.* Vol. 8. New York: Charles Scribner's Sons, 1973.

Holmfeld, John D. "From Amateurs to Professionals in American Science: The Controversy over the Proceedings of an 1853 Meeting." *Proceedings of the American Philosophical Society* 114 (1970): 22–36.

Holt, B. W. G. "Social Aspects in the Emergence of Chemistry as an Exact Science: The British Chemical Profession." *British Journal of Sociology* 2 (1970): 181–99.

Horsford, Eben N. "On Ammonia in Atmospheric Air." *Proceedings of the American Association for the Advancement of Science* 4 (1850): 43–44.

———. "Ammonia in the Atmosphere." *Proceedings of the American Association for the Advancement of Science* 11 (1856): 145–52.

———. "Ammoniakgehalt der Gletscher." *Annalen der Chemie* 59 (1846): 113–16.

———. "Analyse der Asche des Klee's (Trifolium pratense)." *Annalen der Chemie* 58 (1846): 391.

———. "Connection between the Atomic Weights and the Physical and Chemical Properties of Barium, Strontium, Calcium, and Magnesium, and Some of Their Compounds." *American Journal of Science,* 2nd series, 9 (1850): 176–84.

———. "Der Geschichte der condensirten Milch." *Dingler's Polytechnisches Journal* 220 (1876): 539–46.

———. "List of Sweet Bodies and the Formulae." *Proceedings of the American Academy of Arts and Sciences* 1 (1846–48): 302–05.

———. "On the Moisture, Ammonia, and Organic Matter of the Atmosphere." *Proceedings of the American Association for the Advancement of Science* 2 (1849): 124–28.

———. "Notiz über den Ammoniakgehalt der Atmosphäre." *Annalen der Chemie* 74 (1850): 243–44.

———. "On the Relation of the Chemical Constitution of Bodies to Taste." *Proceedings of the American Association for the Advancement of Science* 4 (1850): 216–22.

———. "Report of Eben Horsford to James Hall on Geology of Cattaraugus Co." Appendix to *Geological Report of the Fourth District.* New York State Assembly Document No. 50, 1840. pp. 457–72.

————. "Report of the Consulting Physicians of the City of Boston in Relation to the Action of Cochituate Water upon Mineral Substances." City Document No. 18. Boston: Eastburn, 1848. Appendices XVIII, XIX, X [sic].

————. "Report of the Water Commissioners on the Material Best Adapted for Distribution Water Pipes . . ." City Document No. 32. Boston: Eastburn, 1848. Appendices I, II, III, VI, and VII.

————. *Report on the Phrenological Classification of J. Stanley Grimes.* Albany: J. Munsell, 1840.

————. "Results of Some Experiments on the Explosions of Burning Fluids." *Proceedings of the American Academy of Arts and Sciences* 2 (October 2, 1849): 178–79; (April 6, 1852): 311–17.

————. *Service Pipes for Water: An Investigation Made at the Suggestion of the Board of Consulting Physicians of Boston.* Cambridge Mass.: Metcalf and Co., 1849, repr. from *Proceedings of the American Academy of Arts and Sciences* 2 (November 8, 1848): 62–99.

————. "Solidification of Rocks of Florida Reefs: Sources of Lime in the Growth of Corals." *Proceedings of the American Association for the Advancement of Science* 6 (1851): 207–15.

————. "Solidification of the Rocks of the Florida Reefs, and the Sources of Lime in the Growth of Corals." *American Journal of Science,* 2nd ser., 14 (1852): 245–53.

————. "On the Solidification of the Coral Reefs of Florida, and the Sources of Carbonate of Lime in the Growth of Corals." *Proceedings of the American Association for the Advancement of Science* 7 (1853): 122–47.

————. "Ueber den elektrischen Leitungswiderstand der Flüssigkeiten." *Poggendorfs Annalen der Physik* 70 (1847): 238–42, repr. in *American Journal of Science,* 2nd ser., 5 (1848): 36–39.

————. "Ueber Glycocoll (leimzucker) und einige seiner Zersetzungsproducte." *Annalen der Chemie* 60 (1846): 1–57, repr. in *American Journal of Science,* 2nd ser., 3 (1847): 369–81, and 4 (1847): 58–70, 326–40.

————. "Ueber den Werth verschiedener vegetabilischer Nahrungsmittel, hergeleitet aus ihrem Sticksoffgehalt." *Annalen der Chemie* 58 (1846): 166–212, repr. in *Philosophical Magazine* 29 (1846): 365–97.

Howard, Albert. *An Agricultural Testament.* London: Oxford University Press, 1940 (title page) [1943, next page].

————. *The Soil and Health: A Study of Organic Agriculture.* New York: Devin-Adair Co., 1947.

Howe, Frank B. *Classification and Agricultural Value of New York Soils.* Cornell University Experiment Station Bulletin 619. Ithaca, N.Y., 1934.

Howitt, William. *The Student Life of Germany.* Philadelphia: Carey & Hart, 1842.

Hulbert, Archer B. *Soil: Its Influence on the History of the United States.* New Haven: Yale University Press, 1930.

Hunt, Charles B. *Physiography of the United States.* San Francisco: W. H. Freeman & Co., 1967.

Hunt, T. S. "On the Determination of Phosphoric Acid." *Proceedings of the American Association for the Advancement of Science* 4 (1850): 338.

Hutchinson, George Evelyn. *The Biogeochemistry of Vertebrate Excretion.* Published as *Bulletin of the American Museum of Natural History* 96 (1950).

Hutchinson, William T. *Cyrus Hall McCormick, Seed-Time, 1809–1856.* New York: The Century Co., 1930.

Ihde, Aaron J. "Edmund Ruffin, Soil Chemist of the Old South." *Journal of Chemical Education* 29 (1952): 407–14.

––––––. "Stephen Moulton Babcock—Benevolent Skeptic." In *Perspectives in the History of Science and Technology,* edited by Duane H. D. Roller, pp. 271–82. Norman, Okla.: University of Oklahoma Press, 1971.

In Memoriam, Professor John Addison Porter. Cambridge Mass.: Riverside Press, 1867. In Yale University Archives.

Jablonski, P. E. "Beitrag zur Lösung der Frage, ob durch den Vegetationsprozess chemisch unzerlegbare Stoffe begildet werden?" (*Wiegmann's*) *Archiv für Naturgeschichte* 2 (1836): 206–12.

Jackson, Charles L. "Eben Norton Horsford." *Proceedings of the American Academy of Arts and Sciences* 28 (1893): 294–95, 340–46.

Jackson, Charles T. "Analysis of Soils." *American Quarterly Journal of Agriculture* 4 (1846): 220–38.

––––––. "On the Organic Matters of Soils." *American Journal of Science* 45 (1843): 237–46.

James, W. O. "Julius Sachs and the Nineteenth-Century Renaissance of Botany," *Endeavour* 28 (1969): 60–64.

Jameson, E. O. *The Cogswells in America.* Boston: Alfred Mudge & Sons, [1884].

Jenkins, Edward H. "William Henry Brewer." *American Journal of Science,* 4th series, 31 (1911): 71–74.

Johnson, Samuel W. "Agricultural Chemistry." *Johnson's New Universal Cyclopedia.* Vol 1. New York: A. J. Johnson & Son, 1876.

––––––. "Agricultural Chemistry—Soil Analysis: Notice of the Agricultural Chemistry of the Geological Surveys of Kentucky and Arkansas." *American Journal of Science,* 2nd series, 32 (1861): 233–52.

––––––. "The Agricultural Experiment Stations of Europe." In *Tenth Annual Report of the Sheffield Scientific School of Yale College, 1874–5,* pp. 11–31.

––––––. "Annual Address by the President." In *Proceedings of the Tenth Annual Convention of the Association of American Agricultural Colleges and Ex-*

periment Stations, pp. 43–46. Office of Experiment Stations Bulletin 41. Washington, D.C.: Government Printing Office, 1897.

———. "Chemische Notizen." *Journal für Praktische Chemie* 62 (1854): 261–64.

———. "Chemische Untersuchung verschiedener Pflanzenaschen, Bodenarten und Gewässer" und mit Prof. O. Sendtner, "ihre Beziehungen zu gewissen Vegetationsverhältnissen in Bayern." *Annalen der Chemie* 95 (1855): 226–42.

———. "On the Houghite of Prof. Shepard." *Proceedings of the American Association for the Advancement of Science* 6 (1851): 243–46; repr. in *American Journal of Science* 2nd series, 12 (1851): 361–66 and in *Journal für Praktische Chemie* 55 (1852): 123–24.

———. *How Crops Feed: a Treatise on the Atmosphere and the Soil as Related to the Nutrition of Agricultural Plants.* New York: Orange Judd and Co., 1870.

———. *How Crops Grow: a Treatise on the Chemical Composition, Structure, and Life of the Plant.* New York: Orange Judd and Co., 1868.

———. "Lectures on Agricultural Chemistry." In *Annual Report of the Board of Regents of the Smithsonian Institution, 1859,* pp. 119–94.

———. "On the Relations that Exist between Science and Agriculture." *Transactions of the New York State Agricultural Society* 15 (1855): 73–95.

———. "On Some Points of Agricultural Science." *American Journal of Science,* 2nd series, 28 (1859): 71–85.

———. "Ueber das zweifach schleimsäure Amyloxyd." *Journal für Praktische Chemie* 64 (1855): 157–59; repr. in *American Journal of Science,* 2nd series, 19 (1855): 423–24.

———. "Ueber die schleimsauren Salze der Alkalien." *Annalen der Chemie* 94 (1855): 224–30.

Johnston, James F. W. *Catechism of Agricultural Chemistry and Geology.* Introduction by John Pitkin Norton. Albany: Erastus H. Pease, 1846.

———. *Lectures on Agricultural Chemistry and Geology.* 2 vols. New York: Wiley and Putnam, 1842. Parts 1 and 2 only.

———. *Lectures on Agricultural Chemistry and Geology.* 1 vol. 2nd ed. of parts 1 and 2; 1st ed. of parts 3 and 4. Edinburgh: Blackwood & Sons, 1844.

———. *Lectures on Agricultural Chemistry and Geology.* 2nd ed. Edinburgh: Blackwood and Sons, 1847.

———. *Notes on North America: Agricultural, Economical, and Social.* 2 vols. Edinburgh: Blackwood and Sons, 1851.

Jordan, Weymouth T. "The Peruvian Guano Gospel in the Old South." *Agricultural History* 24 (1950): 211–21.

Judd, Orange. "Analysis of the Ash of a Cotton Stalk." *Proceedings of the American Association for the Advancement of Science* 6 (1851): 219–21.

Kauffman, George B. "American Forerunners of the Periodic Law." *Journal of Chemical Education* 46 (1969): 128–35.

Kellogg, Charles E. "We Seek; We Learn." In *SOILS: Yearbook of the United States Department of Agriculture, 1957,* pp. 1–11. Washington, D.C.: Government Printing Office, 1957. Excellent brief history of soil science.

King, Rolf. "E. N. Horsford's Contribution to the Advancement of Science in America." *New York History* 36 (1955): 307–19.

Kirkland, Edward C. *A History of American Economic Life.* 4th ed. New York: Appleton-Century-Crofts, 1969.

Klemm, Volker. "Albrecht Daniel Thaer, Begründer der landwirtschaftliche Hochschulpädogogik in Deutschland." *Wissenschaftliche Zeitung Humboldt-Universität, Math-Natur Reihe* 16 (1967): 723–27.

Klickstein, Herbert S. "Charles Caldwell and the Controversy in America over Liebig's 'Animal Chemistry.' " *Chymia* 4 (1953): 129–57.

Knoblauch, H. C., E. M. Law, and W. P. Meyer, *State Agricultural Experiment Stations: A History of Research Policy and Procedure.* U.S. Department of Agriculture Miscellaneous Publication 904. Washington, D.C.: Government Printing Office, 1962.

Kononova, M. M. *Soil Organic Matter, Its Nature, Its Role in Soil Formation and in Soil Fertility.* Translated by T. Z. Nowakowski and G. A. Greenwood. New York: Pergamon Press, 1961. Historical first chapter.

Kuslan, Louis I. "The Founding of the Yale School of Applied Chemistry." *Journal of the History of Medicine and Allied Sciences* 24 (1969): 430–51.

Lampard, Eric. E. *The Rise of the Dairy Industry in Wisconsin: A Study in Agricultural Change, 1820–1920.* Madison, Wis.: State Historical Society of Wisconsin, 1963.

[Larned, William]. "John Pitkin Norton." *New Englander* 10 (1852): 613–31.

Laskowski, Nicholas "Ueber die Proteintheorie." *Annalen der Chemie* 58 (1846): 129–66.

Law, Ernest M. "The Agricultural Experiment Station Movement in Connecticut, 1840–1900: A Case Study of Tax-Supported Scientific Research in a Democracy." Ph.D. dissertation, Yale University, 1951.

Lee, Daniel. "The Study of Soils." *Report of the Commissioner of Patents for the Year 1850,* Part II, *Agriculture,* pp. 25–81. Washington, D.C., 1851.

Lemon, James T. "The Agricultural Practices of National Groups in Eighteenth-Century Southeastern Pennsylvania." *Geographical Review* 56 (1966): 467–96.

———. *The Best Poor Man's Country: A Geographical Study of Southeastern Pennsylvania.* Baltimore: Johns Hopkins Press, 1972.

Levitt, Jacob. *Introduction to Plant Physiology.* St. Louis: C. V. Mosby Co., 1969.

Lewis, William D. "University of Delaware: Ancestors, Friends and Neighbors." *Delaware Notes* 34 (1961): 1–242.

Liebig, Justus. *An Address to the Agriculturalists of Great Britain, Explaining the Principles and Use of His Artificial Manures.* Liverpool: Thomas Baines, 1845.

———. *Animal Chemistry, or Organic Chemistry in Its Applications to Physiology and Pathology.* Translated by William Gregory. London: Taylor and Walton, 1842.

———. *Animal Chemistry* . . . . With notes by John W. Webster. Cambridge, Mass.: John Owen, 1842.

———. "An Autobiographical Sketch." Translated by J. Campbell-Brown. In *Annual Report of the Board of Regents of the Smithsonian Institution . . . to July 1891,* pp. 257–68. Washington, D.C.: Government Printing Office, 1893.

———. *Familiar Letters on Chemistry and Its Relation to Commerce, Physiology, and Agriculture.* Edited by John Gardner. New York: J. Winchester, New World Press, 1843.

———. *Letters on Modern Agriculture.* Edited by John Blyth. London: Walton and Maberly, 1859.

———. *(Organic) Chemistry in Its Applications to Agriculture and Physiology.* First published in 1840. See Appendix 1, above, for a listing of the numerous editions of this work.

———. *The Relations of Chemistry to Agriculture and the Agricultural Experiments of Mr. J. B. Lawes.* Translated by Samuel W. Johnson. Albany, N. Y.: Luther Tucker, 1855.

———. *Researches on the Chemistry of Food and the Motion of the Juices in the Animal Body.* Edited by William Gregory, M. D., and Eben N. Horsford, A. M. Lowell, Mass.: Daniel Bixby and Co., 1848.

———. *Traité de chimie organique.* 3rd revised and corrected ed. Brussels: Librairie Polytechnique, 1841.

———. "Ueber die Erscheinungen der Gährung, Fäulness und Verwesung und ihre Ursachen." *Annalen der Chemie* 30 (1839): 250–87.

———. "Ueber den Schwefelgehalt des stickstoffhaltigen Bestandtheils der Erbsen." *Annalen der Chemie* 57 (1846): 131–34.

———. "Zur Charakteristik des Herrn Prof. Mulder in Utrecht." *Annalen der Chemie* 62 (1847): n.p.

Lockridge, Kenneth. "Land, Population and the Evolution of New England Society, 1630–1790." *Past and Present* 39 (1968): 62–80.

Loehr, Rodney C. "Arthur Young and American Agriculture." *Agricultural History* 43 (1969): 43–56.

Love, James Lee. *The Lawrence Scientific School in Harvard University, 1847–1906*. Burlington, N.C., 1944. Good for 1871–1906.

Lukas, Edward. "Einiges über die Wirkung der Kohle bei der Vegetation." *Annalen der Chemie* 39 (1841): 127–28.

Lyon, T. Lyttleton, and Harry O. Buckman. *The Nature and Properties of Soils*. New York: Macmillan Co., 1943.

M., A. M. "Charles Mayer Wetherill." *American Journal of Science*, 3rd ser., 1 (1871): 478–79.

Macaire-Princep, J. "Mémoire pour servir à l'histoire des assolemens." *Mémoires de la Société de Physique et d'Histoire Naturelle de Genève* 5 (1832): 287–302.

——. "Mémoire sur l'influence des poisons sur les plantes douées de mouvements excitables." *Mémoires de la Société de Physique et d'Histoire Naturelle de Genève* 3 (1825): 67–77.

——. "Note sur l'empoissonement des végétaux par les substances vénéneuses qu'ils fouissent eux-mêmes." *Mémoires de la Société de Physique et d'Histoire Naturelle de Genève* 4 (1828): 91–93.

——. *Notice sur la vie et les écrits de Théodore de Saussure*. Geneva: Ferdinand Ramboz, 1845. Repr. from *Bibliothèque universelle de Genève*, May 1845.

——. "Sur le guano." *Bibliothèque universelle de Genève* 51 (1844): 379–84.

McCall, A. G. "The Development of Soil Science." *Agricultural History* 5 (1931): 43–56.

McChesney, J. H. "Report on Agricultural Education in Europe." In *Report of the Commissioner of Agriculture for the Year 1868*, pp. 127–57.

McCollum, Elmer V. *A History of Nutrition: The Sequence of Ideas in Nutrition Investigations*. Boston: Houghton Mifflin Co., 1957.

McKelvey, Blake. "Erie Canal, Mother of Cities." *New York Historical Quarterly* 35 (1951): 55–71.

McLachlan, James. *American Boarding Schools: A Historical Study*. New York: Charles Scribner's Sons, 1970.

McNall, Neil A. *An Agricultural History of the Genesee Valley, 1790–1860*. Philadelphia: University of Pennsylvania Press, 1952.

Marti, Donald B. "Agrarian Thought and Agricultural Progress: The Endeavor for Agricultural Improvement in New England and New York, 1815–1840." Ph.D. dissertation, University of Wisconsin, 1966.

——. "Early Agricultural Societies in New York: The Foundations of Improvement." *New York History* 48 (1967): 313–31.

——. "The Purposes of Agricultural Education: Ideas and Projects in New York State, 1819–1865." *Agricultural History* 45 (1971): 271–83.

Maynard, Leonard A. "Wilbur O. Atwater: A Biographical Sketch." *Journal of Nutrition* 78 (1962): 1–9.

Mead, Sidney Earl. *Nathaniel William Taylor, 1786–1858: A Connecticut Liberal*. Chicago: University of Chicago Press, 1942.

Mellor, C. M., and D. S. L. Cardwell. "Dyes and Dyeing, 1775–1860." *British Journal for the History of Science* 1 (1963): 265–79.

Memorials of John Pitkin Norton. Albany, 1853.

Merrill, George P. *The First One Hundred Years of American Geology*. New Haven: Yale University Press, 1924.

Mierke, Harvey O., Jr. "German Influences on the Sheffield Scientific School, 1850–1900." A.B. thesis, Amherst College, 1959.

Miles, Wyndham D. "Books on Chemistry Printed in the U. S., 1755–1900: A Study of Their Origin." *Library Chronicle* 18 (1952): 51–62.

———. "Public Lectures on Chemistry in the United States." *Ambix* 15 (October 1968): 129–53.

———. " 'Sir Humphrey Davie, The Prince of Agricultural Chemists.' " *Chymia* 7 (1961): 126–34.

Miles, Wyndham D., and Louis Kuslan. "Washington's First Consulting Chemist, Henry Erni." In *Records of the Columbia Historical Society of Washington, D. C., 1966–68*, pp. 154–66.

Miller, Howard S. *Dollars for Research, Science and Its Patrons in Nineteenth-Century America*. Seattle: University of Washington Press, 1970.

Morgan, M. F. *The Soil Characteristics of Connecticut Land Types*. Bulletin 423. New Haven: Connecticut Agricultural Experiment Station, 1939.

Morison, Samuel Eliot, ed. *The Development of Harvard University since the Inauguration of President Eliot, 1869–1929*. Cambridge: Harvard University Press, 1930.

———. *Three Centuries of Harvard, 1636–1936*. Cambridge: Harvard University Press, 1936.

Morrell, J. B. "The Chemist Breeders: The Research Schools of Liebig and Thomas Thomson." *Ambix* 19 (1972): 1–46.

———. "The University of Edinburgh in the Late Eighteenth Century: Its Scientific Eminence and Academic Structure." *Isis* 62 (1971): 158–71.

Moulton, Forest Ray. *Liebig and after Liebig: A Century of Progress in Agricultural Chemistry*. Washington, D.C.: American Association for the Advancement of Science, 1942.

Mulder, G[erhardus] J. *The Chemistry of Vegetable and Animal Physiology*. Introduction by J. F. W. Johnston and Benjamin Silliman, Jr. New York: Wiley & Putnam, 1845.

———. *Liebig's Question to Mulder Tested by Morality and Science*. Translated by P. F. H. Fromberg. Edited by J. F. W. Johnston. Edinburgh: William Blackwood & Sons, 1846.

Munsell, Joel. "Albany Female Academy." In *The Annals of Albany*, 1: 202–05. 2nd ed. Albany: Joel Munsell, 1869.

Muspratt, Edmund Knowles. *My Life and Work*. London: John Lane, 1917. Memoirs of an English student of Liebig.

Nash, Dennison. *A Community in Limbo: An Anthropological Study of an American Community Abroad*. Bloomington, Ind.: Indiana University Press, 1970.

Nash, Leonard K. *Plants and the Atmosphere*. Harvard Case Histories in Experimental Science, Case 5. Cambridge: Harvard University Press, 1966.

Neu, Irene D. *Erastus Corning, Merchant and Financier, 1794–1872*. Ithaca, N.Y.: Cornell University Press, 1960.

Nichols, Roy F. "Latin American Guano Diplomacy." *In Modern Hispanic America*, edited by A. Curtis Wilgus, pp. 517–43. Washington, D.C.: George Washington University Press, 1933.

Nicklès, Jérôme. "On the Permeability of Metals to Mercury." *American Journal of Science*, 2nd ser., 15 (1853): 107–09.

Norton, John P. "An Account of Some Researches on the Protein Bodies of Peas and Almonds, and a Body of a Somewhat Similar Nature Existing in Oats." *American Journal of Science*, 2nd ser., 5 (1848): 22–33.

———. "Address" appended to *Transactions of the Hampden County Agricultural Society for the Year 1851*. Springfield, Mass.: Lucius M. Guernsey, 1851.

———. *An Address before the Hampshire, Franklin, and Hampden Agricultural Society, at Northampton. Mass., October 1849*. Northampton, Mass.: Gazette Office, 1849.

———. *An Address before the Hartford County Agricultural Society, Delivered October 15, 1847*. Hartford: Brown and Parsons, 1847. Partially reprinted in *Cultivator*, n.s. 5 (January 1848): 15–19.

———. *An Address Delivered at the Annual Meeting of the New York State Agricultural Society, at Albany, January 19th, 1848*. Albany: Charles Van Benthuysen, 1848. Repr. in *Transactions of the New York State Agricultural Society* 7 (1847): 62–82.

———. *An Address Delivered at the Annual Show of the N.Y.S. Agricultural Society at Buffalo, September 6, 1848*. Albany: Charles Van Benthuysen, 1848. Reprinted in *Transactions of the New York State Agricultural Society* 8 (1848): 55–72.

———. *An Address Delivered before the Ontario Co. Agricultural Society, October 2, 1850, Canandaigua*. New York: J. J. Mattison, 1850.

———. "Address to the Seneca County Agricultural Society." *Transactions of the N. Y. State Agricultural Society* 10 (1850): 585–600.

————. "On the Analysis of the Oat." *American Journal of Science* 3 (1847): 222–36, 318–33. Partially reprinted in *American Agriculturalist* 6 (February 1847): 47–9, and (March 1847): 80–81.

————. "Connection of Science with Agriculture." *Transactions of the New York State Agricultural Society* 11 (1851): 161–77.

————. "A Description of a New Sand-Bath with Water-Bath and Distilling Apparatus Attached, Erected in the Yale Analytical Laboratory." *American Journal of Science,* 2nd ser., 12 (1851): 52–56.

————. *Elements of Scientific Agriculture.* Albany: Erastus H. Pease, 1850.

————. "Introductory Lecture before the Scientific Department of the Albany University, on Wednesday Evening, January 14, 1852." *Transactions of the New York State Agricultural Society* 12 (1852): 243–51.

————. "The Structure, the Physical Properties, and the Chemical Composition of the Soil: An Address Delivered before the Agricultural Societies of Berkshire and Hampshire Counties, at Their Anniversary Fairs, in Pittsfield and Northampton, in October 1848." In *Transactions of the Agricultural Societies of Massachusetts for the Year 1848,* pp. 221–43.

Norton, John P., and William J. Craw. "On the Value of Soil Analyses and the Points to Which Especial Attention Should Be Directed." *Proceedings of the American Association for the Advancement of Science* 6 (1851): 199–206.

Obituary of Samuel L. Dana, *American Journal of Science,* 2nd ser., 45 (1868): 424–25.

Obituary of Samuel W. Johnson. *U.S. Department of Agriculture Experiment Station Record* 21 (1909): 201–06.

Obituary of James F. W. Johnston. *Quarterly Journal of the Chemical Society* 9 (1857): 157–59.

Obituary of John A. Porter. *American Journal of Science,* 2nd ser., 42 (1866): 290.

Obituary of James E. Teschemacher. *Proceedings of the Boston Society of Natural History* 4 (1851–54): 393–94.

Olcott, Henry S. *Outlines of the First Course of Yale Agricultural Lectures.* Introduction by J. A. Porter. New York: C. M. Saxton, Barker & Co., 1860.

Orwin, Christabel S., and Edith H. Whetham. *History of British Agriculture, 1846–1914.* London: Archon Books, 1964.

Osborne, Elizabeth A., ed. *From the Letter-files of S. W. Johnson.* New Haven: Yale University Press, 1913.

Osborne, Thomas B. "Samuel William Johnson." *Science* 30 (September 24, 1909): 385–89.

Ott, Adolf. "Ueber die Fabrikation des im Horsford'schen Backpulver gebrauchten säuren Calciumphosphates." *Dingler's Polytechnisches Journal* 212 (1874): 438–39.

Paoloni, Carlo, ed. *Justus von Liebig, Eine Bibliographie sämtlicher Veröffentlichungen.* Heidelberg: Carl Winter, Universitätsverlag, 1968. Very useful but weak on American editions.

Partington, J. R. *A History of Chemistry,* 4 vols. London: Macmillan & Co., 1964.

Paullin, Charles O., and John K. Wright. *Atlas of the Historical Geography of the United States.* Carnegie Institution of Washington and American Geographic Society of New York, 1932.

Paulsen, Friedrich. *The German Universities: Their Character and Development.* New York: Macmillan Co., 1895.

Pearson, Henry Greenleaf. *James S. Wadsworth of Geneseo.* New York: C. Scribner's Sons, 1913.

———. *Son of New England, James Jackson Storrow, 1864–1926.* Boston: Thomas Todd Co., 1932. Appendix on Charles S. Storrow, 1809–1904.

Pettenkofer, Max von. *Dr. Justus Freiherrn von Liebig zum Gedächtniss.* Munich: Verlag der K. Akademie, 1874.

Pohl, Johann. *Justus von Liebig und die landwirtschaftliche Lehre.* Berlin: Carl Habel, 1885. Repr. from *Deutsche Zeit- und Streit Fragen* 14 (1885): 419–52.

Poor, Henry V. *History of the Railroads and Canals of the United States of America.* 2 vols. New York: John H. Schultz & Co., 1860.

Porter, John A. "Agricultural Education." *New Englander* 17 (1859): 1056–65.

———. "Ash Analyses." *American Journal of Science,* 2nd ser., 9 (1850): 20.

———. *First Book of Chemistry and Allied Sciences, Including an Outline of Agricultural Chemistry.* New York: A. S. Barnes & Co., 1857.

———. "Plan for An Agricultural School." In *Transactions of the Connecticut State Agricultural Society for the Year 1855,* pp. 157–65. Repr. in *American Journal of Education* 1 (1856): 329–35. With additional notes.

———. *A Poem by John Addison Porter; and the Valedictory Oration by Newton Edwards; Pronounced before the Senior Class in Yale College, July 6, 1842.* New Haven: Hitchcock & Stafford, 1842. In Yale University Archives.

———. *Principles of Chemistry.* New York: A. S. Barnes & Co., 1857.

———. "A Product of the Action of Nitric Acid and Woody Fibre." *American Journal of Science,* 2nd ser., 9 (1850): 20–23.

Porter, Noah. "In Memoriam, John Treadwell Norton." *Hearth and Home* 1 (July 10, 1869): 451.

———. *In Memoriam, Joseph Earl Sheffield: A Commemorative Discourse, June 26, 1882.* New Haven: n.p., 1882.

Potter, Alonzo. *The Principles of Science Applied to the Domestic and Mechanic Arts, and to Manufactures and Agriculture.* Boston: Marsh, Capen, Lyon & Webb, 1840.

Potter, David M. *People of Plenty: Economic Abundance and the American Character.* Chicago: University of Chicago Press, 1954.

Prandtl, Wilhelm. *Das Chemische Laboratorium der Bayerischen Akademie der Wissenschaften in München.* Weinheim: Verlag Chemie, 1952.

"A Preliminary Roll of the Sheffield Scientific School, 1846–69." In *Fourth Annual Report of the Sheffield Scientific School of Yale College, 1868–69*, pp. 33–56. New Haven: Tuttle, Morehouse and Taylor, 1869.

"Proceedings of the Convention of Friends of Agricultural Education, August 24–5, 1871." *Fourth Annual Report of the Board of Trustees of the Illinois Industrial University for the Year 1871.* Springfield: Illinois Journal Printing Office, 1872. Repr. as *An Early View of the Land-Grant Colleges.* Edited by Richard A. Hatch. Urbana: University of Illinois Press, 1967.

Proceedings of the National Agricultural Convention, held at Washington, D.C., February 15, 16, and 17, 1872. U.S., 42d Cong., 2nd Sess., Senate Miscellaneous Document No. 164. Washington, D.C.: Government Printing Office, 1872.

Pursell, Carroll W., and Earl M. Rogers, comps. *A Preliminary List of References for the History of Agricultural Science and Technology in the United States.* Davis, Calif.: Agricultural History Center, University of California, 1966.

Reed, H. Clay. "Student Life at Delaware, 1834–59." *Delaware Notes* 8 (1934): 40–74.

Reed, Howard S. *A Short History of the Plant Sciences.* Waltham, Mass.: Chronica Botanica Co., 1942.

Reid, Wemyss. *Memoirs and Correspondence of Lyon Playfair, Lord Playfair of St. Andrews.* London: Harper & Bros., 1899.

Reingold, Nathan. "American Indifference to Basic Research, A Reappraisal." In *Nineteenth-Century American Science: A Reappraisal,* edited by George Daniels. Evanston: Northwestern University Press, 1972.

———. "Science in the Civil War: The Permanent Commission of the Navy Department." *Isis* 49 (1958): 307–18.

Report of the Commissioners . . . to Examine the Sources from which a Supply of Pure Water May Be Obtained for the City of Boston. City Document 41. Boston: J. H. Eastburn, 1845; Appendix A partially repr. in Benjamin Silliman, Jr., "Chemical Examination of Several Natural Waters." *American Journal of Science,* 2nd ser., 2 (1846): 218–24.

Report of the Joint Committee [of Connecticut General Assembly] on Education . . . on the Subject of the Establishment of Professorships of Agriculture and the Arts. Hartford: John L. Boswell, 1847.

Review of *Chemical Essays Relating to Agriculture,* by E. N. Horsford. *American Journal of Science,* 2nd ser., 3 (1847): 144–45.

Review of *Lectures on the Applications of Chemistry and Geology to Agriculture,* Part 2, by J. F. W. Johnston (1843). *American Journal of Science* 44 (1843): 189.

Review of *A Letter to the President of Harvard College,* by a Member of the Corporation. *North American Review* 68 (1849): 503–09.

Review of *Sketch of the History of Harvard College and Its Present State,* by S. A. Eliot. *North American Review* 68 (1849): 99–128.

Rezneck, Samuel. *Education for a Technological Society: A Sesquicentennial History of Rensselaer Polytechnic Institute.* Troy. N. Y.: Rensselaer Polytechnic Institute, 1968.

———. "The Emergence of a Scientific Community in New York State a Century Ago." *New York History* 43 (1962): 211–38. Centers on James Hall and his correspondents.

———. "The European Education of an American Chemist and Its Influence in Nineteenth-Century America: Eben Norton Horsford." *Technology and Culture* 11 (July 1970): 366–88.

———. "Horsford's Marching Ration for the Civil War Army." *Military Affairs* 33 (April 1969): 249–55.

Rigg, Robert. "Outline of an experimentall Inquiry into a peculiar Property of the Earth; the Chemical Changes which occur during the germination of Seeds; the vegetation of Plants; the formation of vegetable Products; and the renovation of the Atmosphere; with some Observations on the ultimate analysis of Organic Compounds; the whole being in connexion with a series of investigations into the decomposition of Vegetable Matter." *Notices and Abstracts of Communications to the British Association for the Advancement of Science* 6 (1837): 50–51.

Riley, Margaret Tschan. "Evan Pugh of Pennsylvania State University and the Morrill Land-Grant Act." *Pennsylvania History* 27 (1960): 339–60.

Roberts, Isaac Phillips. *Autobiography of a Farm Boy.* Albany: J. B. Lyon, 1916.

[Rogers, Emma, and William T. Sedgwick], eds. *Life and Letters of William Barton Rogers.* 2 vols. Boston: Houghton, Mifflin & Co., 1896.

Rosen, George M. "Carl Ludwig and His American Students." *Bulletin of the History of Medicine* 4 (1936): 609–50.

Rosenberg, Charles E. "The Adams Act: Politics and the Cause of Scientific Research." *Agricultural History* 38 (1964): 3–12.

———. "Science and Social Values in Nineteenth-Century America: A Case Study in the Growth of Scientific Institutions." In press.

———. "Science, Technology, and Economic Growth: The Case of the

Agricultural Experiment Station Scientist, 1875–1914." *Agricultural History* 45 (1971): 1–20.

Rossiter, Margaret W. "Benjamin Silliman and the Lowell Institute: The Popularization of Science in Nineteenth-Century America." *New England Quarterly* 44 (December 1971): 602–26.

———. "The Organization of Agricultural Improvement in the U.S., 1785–1865." (See Hindle entry, above.)

Ruffin, Edmund, *An Essay on Calcareous Manures.* Edited by J. Carlyle Sitterson. Cambridge: Harvard University Press, 1961.

Rüling, E. "Bestimmung des Schwefels in den Schwefel- und Stickstoff-haltigen Bestandtheilen des Pflanzen- und Thierorganismus." *Annalen der Chemie* 58 (1846): 301–15.

Russell, Sir E. John. *A History of Agricultural Science in Great Britain, 1620–1954.* London: Allen & Unwin, 1966.

———. "Rothamstead and Its Experiment Station." *Agricultural History* 16 (1942): 161–83.

Ryden, George H. "The Founding of the University of Delaware and Its First President, Dr. E. W. Gilbert." *Delaware Notes* 8 (1934): 31–39.

Sachs, Julius von. *History of Botany (1530–1860).* Translated by Henry Garnsey. Revised by Isaac B. Balfour. Oxford: Clarendon Press, 1890.

Sauer, Carl O. "Theme of Plant and Animal Destruction in Economic History." In *Land and Life: A Selection from the Writings of Carl Ortwin Sauer,* edited by John Leighly. Berkeley: University of California Press, 1963.

Saussure, [N] Th. de. "De l'action de la fermentation sur le mélange des gaz oxygène et hydrogène." *Bibliothèque universelle* 13 (1838): 380–401.

———. *Recherches chimiques sur la vegetation.* Paris: V. Nyon, 1804.

Schneider, Edward C. "Wilbur Olin Atwater." *Storrs Agricultural Experiment Station Bulletin* 168 (1930): 311–18.

Schödler, Friedrich. "Das chemische Laboratorium unserer Zeit." *Westermanns (Jahrbuch der Illustrierten Deutschen) Monatshefte* 38 (1875): 21–47.

Schreiner, Oswald. "Early Fertilizer Work in the United States." *Soil Science* 40 (1935): 39–47.

Scott, Mark John. "Karl Friedrich Mohr, 1806–1879: Father of Volumetric Analysis." *Chymia* 3 (1950): 191–203.

Scott, Roy V. *The Reluctant Farmer: The Rise of Agricultural Extension to 1914.* Urbana, Ill.: University of Illinois Press, 1970.

Seager, Robert, II. *And Tyler Too: A Biography of John & Julia Gardiner Tyler.* New York: McGraw-Hill, 1963.

Shannon, Fred A. *The Farmer's Last Frontier: Agriculture, 1860–1897.* New York: Farrar & Rinehart, 1945.

Shaw, Ronald E. *Erie Water West: A History of the Erie Canal, 1792–1854.* Lexington, Ky.: University of Kentucky Press, 1966.

Shryock, Richard. "American Indifference to Basic Science during the Nineteenth Century." *Archives internationales d'histoire des Sciences,* 2 (1948): 50–65.

———. "British versus German Traditions in Colonial Agriculture." *Mississippi Valley Historical Review* 26 (1939): 39–54.

———. "The Pennsylvania Germans in American History." *Pennsylvania Magazine of History* 63 (1939): 261–81.

Shumway, Daniel B. "The American Students of the University of Göttingen." *German-American Annals,* o.s. 12 (1910): 171–254.

Siegfried, Robert C. "A Study of Chemical Research Publications from the United States before 1880." Ph.D. dissertation, University of Wisconsin, 1952.

Silliman, Benjamin. *A Visit to Europe in 1851.* 2 vols. New York: G. P. Putnam & Co., 1853.

———. Review of *A Muck Manual for Farmers,* by S. L. Dana. *American Journal of Science* 43 (1842): 192–97.

Silliman, Benjamin, Jr. "Memoir of John Lawrence Smith, 1818–1883." *National Academy of Sciences Biographical Memoirs* 2 (1886); 219–48.

———. Review of *Organic Chemistry in Its Application to Agriculture and Physiology,* by Justus Liebig. *American Journal of Science* 40 (1841): 177–83.

———. Review of *Report on the Geological and Agricultural Survey of the State of Rhode Island in 1839,* by C. T. Jackson. *American Journal of Science* 40 (1841): 182–94.

———. Review of *System of Mineralogy including the Most Recent Discoveries, Foreign and American,* by J. D. Dana. *American Journal of Science* 46 (1843–44): 362–87.

Silverman, Robert, and Mark Beach. "A National University for Upstate New York." *American Quarterly* 22 (1970): 701–13.

Smith, Edgar F. "James C. Booth, Chemist, 1810–1888." *Journal of Chemical Education* 20 (1943): 315–18, 357.

———. "Charles Mayer Wetherill, 1825–1871." *Journal of Chemical Education* 6 (1929): 1076–89, 1215–24, 1461–77, 1668–80, 1916–27, 2160–77.

———. *Chemistry in America.* New York: D. Appleton and Co., 1914.

———. "Martin Hans Boyè, Chemist, 1812–1909." *Journal of Chemical Educatin* 21 (1944): 7–11.

Smith, J. Lawrence. "Abstracts of the Researches of European Chemists [on Guano]." *American Journal of Science* 48 (1845): 181–83.

"Some of Harvard's Endowed Professorships." *Harvard Alumni Bulletin* 29 (November 5, 1926): 145–50.

Spence, Clark C. *Mining Engineers and the American West: The Lace-Boot Brigade, 1849–1933.* New Haven: Yale University Press, 1970.

Stephens, Henry, assisted by John P. Norton. *The Farmer's Guide to Scientific and Practical Agriculture.* 2 vols. New York: Leonard Scott & Co., 1851.

Stephens, Michael D., and Gordon W. Roderick. "The Muspratts of Liverpool." *Annals of Science* 29 (1972): 287–311.

Stevens, Frank Walker. *The Beginnings of the New York Central Railroad: A History.* New York: G. P. Putnam's Sons, 1926.

Stohmann, [   ]. "Liebig's Beziehungen zur Landwirtschaft." *Journal für Praktische Chemie* 8 (1874): 458–76.

Storr, Richard J. *The Beginnings of Graduate Education in America.* Chicago: University of Chicago Press, 1953.

Strother, Horatio T. *The Underground Railroad in Connecticut.* Middletown, Conn.: Wesleyan University Press, 1962.

Struik, Dirk J. *Yankee Science in the Making.* Rev. ed. New York: Collier Books, 1962.

Sullivan, Robert. *The Disappearance of Dr. Parkman.* Boston: Little, Brown and Co., 1971.

Symons, Leslie. *Agricultural Geography.* New York: Frederick Praeger, 1967.

Syndor, Charles S. "State Geological Surveys in the Old South." In *American Studies in Honor of William Keith Boyd,* edited by David K. Jackson, pp. 86–109. Durham,: N.C. Duke University Press, 1940.

Szabadvary, Ferenc. *History of Analytical Chemistry.* Translated by Gyula Svehla. Oxford: Pergamon Press, 1966.

Taylor, Rosser H. "The Sale and Application of Commercial Fertilizers in the South Atlantic States to 1900." *Agricultural History* 21 (1947): 46–52.

Teschemacher, James E. *Essay on Guano.* Boston: A. D. Phelps; New York: Saxton and Huntington, 1845.

Thompson, Louis M., and Frederick R. Troeh, *Soils and Soil Fertility.* 3rd ed. New York: McGraw-Hill Book Co., 1973.

Thompson, M. L. "The Second Agricultural Revolution, 1815–1880." *Economic History Review,* 2nd ser., 21 (1968): 62–77.

Thomson, Helen. *Murder at Harvard.* Boston: Houghton Mifflin Co., 1971.

Thwing, Charles F. *The American and the German University.* New York: Macmillan Co., 1928.

Toepke, Gustav. *Die Matrikel der Universität Heidelberg.* Vols. 4–6. Heidelberg: Carl Winter, 1903–07.

Transactions of the New Haven County Agricultural Society, for 1849, with an Address by Prof. John P. Norton. New Haven: B. L. Hamlen, 1850.

Trowbridge, W. P. "Memoir of William A. Norton, 1810–1883." *National Academy of Sciences Biographical Memoirs* 2 (1886): 189–99.

True, Alfred C. "Agricultural Experiment Stations in the U. S." In

Yearbook of the United States Department of Agriculture, 1899, pp. 513–18. Washington, D.C.: Government Printing Office, 1900.

———. "A Brief Account of the Experiment Station Movement in the United States." In *Office of Experiment Stations Bulletin 1,* pp. 73–78. Washington, D.C.: Government Printing Office, 1889.

———. *A History of Agricultural Education in the United States, 1785–1925.* Miscellaneous Publication no. 36, U.S. Department of Agriculture. Washington, D.C.: Government Printing Office, 1929.

———. *A History of Agricultural Experimentation and Research in the United States, 1607–1925.* Miscellaneous Publication no. 251, U.S. Department of Agriculture. Washington, D.C.: Government Printing Office, 1937.

Tyler, Alice Felt. *Freedom's Ferment: Phases of American Social History from the Colonial Period to the Outbreak of the Civil War.* 1944. Reprint. New York: Harper Torchbooks, 1962.

U.S. Department of Agriculture. *SOIL, Yearbook for 1957.* Washington, D.C.: Government Printing Office, 1957.

———. *Soils and Men: Yearbook of Agriculture, 1938,* Washington, D.C.: Government Printing Office, 1938.

———. *Soil Survey of Livingston County, New York.* Series 1941, no. 15 (August 1956).

U.S. Department of Agriculture, Agricultural Research Service, and Tennessee Valley Authority. *Superphosphate: Its History, Chemistry and Manufacture.* Washington, D.C.: Government Printing Office, 1964.

Van Klooster, H. S. "The Beginnings of Laboratory Instruction in the U.S.A." *Chymia* 2 (1949): 1–15.

———. "Friedrich Wöhler and His American Pupils." *Journal of Chemical Education* 21 (1944): 158–70.

———. "Liebig and His American Pupils." *Journal of Chemical Education* 33 (1956): 493–97.

———. "125 Years of Chemistry at Rensselaer Polytechnic Institute." *Journal of Chemical Education* 26 (1949): 346–52.

Verdeil, Francois. "Schwefelbestimmung einiger organischer Körper." *Annalen der Chemie* 58 (1846): 317–22.

Vickery, Hubert B. "Liebig and Proteins." *Journal of Chemical Education* 19 (1942): 73–79.

———. "The Origin of the Connecticut Agricultural Experiment Station." Unpublished paper, December 1969.

———. "The Origin of the Word 'Protein'." *Yale Journal of Biology and Medicine* 22 (1950): 387–93.

———. "The Relationship of the Sheffield Scientific School to Agriculture." In *The Centennial of the Sheffield Scientific School,* edited by George A. Baitsell, pp. 196–203. New Haven: Yale University Press, 1950.

————. "Samuel W. Johnson and *How Crops Grow.*" In *How Crops Grow, A Century Later,* edited by Peter R. Day. Bulletin 708. New Haven: Connecticut Agricultural Experiment Station, 1969.

Vickery, Hubert B., and C. L. A. Schmidt. "The History of the Discovery of the Amino Acids." *Chemical Reviews* 9 (1931): 169–318.

Vogel, August. *Justus Freiherr von Liebig als Begründer der Agrikultur-Chemie, Eine Denkschrift.* Munich: Verlag der K. Akademie, 1874.

————. *Zur Geschichte der Liebig'schen Mineral-theorie.* Berlin: Carl Habel, 1883. Repr. from *Sammlung gemeinverständlicher wissenschaftlicher Vorträge* 18 (1883): 687–730.

Volhard, Jakob. *Justus von Liebig.* 2 vols. Leipsig: J. A. Barth, 1909.

Walker, Mack. *Germany and the Emigration, 1816–85.* Cambridge: Harvard University Press, 1964. Discusses agricultural problems of Giessen area.

Walther, [   ]. "Schwefelgehalt des Caseins." *Annalen der Chemie* 58 (1846): 315–17.

Ward, Roswell. *Henry A. Ward: Museum Builder to America* published as *Rochester Historical Society Publications* 24 (1948).

Watson, James A. Scott. *The History of the Royal Agricultural Society of England, 1839–1939.* London: Royal Agricultural Society, 1939.

Webster, John W. *A Manual of Chemistry.* Boston: Richardson & Lord, 1826.

————. *A Manual of Chemistry.* 3rd ed. Boston: Marsh, Capen, Lyon and Webb, 1829.

Wells, David A. "Communication." In *Transactions of the Hampden County Agricultural Society for the Year 1851,* pp. 19–22. Springfield, Mass.: Lucius M. Guernsey, 1851.

————. "Notes and Observations on the Analyses and Characters of the Soil of the Scioto Valley, Ohio, with Some General Considerations Respecting the Subject of Soil Analyses." *American Journal of Science* 14 (1852): 11–19.

Wells, H. L. "Samuel William Johnson." *American Journal of Science,* 4th ser. 28 (1909): 405–07.

Weyman, G. W. "Analysis of Bituminous Coal Ash." *Proceedings of the American Association for the Advancement of Science* 6 (1851): 196–98.

White, C. Langdon; Edwin J. Foscue; and Tom L. McKnight. *Regional Geography of Anglo-America,* 3rd ed. Englewood Cliffs, N. J.: Prentice-Hall, 1964.

White, Gerald T. "Benjamin Silliman, Jr., and the Origins of the Sheffield Scientific School." *Ventures Magazine of the Yale Graduate School* 8 (Spring 1968): 19–25.

————. *Scientists in Conflict: The Beginnings of the Oil Industry in California.* San Marino, Calif.: Huntington Library, 1968.

Wiegmann, A. F., and L. Polstorff. *Über die anorganischen Bestandteile der Pflanzen* . . . Braunschweig: F. Vieweg und Sohn, 1842. Reprinted in *Flora* 26 (1843): 21–35.

Wiley, Harvey W. *An Autobiography.* Indianapolis: Bobbs-Merrill Co., 1930.

―――. "The Relation of Chemistry to the Progress of Agriculture." In U.S. Department of Agriculture, *Yearbook for 1899*, pp. 201–58. Good on Davy.

Will, Henry. *Outlines of the Course of Qualitative Analysis Followed in the Giessen Laboratory.* Preface by E. N. Horsford. Boston: James Munroe & Co., 1847.

―――― (Heinrich). *Outlines of Chemical Analysis, Prepared for the Chemical Laboratory at Giessen.* Translated by Daniel Breed, M.D., and Lewis Steiner, M.A., M.D. Boston: James Munroe & Co., 1855.

Wilson, Harold F. *The Hill Country of Northern New England: Its Social and Economic History, 1790–1930.* New York: Columbia University Press, 1936.

Wöhler, Emilie, with A. W. Hofmann. *Aus Justus Liebig's und Friedrich Wöhler's Briefwechsel.* 2 vols. Braunschweig: Vieweg and Sohn, 1888.

[Wöhler, Friedrich]. "Ueber die Zusammensetzung des Guanos." *Annalen der Chemie* 37 (1841): 285–91.

Woodward, Carl R. *The Development of Agriculture in New Jersey, 1640–1880.* New Brunswick, N. J.: Rutgers University, 1927.

Worthen, Edmund L. *Farm Soils: Their Management and Fertilization.* New York: John Wiley & Sons, 1941.

Wyman, Morrell. "Report of Committee on Ventilators and Chimney Tops." *Proceedings of the American Academy of Arts and Sciences* 1 (November 10, 1847): 185, and (March 7, 1848): 307–24.

Index

New York State Agricultural Society, 9,
123, 141; and Horsford, 52-53, 63; and
Johnson, 136, 138
New York State College of Agriculture, 49-
50, 55, 67. *See also* Cornell University
New York State Natural History Survey, 51
New York State Normal School, Albany,
129
Nichols, James R., 219n33
Nicklès, Jerôme, 100
Nitrates, 22, 40, 147. *See also* Boussingault,
J. B.
Nitrogen, in plants, 18, 21-24, 117, 132,
145-46; cycle, 20-23; in animals, 22; in
soils, 23, 43, 209n19; "inert," 143, 147.
See also Ammonia; Dumas, J. B.;
Fertilizers, organic; Nitrates; Nutrition;
Will and Varentrapp
Nobbe, Professor Friedrich, 168
North American Review, 10, 70
Norton, Elizabeth (Mrs. William A.), 54
Norton, Elizabeth Cogswell (Mrs. John T.),
92
Norton, John Pitkin, xiv, 9; agricultural
journalist, 66, 103; family, 91-92; compared to Horsford, 91, 93; reads Liebig,
91, 95; runs family farm, 93, 95; education and career choice, 93-96; desire to
be missionary, 94-95, 109; at Benjamin
Silliman, Jr.'s laboratory, 97; in Edinburgh with Johnston, 98-103; quarrel
with Johnston, 98-99, 105, 220n18; at
BAAS (1845), 99; studies oat, 99, 144;
extension work in Scotland, 102-03; at
Mulder's laboratory in Utrecht, 102, 105-
08; studies avenine and legumin, 106-07
— criticizes powdered charcoal, 38; illness
and death, 84, 124, 225n29; opposes
Liebig, 101, 107, 116-18, 173; leader of
agricultural chemistry movement in U.S.,
109, 115-24; simplistic view of soil
analysis, 109, 118-19; values German education, 112, 128-29; edits *Farmers Guide,*
116; public lectures, 116; writes *Elements
of Scientific Agriculture,* 116, 119,
224n17; influenced by Liebig, 117-18;
defends soil analysis, 120-23; University
of Albany, 124. *See also* Yale University
— at Yale Analytical Laboratory: unconcerned about money, 75, 104-05, 113-14,
210n11; selfless personality, 88, 116,

175; opposes frauds and quacks, 99,
115, 121, 149, 151; professorship established, 104; not funded, 104, 109-10,
139, 222n30; career at Yale, 109-24;
lectures on agricultural chemistry, 112-
13; no research, 113; does soil analyses
below cost, 114-15, 198, 221n26
Norton, John Treadwell, 91-92, 213n17
Norton, William A., 53-54
Nott, Eliphalet, 104
Nutrition, 64-65, 112, 165. *See also*
Boussingault, J. B.

Oat, 99
Ohio State Board of Agriculture, 121
Olcott, Thomas, 52
Olcott family, 92
Olmsted, Denison, 93-94, 111
Osmosis, 82, 145, 147
Ovid Academy, New York, 136, 140

Paris, France, 61, 140
Parker, Joel, 54
Parkman, Dr. George, 84
Pasteur, Louis, 16, 146
Payen, A., 100
Peabody, George, 139
Peat, 149, 155-56, 211n19
Peirce, Benjamin, 68-69, 71-74, 81, 124, 203
Pell, Robert, 37-38
Pennsylvania, University of, 54
Pennsylvania State University, 130
Persoz, J. F., 100
Peter, Robert, 221n26
Pettenkofer, Max von, 83
Philadelphia, Pennsylvania, 80
Philadelphia Society for the Promotion of
Agriculture, 122
Phosphates, 18-19; in soils, 24-25; in dye-
ing, 25; in bone dust, 25, 40; difficulties
of detection, 25, 225n23; in guano, 39;
in proteins, 41-42, 64-65; in soil
analysis, 119-22; veins of irregular, 149;
prices of, 153, 153n, 159
Photosynthesis, 13, 20
Phrenology, 52
Pitkin, Mary Hubbard, 91
Pitkin, Timothy, 91
Plants, growth, 13-18; anatomy and
physiology, 21, 145; excretions, 24;
proteins in, 41-42; analyses, 134, 144-